1820

GEOLOGICAL SURVEY OF
GREAT BRITAIN

FIRST PUBLISHED IN 1952

*George Allen and Unwin, Ltd.,
40, Museum Street, London, W.C.1,
are now the proprietors of
Thomas Murby and Co.*

PRINTED IN GREAT BRITAIN
in 11 point Caslon type,
BY THE WOODBRIDGE PRESS, LTD.,
GUILDFORD.

GEOLOGICAL SURVEY OF
GREAT BRITAIN

by

SIR EDWARD BAILEY

F.R.S.

London

THOMAS MURBY & CO

40 Museum Street

PLATE I.

SIR HENRY THOMAS DE LA BECHE, C.B., F.R.S.

[Frontispiece.

PREFACE

HERE is the story of a survey. It was originally written for the British Council, to appear in their series, *Science in Britain;* but publication of this series had to be suspended before my manuscript was ready. So I turned elsewhere. Meanwhile, during early stages of preparation, I had intended to dedicate my account to my former great chief, Sir Edward Appleton, who was at the time still Secretary of the Department of Scientific and Industrial Research; but here again a change of plan became necessary—I realised as I proceeded that dedication to anyone might perhaps obscure my sole responsibility for certain opinions expressed on debatable topics.

The world has reached a stage when a number of nations annually devote large sums of money to scientific research. Most of their zeal for knowledge is inspired by fear, and seeks continually the development of more and more terrible weapons of destruction; but there is also a genuine associated desire to raise the standard of living throughout the world—to provide more food and clothing, perhaps even more understanding, for the involuntary children of mankind.

My own opinion is that that nation will be most favoured which, behind a façade of necessary precautions, bravely maintains a generous, tolerant sympathy with freedom of research and publication. Is it too much to suggest that experience, won by trial and error during the lifetime of the second oldest national research institute of Britain, may prove of some assistance to framers of present-day policy?

The frontispiece portrait of De la Beche has already appeared in H. B. Woodward's *History of the Geological Society,* published by the Society as a centenary volume. Plate II is from a drawing of T. F. Colby, of equally happy memory, which is hung in the office of the Ordnance Survey. The charming snapshot in Plate III of Peach, Horne and Clough, standing on a pillow lava at Tayvallich, 1904, was taken by J. S. Flett. Plate IV of the Museum of Practical Geology, old and new, reproduces two official photographs. To everyone concerned I offer cordial thanks. Crown copyright of official photographs not previously published is reserved.

Among the line-blocks, *Figs*. 8, 10, 14, 28 have been specially drawn. The remainder are reproductions, almost all taken from memoirs of the Geological Survey very roughly in order of appearance. I wish again to express my thanks, in this case directed to the appropriate heads of the Geological Survey, the Department of Scientific and Industrial Research and H.M. Stationery Office.

The text has been written without quoting references; but those who wish to follow up any particular aspect of the subject will probably find little difficulty. The main sources are, of course, the publications of the Geological Survey itself. In addition, great assistance has been obtained from various historical writings, especially those of Archibald Geikie, H. B. Woodward, F. J. North, and J. S. Flett. The latter's official *First Hundred Years of the Geological Survey of Britain*, 1937, is of special value. The following brief list draws attention to a few publications not included in its bibliographical appendix.

ADAMS, F. D. 1938. *The Birth and Development of the Geological Sciences*, London.

BAILEY, E. B. and D. TAIT, 1921. Geology. *Edinburgh's Place in Scientific Progress*, p. 63. Edinburgh.

BAILEY, E. B. 1939. The Interpretation of Scottish Scenery. *Scot. Geog. Mag.*, vol. 1, p. 308.

—— 1950. James Hutton, Founder of Modern Geology. *Proc. Roy. Soc. Ed.*, vol. lxiii, p. 357.

COX, L. R. 1942. New Light on William Smith and his Work. *Proc. Yorks. Geol. Soc.*, vol. xxv, p. 1.

DOUGLAS, J. A. and J. M. EDMONDS. 1950. John Phillip's Geological Maps of the British Isles. *Ann. Sc.*, vol. vi, p. 361.

EYLES, V. A. 1937. John Macculloch, F.R.S., and his Geological Map : an account of the first Geological Survey of Scotland. *Ann. Sc.*, vol. ii, p. 114.

—— 1939. Macculloch's Geological Map of Scotland, an Additional Note. *Ann. Sc.*, vol. iv, p. 107.

—— 1948. Louis Albert Necker, of Geneva, and his Geological Map of Scotland. *Trans. Ed. Geol. Soc.*, vol. xiv, p. 93.

EYLES, V. A. 1950. The First National Geological Survey. *Geol. Mag.*, vol. lxxxvii, p. 373.

—— 1950. Note on the Original Publication of Hutton's Theory of the Earth, and on the Subsequent Forms in which it was issued. *Proc. Roy. Soc. Ed.*, vol. lxiii, p. 377.

—— and JOAN M. EYLES. 1938. On the Different Issues of the First Geological Map of England and Wales. *Ann. Sc.*, vol. iii, p. 190.

FLETT, J. S. 1937. The First Hundred Years of the Geological Survey of Great Britain. *Mem. Geol. Surv.*

GEIKIE, A. 1898. Introduction. *Sum. Prog. Geol. Surv.* for 1897, p. 1.

MACGREGOR, M. 1950. Life and Times of James Hutton. *Proc. Roy. Soc. Ed.*, vol. lxiii, p. 351.

NORTH, F. J. 1933. From Giraldus Cambrensis to the Geological Map. *Trans. Cardiff Naturalists' Soc.*, vol. lxiv, p. 20.

—— 1943. Centenary of the Glacial Theory. *Proc. Geol. Ass.*, vol. liv, p. 1.

SIMMINGTON, R. C. and A. FARRINGTON. 1949. A Forgotten Pioneer. Patrick Ganly, Geologist, Surveyor and Civil Engineer. *Journal of the Department of Agriculture, Eire,* vol. xlvi, p. 36.

SMITH, BERNARD. 1936. Progress of the Geological Survey, 1920-1935. *Sum. Prog. Geol. Surv.* for 1935, p. 12.

TOMKEIEFF, S. I. 1950. James Hutton and the Philosophy of Geology. *Proc. Roy. Soc. Ed.*, vol. lxiii, p. 387.

TYRRELL, G. W. 1950. Hutton on Arran. *Proc. Roy. Soc. Ed.*, vol. lxiii, p. 369.

E. B. BAILEY

CONTENTS

LIST OF ILLUSTRATIONS

PLATES

FIGURES IN TEXT

xi

PRELUDE

STIRRINGS of geological consciousness have left several traces in the writings of antiquity. We read how from time to time some rare spirit realised that many rocks are consolidated waterborne detritus, or that fossils are remains of bygone organisms, or that certain hills and valleys have been shaped by erosion; but for the most part early geological speculation amounted to little more than mental exercise in astrology and alchemy, confined within limits set by guardians of divine revelation. Our spiritual advisers, it must be remembered, recognised need for control of scientific research long before anyone contemplated disintegration of atoms.

Supplementary, unwritten evidence of at any rate empirical geological knowledge, dispersed among practical men of past ages, is afforded by various notable achievements in civil engineering, including quarrying and mining, where success often depended upon recognition of succession and structure within rock masses, or of the potentialities of weather, rivers and sea. That such empirical knowledge was sometimes combined with deep understanding has been revealed, for instance, through posthumous publication of notebooks of Leonardo da Vinci, who lived from 1452 to 1519. Da Vinci was brought face to face with Nature in the field as an engineer, and formed correct ideas on several topics of the type indicated above.

Miners, though not necessarily sharing da Vinci's insight into geological processes, have always had to think in three dimensions. This is well exemplified in a *Short History of Coal* by George Sinclair, which appeared in 1672 as part of a work entitled *The Hydrostaticks*. Sinclair for 20 years occupied the chair of Philosophy and Mathematics at Glasgow University, though with an interval of enforced retirement due to political difficulties. He found employment during his academic respite as a mining engineer practising

1

in the Lothians; and it is to this circumstance that we owe his *Short History of Coal, and of all the Common, and Proper Accidents thereof; a Subject never Treated of Before*. It will convince anyone of the continuity of geological thought from the seventeenth century onwards to find Sinclair using our current words : crop, dip, rise and strike. Faults and igneous dykes he grouped together, as Scots miners still are wont to do, under the terms gae, dyke or trouble. He understood thoroughly the geometry of an ordinary faulted coal basin. As regard gaes, he cited the experience of the coal hewers that a coal seam will be found ' down ' on the side to which a gae inclines. As regards dip, he agreed with those who contend that dip, unless interrupted by a gae, continues to a centre, where the coal, or whatever it may be, ' takes a contrary course ' which brings it up again to the ' grass.' This proposition he applied to the Mid Lothian coalfield, boldly accepting a hypothesis which carried him in imagination 3,000 ft. below the depth reached by contemporary mining. It appealed to him very strongly that he could follow the outcrop of the Great Seam fairly satisfactorily right round the landward margin of what he correctly interpreted as a basin-shaped structure.

That English coal miners had also by this time comprehended a great deal of the geometry of their fields is revealed in *The Natural History of Staffordshire*, 1686, written by Robert Plot, Keeper of the Ashmolean Museum and Professor of Chemistry in the University of Oxford; and also in a paper on the Coal District of Somerset, which John Strachey contributed, 1719, to the Philosophical Transactions of the Royal Society. In this last Strachey drew a section which shows seven named ' veynes ' (or seams) of coal dipping somewhat steeply and affected by a ' ridge [fault] which breaks off the veynes and makes them trap [step] down or trap up from their regular course.' The dipping veynes and vertical ridge are drawn as truncated above by a horizontal succession which from below upwards consists of (1) ' Yellowish Spungey Earth ' (New Red Sandstone), (2) ' Marle ' and (3) ' Lyas or Limestone ' (both (2) and (3) are now included as Lias). The section further shows

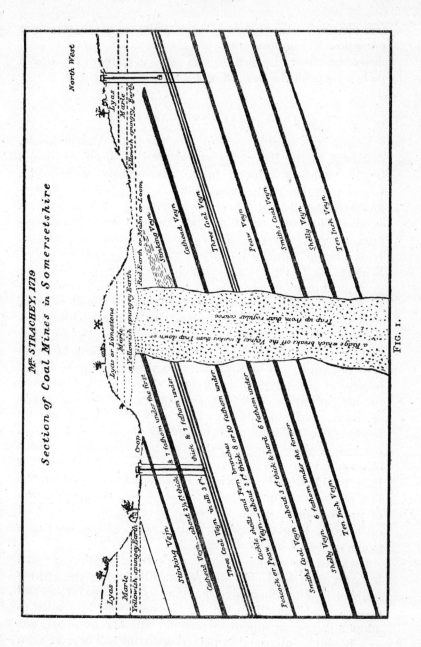

Mr. STRACHEY, 1719

Section of Coal Mines in Somersetshire

FIG. 1.

two pits sunk to coal veynes, one starting in a valley bottom on exposed Coal Measures, the other on a hill top on Liassic limestone cover. In fact, to this day, it conveys as clear a picture as could be desired of a semi-concealed coalfield.

JEAN ÉTIENNE GUETTARD

Going back a little we find in a paper by Martin Lister, delivered to the Royal Society in 1683, a desire expressed for a 'soile or mineral map.' Sixty years later, 1743, Christopher Packe produced such a map, *A New Philoso-phico-chorographical Chart of East Kent,* in which, as a result of close investigation, chalk districts, stone hills, clay-hills, etc., were distinguished. Shortly afterwards, in 1746, Jean Étienne Guettard communicated to the Academy of Sciences in Paris two additional examples of primitive geological maps of more ambitious scope. One covered much of France and England. The other, on a smaller scale, western Europe, including Iceland. It is worth while quot-ing from Sir Archibald Geikie's *Founders of Geology* the first sentences of Guettard's remarkable *Mémoire et Carte Mineralogique:* 'If nothing can contribute more towards the formation of a physical and general theory of the earth than the multiplication of observations among the different kinds of rocks and the fossils which they contain, assuredly nothing can make us more sensible of the utility of such a research than to bring together into one view those various observations by the construction of mineralogical maps. I have travelled with the view of gaining instruction on the first of these two points, and following the recommendation of the Academy, which wished to have my work expressed on a map, I have prepared such a map, which contains a summary of all my observations.'

Guettard was an indefatigable worker and he supplemented his own wide field observations by diligent reading, which enabled him to extend his mapping to districts far beyond those he had himself visited. At the same time he tended to adopt a somewhat superficial outlook. His first approach was as a botanist, interested in plant associations. These he soon found to be in large measure guided by mineral associations; and in the distribution of the latter he detected a methodical pattern capable of presentation on a map. His wide excursions led him clearly to recognise the roles of subaerial and marine erosion, and to correlate these activities with resultant deposition of sediment. They further rewarded him with the exciting discovery of extinct volcanoes in the Auvergne district of central France. Fossils he collected and described in great numbers, as a naturalist; but apparently he did not realise that they could be arranged in tell-tale vertical time-sequence from below upwards.

Guettard's map of France was brought into final form by Monnet, to appear in 1780, in sixteen sheets, under their joint names as an official publication, 'entrepris par ordre du Roi.' Among its other uses it provided a valuable statement of the distribution of mineral industries and possibilities.

ABRAHAM GOTTLOB WERNER

Geological research was by this time receiving quite exceptional impetus from developments in the metalliferous fields of Central Europe. Already during past centuries the region had functioned as a dispersal centre for mining technique and tradition—as is evidenced, for instance, by the quaint name of toadstone still attached to Carboniferous lavas in Derbyshire, where early German miners had apparently found such rocks *tot,* or dead, from the point of view of mineralisation. Now, in 1767, a great step forward was taken through the establishment of a Mining Academy at Freiberg in Saxony; and this was consummated in 1775 by an invitation extended to young Abraham Gottlob Werner to come to the Academy as Inspector and Teacher of Mining and Mineralogy.

Werner was born and bred to the appointment. His ancestors had a long association with the iron industry; while he himself, when scarce able to speak, could find amusement in breaking down pieces of sandstone and marl; and a little later could be bribed to good behaviour by a promise of a peep at his father's collection of minerals. What brought him more especially to the notice of the authorities at the Academy was a short treatise on the external characters of minerals, which he published in 1774 while still a student at Leipzig University. This book enabled readers, without recourse to the infant science of chemistry, to recognise individual minerals, and at the same time furnished them with information regarding economic applications. Werner's stipend at Freiberg was to be 300 thalers, which reminds us that the almighty dollar took its name from Joachimsthal in Bohemia in days when this centre was a rich producer of silver.

Werner's personality soon came to be a dominant factor. He saw that scenery, industry, population, civilisation, architecture, sculpture, agriculture, commerce and war were all regulated by mineral distribution; and he had the gift of being able to communicate this truth to others. Cuvier has recorded how : ' At the little Academy of Freiberg, founded for the purpose of training mining engineers and mine captains for the mines of Saxony, there was renewed the spectacle presented by the universities of the Middle Ages, for students flocked thither from every civilised country. One saw men from the most remote countries, already well advanced in years, men of education holding important positions, engaged with all diligence in the study of the German language, that they might fit themselves to sit at the feet of this " Great oracle of the sciences of the earth." '

To this Cuvier adds, after recording the brilliant array of investigators who started from Werner's school to explore the face of the earth : ' We may say of him, what was never truthfully said before, save of Linnæus, that Nature everywhere found herself interrogated in his name.'

Werner in his enthusiasm developed certain generalisations which have proved to be exaggerations. Thus he claimed not only some rocks, but all, with the exception of products of modern volcanoes, to have been deposited from water, for the most part in the sea. They might be detrital as sandstone, or organic as shelly limestone, or chemical as rock-salt and, according to him, basalt and granite. Again, impressed by the persistent succession of various definable lithological formations in Saxony, Werner thought that there was a universal, or near-universal, succession of formations, starting with granite and ending with superficial gravels; and he considered that this succession was controlled by successive changes in the composition and extent of the ocean. He was not confident as to what had led to the present low-water level of the ocean, but imagined that much of its substance might have escaped into surrounding space. He certainly did not accept steep dips as an indication of earth movement; for he recognised that sedimentation, if accompanied by cementation, might occur at any angle, as can be seen, for instance, on the roof and walls of a cave.

Not unnaturally Werner's followers came to be spoken of as Neptunists, for they referred almost every geological phenomenon to the operation of sea power. Werner taught the non-volcanic origin of basalt as early as 1776, after an examination of a Saxon exposure. He seems to have known at the time that Desmarest in 1774, as a result of researches extending back to 1763 among Guettard's volcanoes of the Auvergne, had already claimed a volcanic origin for basalt, not only locally but generally. Still he himself 'found not a trace of volcanic action, nor the smallest proof of volcanic origin.'

JAMES HUTTON

Those who agreed with Desmarest were called Vulcanists, and among them was a particularly stalwart band, the Plutonists, led by James Hutton of Edinburgh, who interpreted not only basalt, but also granite, as igneous, and deduced from the attitudes and compositions of various sedimentary rocks a story of repeated unheaval, erosion, subsidence and sedimentation, just as we do today.

Hutton had qualified as a doctor of medicine, but subsequently trained and practised as a farmer before devoting himself wholly to philosophic pursuits. It was as a farmer that he learnt to look below turf and soil and to puzzle out for himself the story recorded in underlying rocks. After completing more than 30 years of study Hutton produced his celebrated *Theory of the Earth* in volume i, 1788, of the Transactions of the newly founded Royal Society of Edinburgh. Later, in 1795, in response to criticisms, he brought his *Theory* up to date with considerable additions and issued it in book form. Hutton's main difference from Werner is epitomised in his proposition that land power must be accorded an important role along with sea power in the shaping of world destiny. For him igneous action was of old standing and highly significant. The earth could be regarded as a machine, actuated by deep-seated heat and safeguarded by volcanoes. The Neptunists treated volcanoes merely as a modern accident due to spontaneous combustion of coal seams ignited near the surface.

Hutton made mistakes, some of them serious, but he so frequently referred back to Nature for guidance in developing his theory that most of his conclusions hold good to this day. It is therefore interesting to note that the very foundation upon which he built would not be considered acceptable in any modern court of scientific inquiry. The earth, he contended, is a machine of peculiar construction, divinely adapted for use by plants and animals. This machine, from the beginning, must have followed the same laws of action as control it today—otherwise one would have to admit some flaw in the original design. Strange to say, on this insecure postulate he erected a discipline that has proved trustworthy : anyone who would trace the working of the earth should in the first place study such operations as are carried on before his eyes in accessible regions; and, in the second place, critically examine the products of that other great group of activities which are not themselves open to his scrutiny.

It has been said above that Hutton was leader of the Plutonists, but his dogma that geological agencies have acted in the past with the same general intensity as in the present had to stand or fall quite apart from any interpretation of igneous rocks. Thus he was leader not only of the Plutonists, but also of those who later came to be known as Uniformitarians. In actual fact most of Hutton's Plutonist followers set aside their master's Uniformitarian doctrine.

They thought that the record of the rocks necessitated appeal to catastrophes, much more vigorous and widespread than the floods, earthquakes and eruptions that afflict us today.

Extraordinary bitterness of feeling was manifested in the controversies between Neptunists and Plutonists, Catastrophists and Uniformitarians. Lyell has suggested that allowance should be made for the political excitement engendered by the French Revolution; but it must be admitted that a similar vituperative outburst occurred among geologists in politically peaceful times a hundred years later, provoked by a radical reinterpretation of the structure of the Alps. Anyhow, it is interesting to recall that the inherent tranquillity of Hutton's uniformitarianism proved one of the prime causes of the ensuing uproar. Hutton connected landscape with commonplace erosion in strikingly modern fashion, and to make this possible he lifted all restriction from geological time; whereas Bishop Ussher, it will be remembered, had dated the creation of the world no further back than the year 4004 B.C. My own opinion is that Hutton's chief sin in the eyes of many of his contemporaries was his confident interpretation of God's purpose through thoughtful observation of Nature without accepting guidance from revelation.

WILLIAM SMITH

While this wordy warfare proceeded, William Smith, a plain practical man, a civil and mineral engineer, particularly concerned at first with surveying routes for canals, made a momentous observation on a subject, which, more than anything else, has come to distinguish geology from other sciences. He discovered that each stratum (one would be more inclined now to say each formation) could be identified by its contained fossils. He fully realised not only the scientific but also the practical value of his discovery, which again and again might help in the identification of geological formations concerned in problems of agriculture, mining, transport, drainage and water supply. Smith's list of formations from the Coal up to the Chalk, with a selection of characteristic fossils, was taken down from his dictation in 1799, two years after Hutton's death, and obtained wide publicity. His first geologically coloured map seems to have been of the Bath district, and is also dated 1799. His masterpiece, a geological map of England, Wales and part of Scotland, on the scale of 5 miles to the inch, was published with explanatory memoir in 1815. The map carries a dedication by permission to Sir Joseph Banks, President of the Royal Society, and a prospectus refers to support from the Board of Agriculture, the Royal Institution and the Society of Arts, Manufactures and Commerce. A list of about 400 subscribers is given in the memoir.

Magnificent as was Smith's achievement, we must not forget that his idea of a fossil succession had already been suggested by a few others, though usually without further development even by the authors concerned. This last qualification does not apply to the work of the Abbé Giraud-Soulavie, who between 1780 and 1784 produced a seven-volume *Natural History of Southern France,* in which he divided the local rocks into successive formations characterised by successive fossil faunas. We find him summing up as follows: ' The difference between the shells in the rocks rests on difference of their relative antiquity, and not on mere local causes. If an earthquake were to submerge the ammonite-bearing rocks of the Vivarais beneath the Mediterranean, the sea returning to its old site would not bring back its old shells.'

Though the Abbé Giraud-Soulavie made and recorded enough observations to establish his point, his results seem to have attracted as little attention among geologists of his day as those of the Abbé Mendel among biologists some 80 years later. The reason that has been given for neglect of Giraud-Soulavie's writings is that their poor literary standard blinded readers to their scientific merit. Hutton, too, wrote badly, but fortunately, five years after his death, there appeared in 1802 one of the most attractive books ever penned, *Illustrations of the Huttonian Theory,* written by his friend John Playfair, Professor of Mathematics at Edinburgh University.

Neglect of Giraud-Soulavie did not retard matters very long. Smith's progress we have already indicated. Following closely in date, Georges Cuvier and Alexander Brongniart established, as an independent discovery, a fossil succession in the Paris basin. Cuvier was founder of comparative anatomy and gave much attention to land vertebrates, the modern representatives of which could be regarded as fairly completely listed even in his day. It is interesting to note that some of his earlier findings, and those of fellow naturalists, reached Edinburgh, in spite of war conditions, in time for Playfair to discuss them in his 1802 *Illustrations*. Playfair therein enumerated five genera or species of extinct mammals as definitely demonstrated, and also admitted that shells, corals and plants of the geological past had been shown to differ substantially from their present day representatives. In keeping with this he sagaciously protested against current interpretations of a frozen rhinoceros carcase found in Siberia. He could not admit either far transport of the corpse from some southern haunt or instantaneous change of the local climate. He advanced instead the more reasonable suggestion that these extinct monsters were of a kind that roamed Siberia under much the same climatic conditions as have continued ever since.

Cuvier was an inveterate catastrophist, who again and again in restoration of past times cleared the decks of existent life-forms by some violent revolution. He combated the views of his contemporary, Lamarck, regarding specific variation. For him specific features were constant; and his great influence long retarded the growth of evolutionary speculation. Still, if we feel inclined to criticise, it is well to remember that most of the extinct mammals which Cuvier described have left no descendants in the world today.

Since writing the above I have been delighted to find, in an unpublished manuscript, Hutton's own views in regard to evolution. In reading them one must remember that Hutton died eleven years before Charles Darwin was born. His manuscript, which was intended for publication, discusses possible diversification of species, not on Lamarckian

lines, but through 'continued propagation' of that form
within 'the infinite variation of the breed,' which is 'best
adapted to the exercise of those instinctive arts by which
the species is to live.' 'Thus, for example,' it continues,
'where dogs are to live by the swiftness of their feet and the
sharpness of their sight, the best adapted to that end will be
the most certain of remaining, while those forms that are
least adapted to this manner of chase will be the first to
perish.' According to 'this beautiful system of animal life
(which is also applicable to vegetables)' . . . 'the economy
of this animal [the surviving variety] would always appear
to be in perfect wisdom,' in other words to be in perfect adjustment to environmental needs. This historical revelation
is treated more fully in a Hutton commemorative volume of
the *Proceedings of Royal Society of Edinburgh,* 1950.

Returning from our interesting digression, we may note
that fortunately much of the value of fossils to stratigraphical geology depends upon the mere fact that there is a
determinable fossil succession preserved in the rocks, a fact
that is independent of any theory of the origin or extinction
of species. Smith expresses the position excellently in the
Preface of his 1815 memoir, when he speaks of having discovered a definite arrangement of organic remains, which
holds good in very distant parts of the island; 'which arrangement,' he continues, 'must readily convince every
scientific or discerning person that the earth is formed as
well as governed, like the other works of its great Creator,
according to regular and immutable laws, which are dis-
coverable by human industry and observation, and which
form a legitimate and most important object of science.'

Smith transferred his business quarters to London in 1804;
and in 1807 the Geological Society of the same great city
was instituted, the first of its kind in the world. The two
events approach one another somewhat closely in date, but
in little else. One can hardly imagine that a 15s. dinner
would appeal to Smith as a necessary prelude to a monthly
geological discussion. Admittedly the Society started as a
geological dining club. Its thirteen founder members, including Humphry Davy, Secretary of the Royal Society,

were well-to-do men, keenly interested in scientific questions with a general bias towards chemistry and mineralogy. One of them, however, James Parkinson, was a medical man who published three volumes on the *Organic Remains of a Former World,* 1804-1811. He at any rate appreciated the fact that Smith had given a geological interest to fossils, as we find acknowledged in a paper from his pen on the geology of the London district printed in the first volume of the Society's transactions, 1811.

The original members of the Geological Society seem to have grown impatient of the hostile camps and far-flung war cries that had come to be associated with the name of geology. At their second meeting they elected as Honorary Members Robert Jameson and John Playfair, both of them professors of Edinburgh University; the former was arch-Wernerian in the northern capital; the latter, as we have seen, was Hutton's gifted interpreter. The young Society, starting anew, planned to replace controversy by agreement reached through amicable discussion. It has indeed achieved much in this direction, but it soon had to abolish Article 3 of its first code of rules, which reads as follows : ' All questions on which a difference of opinion may arise shall be determined by ballot at the next ordinary meeting.'

For one year, 1808-9, Sir Joseph Banks, who was President of the Royal Society 1778-1820, was an ordinary member of the Geological Society; but he resigned. Apparently he thought that activities of the new society might cause dissipation of scientific energy. This step led to a special meeting of the Geological Society in 1809 to consider the advisability of consolidating with the Royal Society as an Assistant Society. Instead it was agreed : ' That any proposition tending to render this Society dependent upon, or subservient to, any other Society, does not correspond with the conception this meeting entertains of the original principles upon which the Geological Society was founded.'

The above exchange of opinions probably explains in part why Smith's map, though dedicated, as we have seen, to Sir Joseph Banks, and approved by the Board of Agriculture, the Royal Institution and the Society of Arts, Manufactures and Commerce, carried no indication of assistance from the Geological Society. Fortunately the coolness did not last indefinitely; in 1828 the Geological Society through the mediation of the President and Council of the Royal Society received an invitation from the Lords Commissioners of His Majesty's Treasury to take up quarters in Somerset House, where the Royal Society, the Royal Academy and the Society of Antiquaries had been long in residence; and three years later, in 1831, William Smith was awarded the first medal ever bestowed by the Geological Society—the Wollaston Medal which has since come to be regarded as the premier distinction that can be won in the international field of geological science.

Professor Adam Sedgwick of Cambridge had the congenial task of announcing the prize. He rose to the occasion in characteristic style demanding ' whether we were not compelled, by every motive by which the judgement can approve, and the heart sanction, to perform this act of filial duty, before we thought of the claims of any other man, and to place our first honour on the brow of the Father of English Geology.'

CHARLES LYELL AND CHARLES DARWIN

After speaking of William Smith's achievements, Sedgwick passed on in the course of his Anniversary Address to review many other subjects of geological interest. Here we may single out his comments on volume i of Charles Lyell's *Principles of Geology*, published the previous year. This first volume may be regarded as the natural successor to Playfair's *Illustrations*, enriched with a wealth of new observations. Sedgwick acknowledged very warmly the instruction which he had derived from perusal of Lyell's treatise on ' geological dynamics,' as he styled it; but he inveighed against the author's defence of the ' Huttonian hypothesis,' expressed in the secondary title of the work, which reads: *An Attempt to Explain the Earth's Surface, by Reference to Causes now in Operation*. All know how Charles Darwin, who happened at this time to have imbibed a share of catas-

trophism from Sedgwick, received a copy of Lyell's volume
i in time to take it with him on his five-year voyage in the
Beagle starting from Devonport, December, 1831. All also
know how Lyell's insistence in this volume i upon the
efficacy of natural causes, to use a colloquial expression, in
the realm of dynamical geology influenced Darwin in his
eventual adoption of natural causes to account for the origin
of species. Lyell himself remained, until after the appearance of his friend's epoch-making book on the subject in
1859, a strong advocate of fixity of species, and accounted
for the life succession recorded in the rocks by invoking
special creations distributed through time and space.

G. B. GREENOUGH

From this digression let us return to the Geological
Society and William Smith. So far from helping Smith with
his 1815 map of England and Wales, the Society had actually sponsored a rival map of the same region on the scale
of six miles to the inch, prepared by G. B. Greenough, their
first Chairman and President, 1807-13 (President again,
1818-20, 1833-35). Greenough has explained that he was
aware of Smith's project at any rate as early as 1804, but
shared with others, then and later, the view that completion,
and still more publication, were hopeless. He himself took
up the work of map drawing in 1808 'in obedience to a
recommendation circulated by the Geological Society on its
first establishment'; and with much exertion on his own part
and assistance from others presented a map in manuscript to
the Society in 1812, which was published amended in 1820.
No wonder when Smith received a presentation copy the
iron entered his soul. 'This copy seemed like the ghost of
my old map intruding on my business and retirement, and
mocking me in the disappointments of a science with which
I could scarcely be in temper. It was put out of sight.' No
wonder, too, that further sale of Smith's 1815 map completely faded out. His receipt of a pension of £100 per
annum from William IV in 1832 seems to have been somewhat of a delayed-action recognition in this direction.

Greenough has been blamed in some quarters for unfair, or at least ungenerous, behaviour; and such a view seems to have been accepted by the Society in 1865 when, long after both Smith and Greenough had passed away, they produced a third edition of the latter's map, for they entitled it : 'A Physical and Geological Map of England and Wales, by the late G. B. Greenough, Esq., F.R.S., F.G.S., on the basis of the original Map of William Smith, 1815.' All the same there may be more to say in Greenough's justification than leaps to the eye. He probably sincerely thought in the earlier stages that support to Smith would lead to procrastination without tangible result.

Greenough is sometimes charged with having started with the intention of drawing a Wernerian map (he had been a pupil of Werner at Freiberg), and of having finished with a Smithian map, receiving much assistance on the way from Smith's disciples. In so far as the basis of mapping was lithological, this means that Greenough originally expected to get a useful result by extrapolating the Saxon succession of formations, whereas he soon found it necessary to adopt a British succession—this sort of development one expects in any young progressive science. In so far as the basis of mapping was palæontological, one must realise that geologists in the south and east of England were looking to Paris, rather than Bath or Yorkshire, for guidance. This is well shown in the work of Parkinson in the first volume of the Geological Society in 1811, and of Webster in the second, 1814. Parkinson in relation to the London area stated that geological value can only be got from fossils if their consideration be 'connected with that of the several strata, in which they are found'; and that 'this mode of conducting our inquiries was long since recommended by Mr. W. Smith, who first noticed that *certain fossils are peculiar to and are only found lodged in, particular strata;* and who first ascertained the constancy *in the order of superposition* and *the continuity of the strata of this island.*' Parkinson then pointed out 'that these observations have lately also occurred to Messrs. Cuvier and Brongniart' in the neighbourhood of Paris, and he instituted a comparison of the London and

Parisian successions, finding many agreements with a main difference in the absence of Oligocene (to use a modern term) from the London area—a difference which he thought might perhaps be atttributed to some catastrophe. Webster three years later built largely with Parkinson's assistance, looked for further comparison with Paris, and found Oligocene in the Isle of Wight. Not unnaturally he referred to Cuvier and Brongniart rather than to Smith.

Although the supersession of Smith's map by Greenough's had its poignant aspect, it embodied a great principle. The editors of the first volume of the Society's Transactions, 1811, say in the preface that 'they are persuaded, nothing is more consonant to the wishes of the Society, than that every mineralogist, proposing to visit any part of the kingdom, should have free access to all documents which may happen to be in its possession '—a remark which referred explicitly to 'mineralogical maps, plans, and sections.' There is no doubt that the Society favoured open doors and freedom of research, while Smith to some extent felt that he had won proprietary rights. The Geological Survey of Great Britain, as we shall soon see, is the acknowledged child of the Ordnance Survey and the Geological Society; and it rejoices that co-operate publication of geological information for the good of all came to it as an established aim before it took over part responsibility for mapping and describing the geology of the country. The ideal cannot of course be applied in every case, since the Survey is often entrusted with confidential material; but the broad intention holds all the time.

EARLY GOVERNMENTAL GEOLOGICAL SURVEYS

The Geological Survey of Great Britain was formally instituted as a Geological Ordnance Survey in 1835, and is very generally regarded as the oldest among the national geological surveys of the world. At the same time it did not spring into being quite suddenly, nor was it entirely without forerunners.

Let us begin with the British Isles. L. R. Cox, who has studied the subject with special care, has supplied most of the following facts regarding England. From 1794 onwards for a few years, the Board of Agriculture published a series of county maps of soils and exposed rocks, without any stratigraphical basis. There is no doubt that they proved useful to William Smith.

In 1805 Sir John Sinclair suggested that Smith should be attached to the Ordnance Trigonometrical Survey in a geological capacity, but his proposal came to nothing. Two years later, Smith's pupil, John Farey, was commissioned by the Board of Agriculture, on the advice of Sir Joseph Banks, to survey Derbyshire, so as to combine a report on the strata of that county with information of more direct agricultural significance. Farey's *General View of the Agriculture and Minerals of Derbyshire,* 3 vols., 1811-1817, ranks as the earliest official geological memoir published in Britain, and is a notable achievement.

In 1826 the Ordnance Trigonometrical Survey was placed under the superintendence of Captain T. F. Colby, who remained in charge until he retired in 1846 with the rank of Major-General. Colby was most anxious not to delay his topographical survey, but he also wanted the latter to serve as a groundwork for historical, antiquarian, natural history, geological and statistical surveys. His influence proved most helpful in regard to geological developments. In the first place he encouraged officers of the Ordnance Survey with sufficient knowledge to draw geological boundaries in areas surveyed under their direction, though not to attempt to make geological maps. In 1831 Murchison renewed Sinclair's suggestion that William Smith should be appointed Geological Colourer of the Ordnance maps; but his candidate was by this time rather old for the post. Instead, in 1832, De la Beche, Secretary of the Geological Society, was authorised to affix geological colours to the Ordnance one inch to the mile maps covering Devon, with adjacent parts of Somerset, Dorset and Cornwall. This appointment matured presently with the definite founding of the Geological Survey in 1835.

Now let us turn to Scotland. It is noteworthy that the first appointment of a geologist to the Trigonometrical Survey

PLATE II.

MAJOR-GENERAL T. F. COLBY.

[*To face page* 18

took place some years before Colby became Superintendent; and we are indebted to V. A. Eyles for a very careful investigation of the subject. In 1811 John Macculloch, ranking as a Chemist in the Board of Ordnance, was dispatched to the northern kingdom to undertake certain geological reconnaissances for geophysical purposes. In 1814 he was appointed Geologist, and by 1832, or possibly a little later, had completed a broad geological survey of the kingdom, a very creditable exploit. His results, illustrated by maps, sections and drawings, mostly appeared in publications of the Geological Society and in his famous *Description of the Western Islands of Scotland,* 1819. His geological map of the whole country, on the scale of four miles to the inch, was published officially in 1836, largely owing to exertions of the Highland and Agricultural Society of Scotland. Its busy author had died the previous year as a result of a carrriage accident, whilst on his honeymoon at the age of 62.

In Ireland the work of her greatest geological son, Richard John Griffith, is difficult to separate into two compartments, official and unofficial. From 1809 to 1812 Griffith was engaged as an engineer in a public inquiry into the nature and possibilities of the important peat bogs of his native land. In the latter year he was appointed H.M. Inspector of Mines and also elected Professor of Geology and Mining Engineer to the Royal Dublin Society; and it was at this juncture that he really started work on his famous geological map of Ireland, first definitely published in 1838, on the scale of ten miles to the inch. He undertook the task at the pressing instance of Greenough, which reminds us that Griffith joined the Geological Society of London in 1808, the second year of its existence. From 1822 to 1868 Griffith was continually in official harness in connection with road surveying, boundary fixing or land valuation, subjects which furnished ample scope for geological research directed to the welfare of the nation. In 1835 he exhibited what is sometimes called the second edition of his map to the Geological Section of the British Association at Dublin, over which he presided. Next year the Government ordered it to be reconstructed and engraved under the Board of Ordnance, on the scale of four miles to the inch. The result appeared in 1839, following the smaller-scale 1838 edition mentioned above, and won universal admiration. A revision was engraved by order of the Treasury and published in 1855, a year after the author had received the Wollaston Medal. In 1858 Griffith was rewarded with a baronetcy for his numerous and valuable public services.

Turning back to 1826, when Colby took charge of the Ordnance Trigonometrical Survey, we find J. W. Pringle entrusted with the establishment of a Geological Branch in Ireland. He was followed some six years later by J. E. Portlock, who in 1843 published a capital *Report on the Geology of the County of Londonderry, and of parts of Tyrone and Fermanagh.* Two years afterwards, in 1845, the Irish Survey became part of the compounded Geological Survey of Great Britain and Ireland, and was transferred from the Ordnance Survey to the First Commissioner of Her Majesty's Woods, Forests, Land Revenues, Works and Buildings.

As regards France, we have already noted that Guettard and Monnet's 1780 map received official publication. Later, as Eyles has pointed out, an official geological survey of the country was carried out by five geologists, including Élie de Beaumont and Dufrénoy, between 1825 and 1835. The resultant map was published in 1841 in six sheets, scale 1 : 500,000; while descriptive memoirs began to appear in 1830. It is interesting to recall that as a preliminary measure, in 1823, the two main authors of this important map had been sent to England for six months to gather additional geological, mining and metallurgical experience; and that after the successful completion of their task they were, in 1843, jointly awarded the Wollaston Medal of the Geological Society. In 1868 de Beaumont very fittingly became first Director of the newly established Service de la Carte géologique de la France.

In America, North Carolina, 1824-1828, Massachusetts, 1830-33, and Tennessee, 1831-50, all carried out early State geological surveys.

In India a geologist was attached to the Trigonometrical Survey from 1818 to 1823.

1 8 3 5

DE LA BECHE STARTS ALONE

HENRY Thomas De la Beche, last male representative of a family of Norman barons who came over with the Conqueror, was also first officer of the Geological Survey; in fact from 1835 to 1839 he constituted its whole scientific staff. De la Beche was born in 1796, a year, that is, before Hutton died, and three years before Count Rumford (Benjamin Thompson of Massachusetts) founded the Royal Institution—from which latter De la Beche seems to have derived much of his inspiration. In 1810 he was sent to the Military School of Great Marlow, the Sandhurst of those days; but on the close of the Napoleonic wars he decided to renounce martial ambition and devote himself to scientific research on a moderate income derived from a landed estate in Jamaica. In 1817, when only twenty-one years of age, De la Beche was elected to the Geological Society, and two years later to the Royal Society. His connection with the former was particularly close, for he was Secretary 1831-32, Vice-President 1833-34, Foreign Secretary 1835-47, President 1847-49, and Wollaston medalist 1855. In this last year he died. He had been knighted 1842.

De la Beche loved field geology, because he delighted in nature, both as scientist and artist, and because he had a physique which made him an active pedestrian, not to mention a bold swimmer. He travelled considerably, and his first paper, 1819, deals with *Observations on depth and temperature of the Lake of Geneva;* but his main work lay in south-west England where he had spent much of his boyhood. He read widely and critically and published a number of books, besides papers and official memoirs. The best known, perhaps, is his *Manual of Geology,* 1831, which was so well received that we find him in the preface of the third

English edition, 1833, speaking of German, French and American editions, actually published or in preparation.

Another of De la Beche's publications, his *Theoretical Researches in Geology,* 1834, furnishes a compact statement of the scientific outlook with which its author took up his appointment on the Geological Survey—and here one may interpolate that this appointment marked the second stage in the development of continued governmental scientific research in Britain, initiated in 1675 by the founding of the Royal Observatory at Greenwich ; the position of the Natural History branch of the British Museum is a little difficult to assess, because in early days its research activities tended to be intermittent. In this little book we find De la Beche willing to accept La Place's hypothesis 'that our solar system is a condensation of nebulous matter,' and to consider it extremely probable that the earth has consolidated from a hot fluid spheroid. In his discussion of this and other matters he shows a commendable knowledge of geo-chemistry and physics. He thinks that Élie de Beaumont is probably correct in attributing mountain chains to wrinkling of the earth's surface consequent upon loss of internal heat. He does not follow Hutton and Lyell in the view that the geological record shows 'no vestige of a beginning—no prospect of an end.' On the other hand he interprets gneiss and mica-schist as 'inferior stratified rocks' formed in the earliest hot ocean, and not, as Hutton and Lyell claimed, normal rocks affected by regional metamorphism. He also shows himself a mild catastrophist, rebuking Lyell for thinking that man in his brief experience has seen the full power of Nature's activities. He himself considers the contortion of the Alpine strata as a product of rapid yielding, and commends de Beaumont's 'very simple suggestion . . . that during the last elevating movement which took place in the Alps, the heat evolved from the necessary fissures suddenly melted the snows which previously existed on these mountains, and by these means a large body of water was produced, which swept the blocks through the valleys into those situations where we now find them.' He is also prepared to invoke floods actuated by sudden submarine elevation of mountains as an explanation for the distribution of northern erratic blocks and for much erosion of land forms. He accepts granite as well as basalt as igneous; though for some purposes he prefers to divide rocks into unstratified and stratified, rather than igneous and aqueous, so as not 'to prejudge every question connected with their origin.' He is fully aware of the existence of ancient lavas, as well as intrusions, a matter over which Hutton had stumbled; and he recognises ancient volcanic ashes. He gives much attention to the use of fossils in geology. Certain aspects of his treatment of this matter are outlined below, starting with a quotation from his Chapter xi, which will serve among other things as a further illustration of its author's tangled style of expression, strongly reminiscent of translated German.

> After the remains of animals and vegetables, entombed at various depths and at different periods in the crust of the globe, were fully recognised as the exuviæ of organic life which had once existed on the surface of the earth, it became a somewhat prevalent opinion, particularly after the researches of Cuvier and Brongniart round Paris, and those of Smith in England, that contemporaneous deposits were characterized by the presence of similar organic remains. During the time that such deposits were supposed to be distinguished by similar mineralogical composition, and viewing the subject the other way, that similar mineralogical structure at once proclaimed the geological date of the rock, it was considered somewhat heretical to doubt the possibility of discovering any other than a certain series of organic remains in a given fossiliferous rock wherever found.
>
> This opinion, though somewhat modified, is still so far entertained that similar organic remains are supposed to characterize contemporaneous deposits to considerable distances; at least to this extent, that if a belemnite be discovered on the flanks of the Himalayan mountains, there is a disposition to consider, *à priori*, that it must belong to some part of a series of rocks in which this genus is found in Western Europe. Fossil shells of similar species are also supposed to characterize the same deposit over considerable areas.
>
> In the present comparatively advanced state of geology, it behoves us carefully to weigh the conditions under which animal and vegetable life now exist, before we assume that a given deposit can or cannot be determined.

Then follows a long discussion which takes into account the complexities of modern distribution of life-forms controlled, as they are, by habitat-condition and also by pure geography. De la Beche points out that without any change in the sum total of species mere migration consequent upon local alteration of depth, climate, etc., would furnish successive strata with contrasted faunas, and he emphasises that these faunal successions would be apt to give totally erroneous time‑correlations if subjected uncritically to what may be called Smithian analysis. All this is true; but almost, despite himself, De la Beche accepted as a fact, proved by geological observation, that change of life‑forms has been in large measure controlled by time, and not merely by migration. His summary includes the following : fossils 'teach us that man is a comparatively recent creature on the face of the globe; that creation has succeeded creation on its surface.' As regards this last point, in so far as it concerns the cause of the observed time‑controlled life‑changes, he is less dogmatic in another passage, which reads : ' There are likely to be few, seeing the beauty of design manifest in creation and so apparent in animals and vegetables, who will not rather consider there has been a succession of creations as new conditions arose, than that there should be an accommodating property in organic existence which might ultimately convert a polypus into a man.'

There is no doubt that sometimes a horse runs better in blinkers. Thus De la Beche might well have gone farther if, in his own work, he had been content to follow more closely in Smith's footsteps without an ever‑present consciousness of the difficulties that beset the path. All the same he managed to escape from the indecision and procrastination that might have been expected to accompany his unusually clear perception of these same difficulties. De la Beche realised that within a comparatively short time he could obtain positive results of intrinsic value; and he was prepared to publish such results without waiting for what might prove to be unattainable refinements. If we now compare him with a dog instead of a horse, he was assuredly one who seldom dropped a bone in pursuit of a shadow. This explains the amazing rapidity with which he, and later his staff, produced serviceable geological maps of much of England and Wales, maps that in many cases, as their own authors knew, might have benefited from revision as soon as they appeared.

ORDNANCE SURVEY AND GEOLOGICAL SOCIETY

Our discussion of De la Beche as a scientist on the threshold of his appointment to the Geological Survey has led on to mention of his subsequent publications. Before going farther in this direction let us consider some of the circumstances that attended the actual appointment.

It will be recalled that in 1832 De la Beche was given a preliminary appointment, as one may call it, to colour geologically the Ordnance Survey one inch to a mile maps of south-west England. He made such good progress that Greenough, when President of the Geological Survey in 1834, was able to say that during the previous year : 'Mr. De la Beche, one of our Vice-Presidents, acting under the Direction of the Board of Ordnance, has produced a geological map of the county of Devon, which, for extent and minuteness of information and beauty of execution, has a very high claim to regard. Let us rejoice in the complete success which has attended this first attempt of that honourable Board to exalt the character of English topography by rendering it at once more scientific and very much more useful to the country at large.' And again, in 1835, speaking of 1834 : 'The researches of your Vice-President in the counties of Devon and Somerset have been carried on this year with increased energy. Of the eight sheets of the Ordnance Map upon which he has been engaged, four were published last spring, three others are complete, the eighth is nearly complete, and an explanatory memoir with sheets of sections applying to the whole are to be published before our next anniversary. Let us hope that the work so admirably begun may not be suffered to terminate here.'

The map sheets, to which Greenough referred, are what are now called the Old Series one-inch sheets, each covering an area of some 965 square miles, including in coastal districts a proportion, small or big, of sea. The explanatory memoir, which he mentioned, actually appeared in 1839, after it had been extended to include Cornwall as well as Devon and West Somerset. At the time Greenough spoke he probably knew that his hope for a continuance of De la Beche's survey was likely to be fulfilled. At any rate, at the next anniversary meeting of the Society, on the 20th February, 1836, his successor in the chair, Charles Lyell, was able to say :

Early in the Spring of last year an application was made by the Master-General and Board of Ordnance [Col. Colby once again] to Dr. Buckland and Mr. Sedgwick, as professors of geology in the universities of Oxford and Cambridge, and to myself, as President of this Society, to offer our opinion as to the expediency of combining a geological examination of the English counties with the geographical survey now in progress. In compliance with this requisition we drew up a joint report, in which we endeavoured to state fully our opinion as to the great advantages which must accrue from such an undertaking, not only as calculated to promote geological science, which alone would be a sufficient object, but also as a work of great practical utility, bearing on agriculture, mining, road-making, the formation of canals and railroads, and other branches of national industry. The enlightened views of the Board of Ordnance were warmly seconded by the present Chancellor of the Exchequer, and a grant was obtained from the Treasury to defray the additional expenses which will be incurred in colouring geologically the Ordnance county maps. This arrangement may justly be regarded as an economical one, as those surveyors who have cultivated geology can with small increase of labour, when exploring the minute topography of the ground, trace out the boundaries of the principal mineral groups. This end, however, could only be accomplished by securing the co-operation of an experienced and able geologist, who might organise and direct the operations; and I congratulate the Society that our Foreign Secretary, Mr. De la Beche, has been chosen to discharge an office for which he is so eminently qualified.

The steps taken in 1835 confirmed the policy adopted in 1832 and opened up a prospect of its application to the country at large. There has been a little confusion in certain quarters as to what it meant financially. F. J. North, who took extracts from Ordnance Survey correspondence, since destroyed by enemy action, tells us that De la Beche seems to have already received £300 expenses to cover his eight sheets of Devon (completed to their rectangular margins). Now that he was instructed to 'commence the Geological Survey of Cornwall without delay,' it was on the understanding that the expenses of the new work would come to about £1,000 a year, and that he would be given a salary of £500. A limited amount of mapping assistance was supplied by two geologically minded officers of the

Ordnance Survey, and other help by private geologists investigating the same field. Previous publications were also very useful, many of them in the Transactions of the Royal Geological Society of Cornwall, which had been founded in 1814.

FIRST MEMOIR

In 1839 De la Beche marked the completion of his mapping of the Devon peninsula, from Bridgwater and Axminster to the Scilly Isles, by publishing the first memoir of the Geological Survey, entitled: *Report on the Geology*

FIG. 2.—Plan on large scale of contact of slate and granite. (Quoted from De la Beche, *Report on Cornwall*, 1839, p. 169.)

of Cornwall, Devon and West Somerset. It contains 648 pages of letterpress, with a frontispiece-map in colours, along with numerous other plates presenting geological and mining sections, mining plans and views. It is replete with observation and reasoned deduction, and its methodical arrangement has furnished a pattern for all subsequent Survey memoirs descriptive of particular areas. It is typical of its author that economic geology is given close attention in a chapter of 64 pages dealing with mining, quarrying and agriculture. As all know, the region is of particular variety

and interest, with a major unconformity separating folded
from unfolded sediments. It has in addition lavas, ashes and
intrusions, including granites, these last confined to the
folded formations; while its china clay and china stone and
many of its mineral veins are unique in Britain. It is sometimes said that the *Report* owes most of its permanent value
to the description which it gives of mineral lodes both as
regards geology and method of working. Mining in Cornwall was at the time very prosperous and afforded opportunities for investigation that have since passed away. On the
theoretical side De la Beche thought that many of the veins
had resulted from admission of sea water through fissures
to depths where they found granite still incandescent though
consolidated.

De la Beche's handling, in 1839, of the problems presented by the folded sediments of the peninsula affords an
example of limited achievement. Tacitly accepting a fundamental structural correction advanced by Sedgwick and
Murchison in 1837, he separately mapped the Culm
Measures, or 'carbonaceous rocks,' as an upper, later formation, flanked to north and south by outcrops of the ' greywacke series '; but he opposed the fossil-inspired correlation,
which the same two authors had put forward, of these Culm
Measures with the Carboniferous system of the rest of England and South Wales : the lithological contrast seemed to
him in certain particulars too great.

DEVONIAN SYSTEM

In their 1837 paper Sedgwick and Murchison had considered the underlying greywacke as probably of Cambrian,
or in part perhaps of Lower Silurian, date. This opinion
they soon altered, but not sufficiently early, in print, for
De la Beche to take notice of the fact in his 1839 *Report*.
The new interpretation came to W. Lonsdale, the gifted
Curator of the Geological Society's Museum, in December,
1837; and was, during 1838, communicated by him in conversation to Murchison, Sedgwick, De la Beche and others.
It resulted from a brilliant application of Smithian principles

with due allowance for difficulties introduced by local conditions of sedimentation; how brilliant, may be gathered from the fact that its author, with the help of fossils and field relations, correlated limestones of the greywacke of South Devon with some part of the Old Red Sandstone of Wales, *in spite of the fact that their faunas are strikingly dissimilar!* Lonsdale concluded from the fossils that the limestones in South Devon are of intermediate age between Silurian and Carboniferous; and he knew from field relations, already published, that the Old Red Sandstone in Wales occupies this time interval—with in places a conformable passage at bottom into Silurian and at top into Carboniferous. We shall return to this subject presently.

HOUSES OF PARLIAMENT

Meanwhile we may note that De la Beche in 1838 served along with William Smith and others on a Commission to find the most suitable stone for building new Houses of Parliament at Westminster, in place of those destroyed by fire in 1834. The bulk of the work fell upon De la Beche. The commissioners drove about the country in an old carriage and pair, visiting quarry after quarry and procuring rough samples which were later shaped into six-inch cubes. Eventually Permian dolomite from Anston near Mansfield was selected. Its state of preservation in the Norman front of Southwell church, Nottinghamshire, furnished a good testimonial, though perhaps insufficient for a stone intended for a city atmosphere. Unfortunately, in the sequel, sufficient care was not exercised at the quarry to secure rejection of inferior material, with the result that some 15 per cent. of the stone actually used weathered very badly. De la Beche, however, showed his continued confidence in the Anston stone by using it for the building of his new Museum in Jermyn Street, started in 1848. Here it retained all ornamental detail in perfection until the building was demolished when new quarters were found for the Survey more than eighty years later.

As a postscript we may perhaps quote from the *Summary of Progress of the Geological Survey* for 1934: ' A joint committee of officers of H.M. Office of Works, of the Building Research Station and of the Geological Survey was set up in connexion with the selection of stone suitable for the repair of the stonework of the Houses of Parliament.'

MUSEUM AND STAFF

Having successfully launched his scheme for a geological survey of the kingdom, De la Beche proceeded to point out to the Chancellor of the Exchequer the advantages that would accrue to the country from possession of a museum for display of rocks and minerals of economic significance. The suggestion was approved in 1837, and a building in Craig's Court, Whitehall, adjoining Scotland Yard, was assigned for Survey offices and museum. The latter was opened in 1841 under the title of Museum of Economic Geology. Its first Curator, also Chemist, was Richard Phillips, appointed along with an Assistant Curator in 1839. Phillips was one of the founder members of the Geological Society, and at the time of his death, which occurred on the eve of the opening of the Jermyn Street Museum in 1851, had come to be President of the Chemical Society. Phillips was furnished with a laboratory at the Museum, where the public might obtain analyses of rocks, minerals and soils. Although De la Beche was Director of the new Museum, this institution was administered by the Office of Woods, Forests, etc., and not by the Ordnance Survey, to which for the time being the Geological Survey still remained attached.

The exhibits were all of economic appeal : building stones, including the specimens collected by the Parliament Commission, ornamental stones, marbles, granites, serpentines; plasters, tiles, pottery, earthenware; ores of the metals, with Devon and Cornwall strongly represented, but with many other examples, British and foreign; metallurgical products such as castings, electrotypes, gun barrels; coal and other fuels.

Another extremely important addition to the responsibilities of the Geological Survey dates from this period. In 1836 there was disastrous loss of life in a Co. Durham coal

mine due to flooding from old forgotten workings. Following upon this the Council of the British Association approached the Government, who in 1839 placed De la Beche
in charge of the collection and preservation of plans of
abandoned mines. A Mining Record Office was established
alongside the Museum, and in 1840 T. B. Jordan, who had
previously been Secretary of the Royal Polytechnic Society
of Cornwall, was appointed Keeper. This Record Office
acted in some ways as an extension of the Museum, for it
exhibited models of mines and mining machinery. It continued to function under the Director (presently Director
General) of the Survey until 1883, when, as we shall see, it
passed to the Mines Department of the Home Office.

ANDREW CROMBIE RAMSAY

From 1839 to 1844 seven prospective field geologists were
added to the staff of the Geological Survey, most of them
with no previous training; and two paleontologists. Among
the fieldsmen the most interesting proved to be W. T.
Aveline, 1840, A. C. Ramsay, 1841, and H. W. Bristow,
1842. Andrew Crombie Ramsay, destined to be third
Director General of the Survey, was 27 years old when he
got his great opportunity. Till then his life had been one of
mixed fortunes. His father had been a successful manufacturing chemist,* but died in 1827, leaving a young family
of four. Thus Andrew at thirteen years of age had to forego
further schooling and enter an office in Glasgow. However,
he kept contact with teachers and students at the University
and elsewhere. Among them was a brilliant boy, Lyon
Playfair, some five years younger than himself, who lived
as a boarder in Mrs. Ramsay's house, while studying under
the famous chemist, Thomas Graham, at the Andersonian
Institute. Playfair joined the Survey a few years later; but
at the moment a holiday trip, which he made to Arran in
1836, is all that concerns us.

Playfair tells how, while sitting on the steamer and reading Lyell's *Principles,* a prize won in Professor Graham's

*Whose grandson, William Ramsay, was co-discoverer of argon.

class, he spoke to a charming lady by his side, and, showing her the book, expressed admiration for the author. As luck would have it, he was addressing the author's wife, who straightway called to Charles Lyell to come and be introduced. Ramsay followed Playfair to Arran within a few days, and was asked by Lyell to join in the geological excursions which the latter was making in the island. This proved a great tonic to young Ramsay, as also did his share in preparing for a visit of the British Association to Glasgow, due for 1840.

When the British Association assembled Ramsay was able to display a geologically coloured model of Arran on the scale of two inches to the mile, along with a map, sections and specimens in illustration of his first scientific paper. Lyell was geological President and arranged for Ramsay to read this paper on Friday—which he did successfully to a very distinguished audience—and next day to help in leading an excursion to examine some of the features he had just described. Alas, when Saturday morning came the excited leader overslept and missed the boat!

Murchison had been one of Ramsay's audience at Glasgow, and, apparently not frightened at the subsequent *contretemps,* he wrote asking the young man to join him as companion and assistant on a projected trip to America, Ramsay was delighted, but on reaching London found that Murchison had changed his mind. Fortunately, however, the latter had no difficulty in persuading De la Beche, who had also been at the Glasgow meeting, to secure for Ramsay a post on the Geological Survey.

WILLIAM EDMOND LOGAN

About 1839 De la Beche had transferred his operations from South-west England to South Wales and neighbouring English counties. Most of the geological formations ranged from Ordovician to Coal Measures inclusive, and the dominant structure was the South Wales coal basin. De la Beche received important help from William Edmond Logan, a member of a mining firm operating in the district. Logan had commenced mapping coal seams and other geological data on the one-inch Ordnance sheets as soon as these were issued, and in 1837 had exhibited his handiwork at the Liverpool meeting of the British Association, where it attracted the attention of De la Beche. When the Geological Survey entered South Wales, Logan placed his accumulated results at De la Beche's disposal; and, until he left the country in 1842, to found the Geological Survey of Canada, he continued an enthusiastic amateur, eager to render gratuitous assistance.

Logan, like De la Beche and his staff, mapped on the one inch to the mile scale, but he introduced an important refinement, which was soon adopted officially. He surveyed certain selected lines of country instrumentally, with chain, theodolite and level, to get the topographical detail accurate on a scale of 6 inches to a mile; and along these selected lines he made particularly close geological observations and plotted the combined results (true to scale) on paper in the form of sections with comparatively shallow vertical depth and comparatively long horizontal extension. Such sections are usually spoken of as horizontal sections by the Geological Survey. In addition to horizontal sections Logan drew vertical sections, in which the horizontal breadth is very small compared with the vertical depth. Commonly these vertical sections aim at furnishing a graphical record on a large scale, say one inch to 40 feet, of the thicknesses of all items in a local geological succession. Where the strata of the district lie flat, a vertical section corresponds with the record furnished by a vertical shaft or bore. Where the strata are tilted, if thicknesses are to be presented, rather than depths, correction has to be made for angle of dip. The Geological Survey since 1844 has published, in two separate series, large numbers of sheets carrying groups of horizontal or vertical sections, as the case may be; but the preparation of horizontal sections has latterly been discontinued as an aftermath of the availability of contoured six inch to a mile maps. Another legacy from Logan is the true interpretation of the underclays found beneath coal seams. Here he introduced the growth-in-place interpretation of coal origin, a very great advance.

PROGRESS TO 1846

De la Beche, though now responsible for the training and supervision of a field staff, and for the care of a Museum and Record Office, still for some years found time for personal mapping. By 1846 the combined efforts of the little party were so successful that one-inch geological maps, advertised for sale, covered a compact block of country south of Cardigan and Hereford and west of Gloucester and Bath, with a shorter eastern limit on the English Channel at Lyme Regis (*Fig.* 8). This represents over 6,000 square miles, and includes Cornwall and Devon with their metalliferous riches, and South Wales, the Forest of Dean and Bristol with their coal and iron. In addition, a large number of sections, both horizontal and vertical, had been issued.

We have already mentioned the early appointment of two paleontologists. Unlike most of the field staff, both were men of established reputation : John Phillips, 1841, and Edward Forbes, 1844, the latter not long home from the Ægean.

John Phillips, who remained on the Geological Survey until 1849, was a nephew of William Smith, and one of the ablest geologists of his day. He had been Professor at King's College, London; and after leaving the Survey went on to be Professor at Trinity College, Dublin, and later at Oxford. His first big contribution to the Survey was its second memoir : *Figures and Descriptions of the Palæozoic Fossils of Cornwall, Devon and West Somerset,* 1841. While in the main descriptive, this memoir discusses the age significance of the pre-Culm-Measure fossils. Phillips had already been responsible for grouping geological systems under the three terms, Palæozoic, Mesozoic and Cainozoic; and his cautious conclusion regarding the stratigraphical equivalence of the South Devon limestones appears to be conveyed in the following statements : the *Palæozoic* may be divided into *Lower,* with Primary Strata followed by Transition; *Middle,* including both Eifel and South Devon Strata; and *Upper* with the Carboniferous System followed by the Magnesian Limestone Formation. In other words, Phillips seems, after very detailed and critical examination, to follow

Lonsdale in correlating the limestones of South Devon, that is the lower part of De la Beche's greywacke, with some portion of the Old Red Sandstone of Wales; but he also seems to hesitate whether to go the whole way with Sedgwick and Murchison, who included the upper as well as the lower part of De la Beche's greywacke in the Old Red correlation. Nowadays Sedgwick and Murchison's view is very generally adopted.

IRELAND AND REORGANISATION

The geological branch of the Ordnance Survey in Ireland, referred to previously, may be said to have ended in 1843, when Portlock produced his Report on the *Geology of the County of Londonderry and of Parts of Tyrone and Fermanagh*. It is a magnificent memoir, written by a single author and yet combining areal and palæontological features such as were dealt with separately in De la Beche's *Report,* 1839, and Phillips' *Figures and Descriptions,* 1841. Among other points of interest Portlock emphasises that the local Silurian fauna (in which he included Ordovician, as we call it today) is ' remarkable in supplying species as yet undiscovered in England . . . thus serving as a link of connexion between the Silurian deposits of Great Britain and those of the Continents of Europe and America.'

A new beginning was made in 1845, when De la Beche was appointed Director General of the Geological Survey of Great Britain and Ireland, with Ramsay and Henry James, R.E., as Local Directors for Great Britain and Ireland respectively. James resigned next year to be followed by Thomas Oldham, 1846-50.

Jukes went to Ireland in 1850 as Local Director in succession to Oldham, who left to take charge of the Geological Survey of India. The same year Edward Hull and H. H. Howell joined the staff. Both later played a particularly important part in coalfield research. Both eventually became Directors: Hull for Ireland, 1869; Howell for Scotland, 1882, and for Great Britain, 1888. It is of course impossible to notice more than a few of the accessions to the Survey, which occurred from time to time; but those who have the cause of Irish geology at heart like to remember that G. H. Kinahan was appointed to the Survey in 1854.

The Irish surveyors started with a great advantage over their colleagues in England and Wales, in that from the first they conducted their mapping on Ordnance sheets on the scale of six inches to the mile. In course of time they covered the whole country, publishing on the one inch scale, and accompanying each of their one-inch sheets with an explanatory memoir. In this last accomplishment they have been more successful in Dublin than their fellows in London or, in later years, in Edinburgh. It would, however, be idle to suggest that existing Irish maps and memoirs do not in many cases call out for revision.

Ramsay's field staff, centred on London in 1845, consisted of six in addition to himself. Among them was A. R. C. Selwyn, who eventually succeeded Logan in Canada; while J. B. Jukes came in next year, bringing with him geological experience won in New South Wales and Newfoundland. Several changes occurred at headquarters in 1845 : Robert Hunt took Jordan's place as Keeper of Mining Records; Warington W. Smyth was appointed as Mining Geologist; Lyon Playfair as an additional Chemist; A. Henfrey as Botanist, soon giving place to Joseph Dalton Hooker, 1846-7; and C. R. Bone as Artist. Next year, 1846, J. W. Salter was added as Assistant Palæontologist.

There is music in the name of some of the men whom De la Beche gathered around him. It is good to think of Hooker, already confidant of Darwin in relation to natural selection, finding time to devote to fossil plants while completing his *Flora Antarctica*. He was newly returned from serving under Captain Ross on the voyage of the Erebus and Terror; in front of him rose the Himalayas.

Playfair was of a rather different type. We have already met him as a boy in Ramsay's home. During 1839-40 he worked with Liebig in Germany, when the latter was taking up the chemistry of agriculture and plant physiology. After his return, in 1842, he joined Liebig and Dean Buckland on a visit to different parts of England, and was present when abundance of coprolites in the Lias near Clifton sug-

gested manurial applications. Liebig presently analysed the
material and expressed himself in memorable words : ' What
a curious and interesting subject for contemplation ! In the
remains of an extinct *animal* world England is to find the
means of increasing her wealth in agricultural· produce, as
she has already found the great support of her manufacturing industry in fossil fuel—the preserved matter of primeval
forests—the remains of a vegetable world !' The same year
Sir Robert Peel persuaded Playfair not to leave the country
for a professorship at Toronto. His appointment under De
la Beche in 1845 introduced into the Survey circle an
organiser equal in calibre to that of the chief himself. His
influence manifests itself later in our story. Meanwhile we
may anticipate by noticing that he is the only member of
staff who has had quite such intimate relations with royalty
as to be Gentleman Usher in the household of the Prince
Consort, 1851, or who has attained to the title of Baron,
1892.

The expansion of De la Beche's field of activities from
1839 to 1845 was symptomatic of the times : in 1840 Kew
Gardens were adopted as a national establishment; in 1843
Lawes and Gilbert, in some respects bitterly antagonistic to
Liebig, started the Rothamsted Experimental Station for
Agriculture as a private venture; and in 1845 A. W. Hofmann, isolator of benzine from coal tar, was appointed first
professor of a newly founded Royal College of Chemistry,
of which the Prince Consort had accepted the presidency.

The reorganisation of De la Beche's command in 1845 led
to transfer of the Geological Survey from the Ordnance Survey to the Office of Woods, Forests and other things, which
already administered the Craig's Court Museum of Economic Geology. One outward and visible sign brightened the
lives of the field staff. They were no longer called upon to
carry out their arduous duties arrayed in blue uniform, brass
buttons and top hat.

EARLY MEMOIRS

De la Beche now decided to initiate two serial publications
entitled *Memoirs of the Geological Survey of Great Britain*

(or *Ireland* as the case might be) *and the Museum of Economic Geology in London* (or *Dublin*). Each volume of these *Memoirs* was to contain independent essays, as is ordinarily the case with publications issued by a learned society. In actual fact Irish Memoirs on this pattern never materialised.

FIG. 3.—Unconformity of New Red Sandstone on Coal Measures, South Wales. (Quoted from De la Beche, *Mem.,* vol. i, 1846, p. 248.)

The system cannot be recommended for routine publication by a geological survey, since users should be able to buy a separate memoir on any particular map sheet in which they happen to be specially interested; at the same time vol. i, 1846, vol. ii, pt. 1, 1846, and vol. ii, pt. 2, 1848, of the

Memoirs for Great Britain furnish very convenient indications of the activities of much of De la Beche's organisation at this period. The series ended with volume iv. in 1872.

In volume i, 296 pages, constituting more than half of the whole, are supplied by De la Beche in the form of an essay *on the Formation of the Rocks of South Wales and South-Western England.* It is essentially stratigraphical, and when it comes to South-West England it takes the opportunity of rediscussing the Devonian-Old Red Sandstone correlation. After elaborate fossil analysis, in which recent publications by R. J. Griffith on Ireland are considered, De la Beche adopts much the same attitude as John Phillips, but with a stronger bias towards placing some of the upper part of the pre-Culm greywacke into the Carboniferous. Ramsay supplies the second essay *on the Denudation of South Wales and the adjacent Counties of England.* The horizontal sections issued by the Survey allow him to give minimal quantitative estimates of the prodigious achievements of denudation. Unfortunately, at this time, he had not yet attained to Hutton's realisation of the full significance of subaerial erosion, including the work of rivers. Like Lyell, he considers marine erosion of much greater importance, and in imagination distributes its effects by slowly raising or lowering land masses through the fretful surf. His introduction of the conception of plain of marine denudation still has much value, though replaced in many applications by the American idea of peneplane, produced subaerially. His acceptance of De la Beche's catastrophism so far as folded mountains are concerned leads him to speak of 'the mighty catastrophe that closed the coal measure period' in the Mendip region (and brings letters of protest from both Lyell and Darwin). The third essay, by Edward Forbes, is *on the Connexion between the Distribution of the existing Fauna and Flora of the British Isles and the Geological Changes which have affected their area, especially during the epoch of the Northern Drift.* It is one of the most famous attempts ever made to account for geographical distribution of species. It will always be remembered for its discussion of the arctic-alpine elements found on our mountain tops, and of certain cold water assemblages isolated in deep pockets off our coasts. The concluding seven essays deal with the physics, chemistry, and exploitation of minerals, and also with the Mining Academies of Saxony and Hungary and the Mining Establishment of France. The authors are Hunt, Playfair and Warington Smyth.

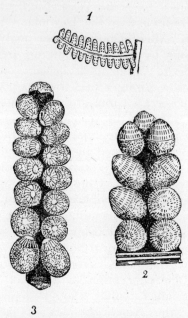

FIG. 4.—Carboniferous Seftenbergia Corda (1, 2) compared with Recent *Aneimidictyon* (3). (Quoted from Hooker, *Mem.*, vol. ii, pt. 2, 1848, p. 402.)

Volume ii, pt. 1, by John Phillips, with assistance from Salter, monographs the stratigraphy and palæontology of *the Malvern Hills, compared with the Palæozoic Districts of Abberley, Woolhope, Mayhill, Tortworth and Usk;* and is a fine district memoir in every respect.

Volume ii, pt. 2, starts with three essays by Hooker. The first is of a semi-popular nature comparing the vegetation of the Carboniferous Period with that of the present day. Its author explains that it is based on 'the first impression received by a naturalist, who, having been almost exclusively occupied with an existing Flora, is called upon to contrast it with the fragmentary remains of another Flora, whose species are, without an exception, different from those now living.' Then follow two essays on Asteriadæ and Cystideæ, by Forbes, and a long *First Report on the Coals suited to the Steam Navy,* pp. 530-630, by De la Beche and Playfair. This last, an early example of fuel research, necessitated the setting up of boilers and the execution of many thermal, chemical and other tests. The experiments were carried out by skilled operators temporarily engaged for the purpose at the expense of the Admiralty. In the end this *First Report* furnished the Navy with important practical data in a field hitherto scarcely entered except in America; but it wisely refrained from giving positive advice, since the suitability under discussion depends upon a number of totally independent qualities, the relative importance of which must be assessed by the users. (Two further *Reports* were supplied to the Admiralty, but were not published between Geological Survey covers.) Four of the remaining six essays deal with metalliferous ores, mainly of lead. Of these, two concern the mining district of Cardiganshire and Montgomeryshire, pp. 635-684, and are by Hunt and Smyth; and two are particularly noteworthy as initiating a long series of Mineral Statistics extracted by Hunt from voluntary returns made to the Mining Record Office.

In 1844 De la Beche introduced a new series of publications, *Figures and Descriptions Illustrative of British Organic Remains.* Each issue contains 10 plates and is called a *Decade,* an old fashioned use of the word. The first four Decades were by Forbes. The last, No. 13, by three other specialists, including T. H. Huxley, appeared in 1872.

UNOFFICIAL PUBLICATION

Meanwhile, in 1848, a most important precedent was established. Jukes and Selwyn, followed by Ramsay and Aveline, read papers before the Geological Society on certain results obtained during the official survey of Wales. De la

Beche had been hesitant about such outside publication, but eventually agreed, so long as intended communications were submitted for his approval in advance. This procedure has been of great value to the institution. Perfect adjustment of what is best put out to learned or technical societies and what is best retained for the Survey itself will never be attained; but on the whole, with ups and downs, a reasonable working practice has prevailed during most of the subsequent years.

GLACIATION AND DRIFT

Geological readers may have wondered that the 1840 meeting of the British Association at Glasgow should have been cited in connexion with Ramsay's introduction to the Survey without any mention of Agassiz's announcement there of his *Études sur les Glaciers de la Suisse,* in which he sketched a hypothesis of a former glaciation of Northern Europe. As a matter of fact for some years to come the announcement meant very little to the Geological Survey.

Let us go back behind 1840. Critics of uniformitarianism in its early days had a strong card to play when they pointed to the dispersal of enormous erratic blocks, characteristic of Switzerland and Northern Europe. A million successive pushes will not transport a boulder, if each push in itself is too small to produce any displacement at all. Hutton realised the strength of the argument, and to this we owe the first suggestion that glaciers in the past may have had a much greater extension than today. His remarks applied to Switzerland, where his task was to account for de Saussure's record of the distribution of Mont Blanc granite boulders, without invoking the assistance of a deluge. He pictured a condition with the Alps higher than at present, when ' there would have been immense valleys of ice sliding down in all directions towards the lower country, and carrying blocks of granite to a great distance, where they would be variously deposited, and many of them remain an object of admiration to after ages, conjecturing from whence or how they came.' From the termination of the glaciers to the passes of the Jura, Hutton proposed to conduct the boulders, ice-rafted, down river courses which existed before the present-day hollow of Lake Geneva was eroded.

After Waterloo, Playfair, 67 years old, realised his ambition to examine the evidence of some of his master's interpretations affecting the continent of Europe. In 1815 we find him standing among great boulders on the slopes of the Jura. He saw one monster, 2,520 tons in weight, which had performed a journey of fully 70 miles and still remained rough and angular. He did not flinch; but decided that ' a glacier which fills up valleys in its course, and which conveys the rocks on its surface free of attrition, is the only agent we now see capable of transporting them to such a distance, without destroying that sharpness of the angles so distinctive of these masses.'

Passing on, we find it recorded that Professor Jameson taught his Edinburgh classes, as early at any rate as 1827, that the erratic phenomena of Scotland might point to the past existence of glaciers. Other pioneers include Esmark of Oslo, 1827, and Goethe in the 1829 edition of his *Wilhelm Meister*.

Before long there followed much more intensive studies in the Alps by Venetz and Charpentier, presently joined by Louis Agassiz. In 1838 the latter explained to Buckland on the south-east slopes of the Jura mountains, various well characterised glacial phenomena. Buckland did not allow himself to be convinced until he had crossed the Swiss plain to examine for himself glaciers still at work in the Alps. Then he returned and told Agassiz that he had similar evidences in Scotland and England (which Agassiz knew quite well), but had hitherto grouped them with his other *Reliquiæ Diluvianæ* (the title of a book on Noah's flood which he had published 1823). As a consequence he persuaded Agassiz to come to the Glasgow meeting of the British Association, where he would be sure to see fossil fishes even if the evidence for vanished glaciers melted away on closer examination.

Buckland had started a tour of glacial investigation before joining Agassiz at Glasgow; and after the Association meeting the two roamed far and wide through Scotland, England

and Ireland. An epitome of their results was communicated to
the Geological Society in November and December of 1840.
It is easy to find fault with important details, but the evidence which they gave of land glaciation of Britain by ice-
sheets comparable with that existing today in Greenland has
held its own triumphantly. To read merely the *Proceedings*
of the Society, especially remembering that Buckland spoke
as its President and that Lyell joined in the chorus with a
paper *On the Geological Evidence of the former existence
of Glaciers in Forfarshire*, might lead one to imagine that
the fight had been won at the first charge. Moreover, one
knows that the defences of probable opponents had been
weakened in advance. On the one hand, the yachting
naturalist, James Smith, of Jordan Hill, had already in 1839
started publication regarding arctic shells in the post-boulder-
clay, uplifted, marine deposits of the Clyde valley, while
similar evidence had come from Canada and Sweden ; and
on the other, uniformitarian Lyell had already in 1836 begun
to account for distribution of erratics by invoking floating
ice. Accordingly the new glacial theory was addressed to an
audience familiar with the idea of an arctic climate and of
transport of boulders by ice of a kind. Fortunately for our
understanding of the case we can turn from the Society's
Proceedings to a contemporaneous report of the discussions
which took place following the delivery of the papers. This
invaluable account is reproduced in H. B. Woodward's *History of the Geological Society of London*. One of the discussions continued until midnight, and on the whole the
opinions expressed were extremely damnatory.

In his succeeding Presidential Address, February, 1841,
Buckland reviewed the situation in a very conciliatory style.
The contest between the adherents of land ice and sea ice he
thinks, ' will probably be settled, as in most cases of extreme
opinions and exclusive theories, by a compromise ; the
glacialist will probably abandon his universal covering of
ice and snow, and will be content with glaciers on the ele-
vated regions of more southern latitudes than now allow of
their formation ; the diluvialist, retaining his floating ice-
bergs as the most efficient agents in the transport of drift and

erratic blocks to regions distant from their place of origin, may also allow to glaciers their due share in the formation of moraines and striated surfaces, in latitudes and elevations that are no longer within the zones of perpetual congelation.' It is true that important features of Agassiz's conception deserved to be jettisoned, but Buckland retreated much too close to the mountains as a result of the rough handling he had received from his critics. He was not alone in his timidity, since for a long time most British geologists accepted the boulder clay of the lowlands as a product of ice floes carried by marine currents.

It has been said above that the announcement of the glacial theory at first meant little to the Geological Survey. This is well exemplified in an entry Ramsay made in his diary for the 16th April, 1845. He had been to the Geological Society to hear A. F. Macintosh read a paper *On the Supposed Evidences of the former Existence of Glaciers in North Wales.* Ramsay's jotting is: 'Jolly night at the Geological. Buckland's glaciers smashed.' This comes amusingly, in retrospect, from one who was destined to become an international figure in glaciology. His conversion seems to date from 1848, when Robert Chambers, who had come south to compare Welsh glaciers with Scottish, gave him a valuable lesson in the Pass of Llanberis. Next year at the Royal Institution Ramsay delivered a discourse on *the Geological Phenomena that have produced or modified the Scenery of North Wales,* in which he assigned great importance to glacial action. He has recorded that the praise he got from Herschel, De la Beche and others was almost too much to be good for him. Faraday ran up to him at the close and shook him by both hands, asking: 'Where *did* you learn to lecture?' Ramsay had now reached the compromise position anticipated by Buckland. He still attributed the general smooth mantle of drift up to 2,300 ft. to glacial marine deposit.

Interest in glaciation has provided a very effective incentive towards the production of drift maps, that is of maps showing the nature of the post-Tertiary superficial accumulations. Such maps are keenly desired by agriculturists and town planners. Unfortunately they are relatively difficult to produce since the distribution of drift is much less methodical than that of the underlying so-called solid formations. Very little could be achieved in the way of drift mapping so long as field work was carried out on the scale of one inch to the mile. Still, a start was actually made, covering a large part of Norfolk, by Joshua Trimmer, 1844-46. His results are given in the Journal of the Agricultural Society for 1847, and of the Geological Society, 1851. Trimmer's interest in diluvial phenomena was of old standing, for in 1831 he had announced the discovery of marine shells in gravel well over 1,000 ft. on Moel Tryfan, Snowdonia. In 1846 he joined the Survey, continuing till 1854, always keen on superficial deposits.

CONSUMMATION OF DE LA BECHE'S HOPES

The quarters at Craig's Court soon proved too cramped for the staff and exhibits marshalled by De la Beche. Moreover, in 1839 the Treasury had sanctioned a proposal for lectures on the practical applications of geology, and Craig's Court failed to afford opportunities to make even a start in this direction. De la Beche had been greatly impressed by the achievements of the Mining Academy at Freiberg and of its virtual offspring, the Écoles des Mines, established in Paris in 1783 and re-established, despite political turmoil, in 1794; and accordingly he attached great importance to personal teaching as supplementary to research and publication. He was a persistent planner, and his ambitions were of such a kind as appealed very strongly to the Prince Consort. The year 1851 brought to both these great men the consummation of their dearest hopes: to De la Beche, the opening of his new Museum of Practical Geology at 28, Jermyn Street, off Piccadilly, with accommodation not only for the Geological Survey and Mining Record Office, but also for a Government School of Mines and of Science applied to the Arts; and to the Prince, the triumphantly successful Great Exhibition of the Industry of all Nations.

His Royal Highness opened the Museum on the 12th of

May, 1851, in the presence of a brilliant gathering. After receiving an address from Sir Henry De la Beche, he spoke as follows :—

In thanking you for the address which you have just read to me, I would express the sincere gratification with which I witness the opening, in a form more likely to make it generally and practically useful, of an institution, the progress of which I have long watched with great interest, and the want of which had long been felt in this country.

I rejoice in the proof thus afforded of the general and still increasing interest taken in scientific pursuits, while science herself, by the subdivision into various and distinct fields of her study, aims daily more and more at the attainment of useful and practical results.

In this view it is impossible to estimate too highly the advantages to be derived from an institution like this, intended to direct the researches of scence, and to apply their results to the development of the immense mineral riches granted by the bounty of Providence to our isles and their numerous colonial dependencies.

It will always give me the greatest pleasure to hear of, and, as far as I am able, to contribute to the continued success of the Museum of Practical Geology.

At the time of the opening of the School of Mines and Science in Jermyn Street the following were professors or lecturers under the presidency of De la Beche: Chemistry, Playfair; Geology, Ramsay; Mechanical Science, Hunt; Metallurgy, John Percy; Mining and Mineralogy, Warington Smyth; Natural History, Forbes. Four out of the six were already Fellows of the Royal Society.

Next year saw the initiation of a new series of publications for the Museum of Practical Geology and Geological Survey, entitled : *Records of the School of Mines and of Science applied to the Arts.* Vol. i, pt. i preserves for us the *Inaugural and Introductory Lectures to the Courses for the Session* 1851-2, delivered by De la Beche and his six professors. De la Beche's own discourse is particularly delightful, free from all the parenthetical complexity we have noticed in his writings of earlier date. Its author glows with quiet enthusiasm and confidence. He explains that the exhibits in the Museum are intended to illustrate the lectures of the School, though also open to the general public. He communicates to the reader some of his own feeling for the building stones, pottery, glass, ores and metals, which he has gathered together, in large measure as presentations from generous donors. He tells how such matters as the working of coal and the ventilation of mines receive ample attention. He emphasises the value of the fossil collection, 'the most perfect of its kind,' and of the rock collection too —showing that new features of first class importance have been introduced as a result of transfer from overcrowded Craig's Court. He has evidently been subjected to criticism from carpers who prefer practice to science; but he feels that this criticism is already losing ground : 'Those whose duties or inclinations take them among our industrial population can scarcely fail to observe how much the term *practical* is becoming appreciated in its true sense. . . . Science and practice are not antagonistic, they are mutual aids.' For himself he has chosen for his new building the proud title of Museum of Practical Geology.

The theme of fruitful co-operation between science and practice is developed in succession by the specialist professors, each giving a most interesting account of the achievements of applied science in his own field. It is characteristic that Percy declares himself 'no believer in useless metals,' and foretells a future for tungsten, at that time thrown away as waste at the Cornish tin mines.

A syllabus is provided of the courses of instruction in lecture hall, laboratory and field, leading up to a diploma, and of the corresponding fees. This must be taken in conjunction with a passage in De la Beche's discourse, which reminds us that : 'The history of the greatest discoveries teaches us, that it is not only by the rich that mankind has been advanced. As far as may be in our power, we propose to explain by evening lectures to the working men of London, those really engaged in business, and whose characters can be vouched for by their employers, such part of our collections as may be thought usefully interesting to them. Some slight payment may be required, sufficient to prove that those attending desire to do so. At the time when our collections are open gratuitously to the public the working man is usually engaged in his occupation, and yet we have much to show—much that may be important to him in his calling.' De la Beche's solicitude for the working man is distinctly reminiscent of Count Rumford's. All the lecturers participated in the evening course, which proved a most attractive perennial feature of the school's curriculum.

At the opening of Parliament in 1852 Queen Victoria announced that a comprehensive scheme was in preparation to ensure the advancement of practical science and the fine arts. Thus the Department of Science and Art was established under the Board of Trade, and on its recommendation the Royal School of Chemistry was absorbed in 1853 into De la Beche's School, which now assumed the title of Metropolitan School of Mines, and of Science applied to the Arts. Hofmann, largely concerned with distillation products of coal, remained Professor of Chemistry; while Playfair resigned to become Secretary for Science in the new Department. Playfair's transfer was not surprising, for in 1850 he had acted as one of the Commissioners organising the Great Exhibition; nor can one wonder that next year, 1854, De la Beche found himself, with his Survey, Museum, Records Office and School, following Playfair from the Office of Woods and Forests into the Department of Science and Art.

Playfair's zeal to employ the profits of the Great Exhibition in the advancement of science held the seeds of eventual dismemberment of De la Beche's creation; but the prestige of the creator and of his immediate successor, coupled with the expenses of the Crimean war, 1854-56, and the untimely death of the Prince Consort, 1861, delayed the operation until 1871.

Reference has already been made to the death of the first Curator of the Museum, Richard Phillips, the day before the new building was opened. His place was taken by Trenham Reeks, who had been Assistant Curator since the beginning in 1839.

START IN SCOTLAND

The general awakening in the country after the Great Exhibition led among other things to an agitation in Scotland for a share in the benefits of the Geological Survey. Extension to the northern kingdom had already been voted in Parliament, but so far had had to wait upon the progress of the Ordnance Survey. Now six inch to the mile maps began to be issued, and Ramsay, who had been commissioned by De la Beche to examine the situation, decided if possible to take advantage of their facilities. Accordingly he crossed to Ireland to learn from Jukes and his men the technique of six-inch field work. Thus it was that in the autumn of 1854 the geological survey of Scotland was started by Ramsay himself, and, most fortunately, on the six-inch scale.

THOMAS H. HUXLEY

Another great event in Survey annals dates from 1854. Thomas H. Huxley, born 1825, had returned in 1850 from a long voyage in H.M.S. Rattlesnake, during which he had investigated with outstanding success marine life near the Great Barrier Reef of Australia. Till 1854 the Admiralty had allowed him to work up results at home, but had then countered an application for money to secure full publication with an order to report for duty as an ordinary ship's doctor. Huxley resigned, and consented to take over Forbes' position as Professor of Biology at the School of Mines—Forbes was leaving for an Edinburgh chair which he scarcely lived to occupy. Huxley in addition was appointed Naturalist to the Survey. He refused ' point blank ' De la Beche's offer of employment as Palæontologist, as he did not care for fossils and intended to give up natural history for physiology. Actually he held his Survey post for thirty-one years, and a large part of his life-work was palæontological.

PROGRESS TO 1855

Now let us take a glance at the progress made in field work generally by the end of 1855 (*Fig.* 8). The western half of that part of England and Wales which lies south of the latitude of Liverpool, including the whole of the principality, had been covered by geological one-inch sheets actually published. In Ireland a definite start of map publication had been made, mainly in Wicklow; though progress had been delayed through non-appearance of Ordnance one-inch maps required for reduction purposes. In Scotland there was no publication, but field work had begun in East Lothian.

The field staff at the beginning of the year numbered six under Ramsay in Great Britain; and seven under Jukes in Ireland.

Of memoirs not already mentioned we may list parts 2-4 of vol. i of the *Records of the School of Mines,* all issued in 1853. Part 2 consists almost wholly of an account by Jukes of the *Geology of the South Staffordshire Coalfield.* It may be taken as a good first example of a long succession of coal-field memoirs continued to this day and of pre-eminent economic importance. Parts 3 and 4 relate to *Mines of Wicklow and Wexford* and *Mineral Statistics,* 1848-1852. Part 4 marks the end of the *Records;* but not of *Mineral Statistics,* for Hunt continued their separate publication under the ægis of the Survey until 1880 had been covered.

CLOSE OF DE LA BECHE'S REIGN

De la Beche began to fail from partial paralysis in 1853, although still able to undertake an inspection tour in Ireland the following year. 'Up to the very end,' says Sir Archibald Geikie, 'Sir Henry came to the Museum, even though he could not leave the chair in which he was wheeled into the building, and his loud voice and hearty laugh could be heard all over the place. He had still his joke for each member of the staff, and his kindly word of inquiry and encouragement for the attendants and cleaners.' He appeared for the last time two days before his death, which occurred on the 13th April, 1855.

In February of the same year De la Beche had been awarded the Wollaston Medal of the Geological Society. He was too ill to attend, so that Sir Roderick Murchison in accepting the medal for transmission was able to speak of his friend's field work and also of his 'successful completion of a great National Establishment, . . . which to the imperishable credit of its author, stands as the first Palace ever raised from the ground in Britain, which is entirely devoted to the Advancement of Science!' Sir John Flett, in writing *The First Hundred Years of the Geological Survey of Great Britain,* was able to add: 'Nothing that he [De la Beche] did has failed and with the progess of the years all his projected enterprises have expanded and developed.'

1 8 5 5

GEIKIE, in his Memoir of Sir A. C. Ramsay, tells how on various occasions De la Beche had led his lieutenant to understand that he regarded him as his natural successor, and that he would in due season press his claims. Towards the end, however, De le Beche seems to have changed his mind. Geikie suggests that he may have become impatient of Ramsay's opposition to certain of his own latter day plans, which, in the opinion of members of staff, sometimes reflected a mental failure connected with his bodily disablement. Another cause may perhaps be suggested. De la Beche knew full well of a desire at higher levels for expansion of his great institution under conditions that might dissolve the geological cement to which he himself attributed great importance. It is quite possible that he doubted whether Ramsay's standing in official quarters would enable him to hold at bay such unwelcome tendencies. He might quite well have come to this conclusion, and yet have continued to subscribe to the oft-repeated description of Ramsay as the best field geologist in Europe.

Soon after De la Beche's death Ramsay found that vigorous efforts were on foot in favour of the appointment of a most estimable man of good family, who unfortunately possessed only a very slender acquaintance with geology. To counter this danger Ramsay proposed at a meeting of the Jermyn Street professors that Sir Roderick Murchison should be suggested as their next chief. His proposal was accepted and communicated to the President of the Board of Trade. A memorial in the same sense, signed by many distinguished outside geologists, was also dispatched to the Government. Within less than a fortnight Murchison was appointed; and the announcement was received with general cheers in the House of Commons.

Roderick Impey Murchison was born in 1782 in Ross-shire, the scion of a North-West Highland family. He passed through Great Marlow, and as a boy of seventeen carried the colours of his regiment during the retreat on Corunna. After that, through no fault of his own, he saw little real warfare; and, with Waterloo passed, in 1815, he married and demobilised. His main interest for the next eight years was fox hunting, which showed at least that he had the stamina for a field geologist. We hear of him in the course of one period of 160 days riding to hounds 110 times; and again, during a trip to Switzerland, in 14 days walking 452 miles, 57 of which he covered on the last day of the outing.

All these years his wife was aiming at something more intellectual; and in 1823 got her reward. Shooting partridges one morning with Sir Humphry Davy, Murchison discovered that one may pursue philosophy without abandoning field sports, and that entry to the Royal Society could easily be arranged for such as himself. He sold his hunters and settled in London to attend lectures at the Royal Institution and discussions at the Geological Society. He received his baptism in field geology in 1825 from the merry though reverend Professor Buckland, when he rode out with a party of Oxford students to listen enthralled while a landscape was geologically dissected. Next winter he read his first paper to the Geological Society, *A Geological Sketch of the North-western extremity of Sussex and the adjoining parts of Hants and Surrey.* From this beginning he continued, spending summer after summer geologising at home or on the continent, with a break for the British Association, and with papers written to present each succeeding winter at the Geological Society. His impetuous zeal led to his election to the secretaryship of the Society 1826-31, and to its presidency 1831-33 and again 1841-43. His master subject was stratigraphy. He was an apostle of William Smith, with whom he had the good fortune to see coastal sections of Yorkshire; and he constantly carried in his pocket Cony-

5

beare and William Phillips' *Outlines of the Geology of England and Wales*. He had no financial worries, and undertook his self-imposed tasks in admirably methodical fashion : he procured the best maps available, studied the literature, inspected museums and consulted anyone who might supply useful information, always taking copious notes. He received great assistance from co-workers, especially palæontologists; and several of his papers were joint products with one or more of his friends. He himself was famous for his quick perception of the geological significance of topographical features; and he enjoyed the exertion and excitement of field work.

In 1831 Murchison broke ground beneath the Old Red Sandstone of the Welsh borders; and in 1834 introduced the name Silurian to cover the succession of fossiliferous formations he had there disinterred from oblivion. Sedgwick since 1822 had been engaged on a similar task in the Lake District, and in 1831 extended his investigations to North Wales. One difference between Sedgwick's work and Murchison's lay in the fact that Sedgwick's old rocks, to which in 1835 he gave the name of Cambrian, do not possess a natural top in the districts investigated—whereas Murchison's do. Another difference was characteristic of the two men themselves; Sedgwick delayed completion of his researches, so that only a very imperfect knowledge of his results was for long available; Murchison, on the other hand, had his fossils determined season by season and promptly published his findings. For some years the two friends were happily ignorant of the fact that Cambrian and Silurian were in large measure synonymous terms. In 1842, however, a much regretted controversy arose as to ownership. A postmortem adjudication by Charles Lapworth has since inserted a buffer system, Ordovician, between reduced representatives of Cambrian and Silurian. 'He took the oyster,' McKenny Hughes is reported as saying, 'and left the discoverers to hold the shells.' Reverting to the relations that existed between these two great discoverers one may recall that Sedgwick, though in 1855 bitterly resentful on the Silurian issue, was among the signatories who advocated

Murchison's appointment to the Director-Generalship of the Geological Survey.

Murchison's other claims to geological fame are so numerous that only the briefest selection can be mentioned. With Sedgwick he correlated the Culm Measures of Devon with the Carboniferous; and soon afterwards, with the same companion, following Lonsdale's as yet unpublished lead, established the Devonian system as time-equivalent in its home county of the Old Red Sandstone farther north. A little later, again with Sedgwick, he equated much of the greywacke of the Rhenish provinces with this Devonian. Then with A. von Keyserling and E. de Verneuil he investigated the geology of Russia, incidentally introducing the title Permian for the lower portion of certain post-Carboniferous red rocks and limestone long studied in Germany. Besides this he made important contributions to the geology of all countries from Italy to Scandinavia. In fact he did more than anyone else to establish and harmonise the main Palæozoic stratigraphical features of Europe and, indirectly, of the world. In addition to a multitude of papers he published three important books: *The Silurian System*, 1839; *The Geology of Russia in Europe and the Ural Mountains*, 1845; and *Siluria*, 1854.

He was elected into the Royal Society in 1826, because, as the President, Sir Humphry Davy, told him, he was an independent gentleman with a taste for science and plenty of time and money for its gratification. He seems to have given little cause for regret to his supporters, since in 1849 we find him awarded the Copley Medal, the highest honour at the Society's disposal. Of the 59 Fellows of the Royal Society who figure on the staff list of the Geological Survey and Museum, only the chemists Hoffmann and Frankland, the physicist Stokes and the biologists Huxley and Hooker share this distinction with the geologist Murchison. He was a founder member and pillar of strength of both the Royal Geographical Society, 1830, and the British Association, 1831. He was knighted in 1846. All this before he took up official duties. In 1864 he received the Wollaston Medal, and in 1866 was created a baronet. He died in 1871.

Murchison's dynamic interest in sport, art, travel and science made him welcome in a wide circle. The receptions which he and Lady Murchison gave were a feature of the life of the Metropolis. Abroad, the crowned heads of Europe invited him to their palaces, for the interest of his conversation and the advantages which his researches brought to their several countries. The presents received from successive Czars are today treasured exhibits in the Museum of Practical Geology. The memory of his services has survived the October Revolution. In 1942 the Geological Society received the following congratulatory telegram from the Ural Geologists at the State University of Svendlovsk : ' We are sending to English geologists with the centenary of Sir Roderick Murchison's establishing the Permian period. We are struggling together for the quickest extermination of our common enemy, the German Nazism.'

Having said so much in favour of Murchison, especially as a pioneer in stratigraphy, it is only fair to recall some of his failings. He was a catastrophist like De la Beche, and a strong opponent of glacial theories. Moreover, he was already 63 years of age on his appointment as Director General.

THE BEGINNING

On his first day of office Murchison called a council of Professors to consider the problem of cataloguing the contents of the Museum. Though he inherited only one catalogue from De la Beche, it happened to cover the well chosen collection of *Pottery and Porcelain;* and it served him in good stead a few days later when the Prince Consort came to talk over plans for the future. The Prince hoped to see the Jermyn Street collections expanded to illustrate all important aspects of applied science, art and manufacture, and spoke of housing the whole in one great building. In the process of time it has required half a suburb, rather than a single building, to accommodate a partial fulfilment of his princely dream.

In 1857 a general descriptive catalogue of the Museum of Practical Geology appeared, followed in 1858-65 by others on *Rocks, Minerals, Mining and Metallurgical Models* and *Fossils.* Huxley was as keen as any of his fellow professors. In 1856 he produced an admirable essay on the *Methods of Palæontology,* which, reprinted, served as preface to a fossil catalogue prepared by himself and Etheridge and issued 1865.

Three months after his appointment Murchison drew up a memorandum of 12 points which he had settled up to date. All are interesting, but only three can be mentioned here.

2. I have ordered the lettering of all the colours on the maps.

9. I have rendered the titles of all our future volumes uniform—Records of Mines, Decades, Memoirs are all to appear under the general title of *Memoirs of the Geological Survey.*

11. On entering office I made a vigorous stand against a Parliamentary document, drawn up by Playfair as Secretary of the Department at the Board of Trade, whereby Mr. Cole was appointed ' Inspector General ' of all schools and *Museums,* whether in the metropolis or country. I insisted upon a special exemption of this establishment from such a rule, and a paragraph to that effect was accordingly inserted.

In relation to item 11 it is interesting to note that next year, 1856, Playfair himself became Inspector General; and that, also in 1856, the Department of Science and Art was transferred to the Education Department of the Privy Council, carrying with it Murchison and his charge. Murchison had protested vigorously against leaving the Board of Trade; but Geikie thinks his objection ' was in good measure personal. Previously the Director General of the Geological Survey had reported direct to a Minister of State, now he would have to conduct his communications through Mr. Henry Cole.' In 1862 Cole acted as Secretary to a small Commission which prefixed *Royal* to the title of the *School of Mines,* and established an *Associateship* in place of the original Diploma.

MEMOIRS OF MURCHISON'S FIRST TWELVE YEARS

One of Murchison's earliest reforms was the introduction of Sheet Memoirs, or Explanations, to accompany individual one-inch maps. As already mentioned, his instruction in this

matter has fully materialised only in Ireland; but enough
has been achieved in Great Britain to make us eternally
grateful. England was first starter with Cheltenham by Hull
in 1857; Ireland followed in 1858; Scotland in 1861.

Only three District Memoirs were published during Murchison's first twelve years. Two cover England's geological
treasure island, the *Isle of Wight,* with its Fluvio-Marine
Formation described by Forbes (posthumous) in 1856, and
its General Geology by Bristow in 1862. The third describes
North Wales, 1866, and is numbered volume iii of De la
Beche's serial memoirs. In it Ramsay speaks for himself

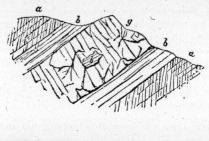

Fig. 5.—Top : a, slate; b, baked shale, uncleaved;
g, intrusive greenstone. Bottom : Pebbles
elongated along cleavage. (Quoted from Ramsay, Mem., vol. iii, 1866, pp. 97, 145.)

and his field colleagues, while Salter, who had retired in
1863, contributes a copiously illustrated palæontological
appendix.

Ramsay starts with an historical introduction, pointing out
that the Geological Survey under De la Beche had in essence
accepted and applied Murchison's vocabulary. ' Differences of
opinion still exist, but chiefly respecting names and classification, and though these may be interesting to individuals,
they neither affect the order of stratification nor the palæontological facts, both of which can be readily understood by
whatever names the strata are called.' Ramsay restricts the

name *Cambrian* to relatively old rocks 'which, excepting annelid burrows, and a doubtful trilobite, have nowhere yielded in England or Wales any well authenticated organic remains.' In fact, much of what Ramsay classes as Cambrian, for instance in Anglesey and the Longmynd, is now called Precambrian. Everything in which respectable Early Palæozoic fossils are found he includes as Silurian. 'Although there are great generic and specific differences in the fossils of some of the Silurian formations, trilobites, cystideæ, brachiopods, etc., are found throughout, and graptolites everywhere except in the Lingula flags.'

The development of knowledge that has come during the progress of the work is sketched, with emphasis on the widespread unconformity detected at the junction of what have later come to be known as the Ordovician and Silurian. A general account of the Palæozoic rocks of Wales and Shropshire follows—the memoir has as frontispiece a geologically coloured map on the scale of ten miles to one inch, which reaches south to the Bristol Channel and west to the Malverns. The difficult matter of local detail for the various sub-districts is admirably handled in a series of short chapters. Slate, copper and gold are mentioned where they occur, but the treatment of economic subjects is disappointing, even when we recall that some have already received separate attention. A strange example of secondary enrichment is noted where the peat of a small moss, after burning in kilns, yielded many thousand pounds worth of copper.

Ramsay's physiographic treatment is according to his new outlook, to be explained more fully later; but it is brief, probably at the request of the Director General, who thought it mistaken. It is, however, good to read of the corries of Snowdonia, ascribed to glacial action. 'In all glacial regions, past and present, high circular hollows like these are exceedingly characteristic.'

On turning to Salter's appendix, one feels, so far as stratigraphy is concerned, lifted to a higher, more international, level. Joachim Barrande in 1851 paid a visit to England with the express purpose of comparing his rich palæontological material from Bohemia with British equivalents. He had already distinguished in the Bohemian Silurian (*sensu lato*) three successive faunas, of which the earliest, or Primordial, corresponds with what we now called Cambrian. He found from an inspection of the Survey collections that the Lingula Flag of Sedgwick was the exact equivalent of his own Primordial. To follow up this clue entailed much work by

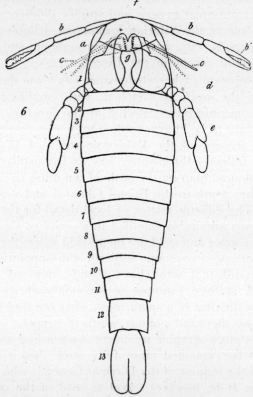

Fig. 6.—Restoration of *Pterygotus bilobus* (length 6in.) (Quoted from Huxley, *Monograph I*, 1859, pl. xv.)

Salter, not only in the cabinets, but also in the field, where especially he came to realise the outstanding value of some of Sedgwick's subdivisions, such as the Tremadoc Slate and the Arenig or Skiddaw group—although, till Salter took up the matter, these subdivisions were little more than lithological.

Here it may be recalled that Salter in 1862 had discovered *Paradoxides* in South Wales, thus opening the door in Britain to palæontological research in what is now known as the Middle Cambrian.

His visit to the district was doubly blessed, for it enabled him to enlist the interest of a doctor practising at St. Davids, the redoubtable Henry Hicks, who in company with himself, and before long independently, was destined to accomplish more than any other in zoning the Welsh Lower

FIG. 7.—Section of Hæmatite at Todholes, near Whitehaven. 1. Drift with limestone fragments. 2. Impure limestone ' roof.' 3. Hæmatite, 20ft. thick. 4. White ' shale floor.' (Quoted from Warington Smyth, *Iron Ores Mem.,* 1856, p. 21.)

Palæozoic formations by their contained trilobites. Salter's appendix was written in 1865—too early for him to make use in it of his joint report with Hicks to the British Association meeting of that year at Birmingham, in which, for instance, the Menevian formation was erected to take the lower, that is paradoxidian, part of the Lingula Flags.

Before the North Wales memoir appeared a new group of publications had been started, illustrative of *British Organic Remains.* Monograph I, by Huxley, dated 1859, was devoted to the genus *Pterygotus,*

The *Warwickshire* (1859) and *Leicestershire* (1860) coalfields were given individual memoirs; and the *South Staffordshire* coalfield a second edition (1859); while the *Iron
Ores of Britain* were treated in four parts, 1856-62, which
cover most of England and Wales.

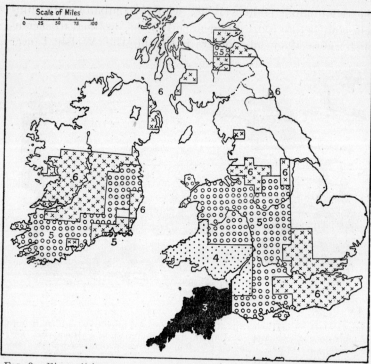

FIG. 8.—First-edition one-inch map publication in decades 1830-39 (3), 40-49
(4), 50-59 (5), 60-79 (6). (See *Figs.* 10, 28, pp. 83, 159.)

MAPS OF MURCHISON'S FIRST TWELVE YEARS

The year 1858 was marked by the appearance of the first
Geological Survey map-sheets on the scale of four miles to
the inch. Six beautiful examples were issued, covering
Wales and the West of England.

Publication of one-inch maps, principal object of the Survey, continued happily: in England spreading mainly east-
wards to complete the Midland coalfields and the approaches

to London; in Ireland, south and south-west from Dublin; in Scotland, through the Lothians and Fife (*Fig.* 8).

Ordnance Survey facilities, it will be remembered, had allowed of field work in Ireland and Scotland being started on maps on the scale of six inches to a mile. By 1859 a skeleton six-inch Ordnance map became available for London and its environs. Murchison seized the opportunity to use it as a basis for geological work. He was most anxious that engineers and proprietors should see the variations of soil and subsoil in and around the Metropolis delineated with as much fullness and accuracy as could reasonably be expected. The mapping required special characteristics on the part of the surveyor, and was mainly entrusted to W. Whitaker, who showed a flair for interpreting records kept by engineers and others of temporary exposures for foundations and sewers and of bore-holes for water—he himself had been trained as an engineer. In an obituary, 1925, it has been said: 'Probably no one has rendered better service to his fellow men than Whitaker in the applications of geology to the needs of civilised life.'

In 1860 Hull was able to start mapping the Lancashire coalfield on the six-inch scale, and this practice was continued in after years northwards from coast to coast. The quality of solid mapping was much improved, and drift mapping became general. Publication of selected six-inch geological maps dates from 1860 in Lancashire and 1861 in Scotland.

STAFF ADDITIONS DURING MURCHISON'S FIRST TWELVE YEARS

As might have been expected from the man, Murchison saw to it that his field staff was increased. The main change was delayed twelve years, but even in the interval his fieldsmen numbered on the average 24.4, nearly double the corresponding figure for De la Beche's last ten years. The most interesting acquisitions during this stage were the brothers Archibald and James Geikie (1855 and 1861), W. Whitaker (1857), A. H. Green (1861), Ben N. Peach (1862) and R. H. Tiddeman (1864).

The Geikies came of a gifted Edinburgh family, and from boyhood onward revealed a strong interest in science and literature. Archibald counted among his senior friends, Hugh Miller, editor of the *Witness,* better known, perhaps, as the Stone Mason of Cromarty. It was to this great man that he owed his first introduction to Murchison. Green was a 6th Wrangler, who both at school and college had learnt to love geology. Ben N. Peach was son of a famous naturalist, Charles W. Peach, employed in the Customs Service.

For many years Peach senior was stationed at Fowey, in Cornwall, where he made striking discoveries in relation to modern and extinct forms of life. Ben used to tell in after years of how his father once wrote to Murchison about a find he had made in 1837 of Ordovician fossils at Gorran Haven. Murchison replied cautiously, suggesting a possible misidentification; but Peach banished doubt by sealing his next envelope with a cast of a diagnostic species. Transferred to Wick in Caithness, Charles Peach continued to use his opportunities. In 1854 he paid a visit to Durness on the Sutherland coast to 'receive' a wreck, and there he noticed fossils, poorly preserved, in the Durness Limestone. This discovery reawoke general interest in the North-West Highlands, more especially when a subsequent visit in 1857 yielded Peach better specimens, undoubtedly Ordovician in age. Murchison felt so indebted to his friend that he undertook to send young Ben to the School of Mines, at which the latter graduated with the newly established Associateship, to remain eternally grateful for having been brought under the tutelage of Huxley.

Tiddeman was a student of Phillips at Oxford. He achieved fame in his Survey career mainly through his theory of reef-knolls in the Carboniferous Limestone of the North of England, to which we shall recur when we come to the 1888 meeting of the International Geological Congress in London.

Murchison did little to increase De la Beche's final Headquarter Staff. He did, however, introduce G. G. Stokes, 1855, as Professor of Physics, to be followed in 1859 by J. Tyndall, who took particular interest in glacial motion. He also secured E. Frankland as Professor of Chemistry, when Hofmann retired in 1865. His palæontological appointments included Robert Etheridge, 1857, and E. T. Newton, 1865. Murchison first met Etheridge while geologising with Lord Ducie in the Cotteswold Hills. ' Judging from his celerity, his quickness in finding shells and naming them, and in drawing sections, I said to Ramsay [who was one of the party], " This is the man we must have to put our Jermyn Street Museum in order." '

RESEARCH DURING MURCHISON'S FIRST TWELVE YEARS

The first twelve years of Murchison's reign fell in the most brilliant period of Natural History Sciences in the story of Britain ; and the Geological Survey played a becoming part —though Murchison himself, in the long run, did more harm than good to his scientific reputation. The novelty of Smithian stratigraphical research had waned, but the accumulated knowledge, combined with better topographical maps, increased the opportunities for preparing geological maps of permanent value for industrial or purely scientific use. Moreover, Darwin's release of his ideas on evolution gave new values to both stratigraphy and palæontology ; while a marked renaissance affected the study of scenery and glaciation.

During this period Murchison polished up a number of his past stratigraphical achievements. Probably his most important contribution was made in 1858 and 1859, when he emphasised faunal comparisons between the Scottish and Russian developments of the Old Red Sandstone, basing largely upon discoveries of Hugh Miller and Robert Dick. Much more attention, however, was attracted to his abortive investigation of the age of the crystalline schists of the Scottish Highlands.

Scottish Highlands.—In Sutherland and Ross, Macculloch, between 1814 and 1824, had described a succession which, to use modern names, may be summarised thus : Lewisian gneiss, covered unconformably by Torridonian sandstone, overlain by quartzites and limestone, which alternate with and are succeeded by gneiss and schist forming the main mass of the Highlands. He also pointed to the existence of fossils, including one now called *Salterella,* in the quartzite series. *Salterella* is a difficult fossil to place zoologically, and did not seem till much later sufficiently definite to give a geological date; but Charles Peach's find of more hopeful remains in the limestone in 1854 led Murchison next year to visit the district in company with Professor J. Nicol of Aberdeen. The two observers did not agree in all details, nor did they afterwards adhere in all particulars to the views they formed individually in 1855. Both returned a number of times to the scene of operations. Murchison in 1858 with Charles Peach, who by this time had got his clearly determinable Ordovician fossils; in 1859, with Ramsay; and in 1860, with Archibald Geikie. Murchison and his two Survey colleagues (Peach's view is not recorded) satisfied themselves that Macculloch's reading of the sections was essentially correct, and that the schists overlying the fossiliferous quartzite-limestone series must be a conformable upward continuation of the latter—and therefore Ordovician. Nicol, on the other hand, considered in 1860 that 'the line of junction [of schists and fossiliferous formations], where this conformable succession is said to occur, is clearly a line of fault, everywhere indicated by proofs of fracture, contortion of the strata, and powerful igneous action.' Nicol, in his sections, always drew his fault very steep or vertical. The true answer, found more than 20 years later, is that the Highland schists here considered have been thrust at a low angle for miles forward over the fossiliferous Ordovician. Nicol was dimly groping towards a realisation of this great structural fact. Murchison, if he ever considered it, dismissed it as impossible. Murchison's failure in this matter is difficult to understand, even allowing for his age and the confidence which long success had given him. As recently as 1848 he had described with detail and conviction a comparable overthrust in the Glarus Alps, which had been demonstrated to him in the field by its discoverer, Escher von der Linth—but then the significance of the Swiss structure was vouched for by fossils, above as well as below the great dislocation.

The authority of Murchison, Ramsay and Geikie's reading of the North-West Highland sections won almost universal acceptance for their views. To the end of his days Murchison could think with self-satisfied smile of the part he had played in the geological interpretation of the home of his fathers. Unfortunately Nicol could not share this pleasure. He died discredited, an object of pity.

Quite apart from their bearing on the age of the Highland schists, Peach's 1857 fossils proved exceptionally interesting. They were determined by Salter, not only as Ordovician, but also as typical of the North American development of the Ordovician. This recalls Portlock's remark of 1843 about the American character of some of the Early Palæozoic fossils of Ireland.

Here, perhaps, we may turn aside to note two remarkable coincidences connected with this research. In the first place Logan had shortly before brought to England his Canadian collections for study by Salter as Palæontologist of the home Survey; and it was this circumstance that made it possible for Salter to realise at once the full significance of Charles Peach's material. In the second place, when the question of structural relations of schist and limestone was reopened in the 80's, no one played a more glorious part in its solution than Ben N. Peach, who owed his education at the School of Mines to his father's discovery of fossils at Durness.

Evolution.—In many other directions Murchison did not carry his colleagues with him as he did in the North-West Highlands. This was the case in a paper he published in 1859 on the reptiliferous sandstones of Elgin. Here he was led by field appearances to urge that the reptiliferous sandstones of Elgin are an upward conformable continuation of the Old Red Sandstone of the district; but he admitted in a postscript that in view of Huxley's careful examination of all the fossils up to date 'it becomes me to pause in my geological conclusions.'

Murchison had long been a progressionist, and, quite apart from Huxley's influence, he had felt that reptiles seemed out of place in the Old Red Sandstone. Still his progressionist views did not bring him to favour Darwin's evolutionary claims as set out in the *Origin of Species,* 1859. On the other hand, Huxley and many of his colleagues were ready converts. Thus in 1860 Huxley chose the *Relation of Man to the Lower Animals* as subject for his six-lecture evening course to working men—like the other professors at Jermyn Street, he found these classes particularly stimulating. Similarly, later the same year, he rendered the Oxford meeting of the British Association journalistically memorable with his better-ape-ancestor-than-bishop repartee addressed to an episcopal opponent, the doughty Wilberforce. Murchison, for his part, said little in public, but his private view is recorded in a letter : ' I flatter myself that I have seen as much of nature in her rough moods as any living man, and I fearlessly say that our geological record does not afford one scintilla of evidence in support of Darwin's theory.'

Rivers.—The year 1862 saw the publication by the Geological Society of a famous classic, in which Jukes analysed the river development of Southern Ireland. Jukes explains how, when Murchison decided upon routine publication of Sheet Explanations, he gave him instructions to include descriptions of the *form of the ground.* Jukes had already devoted much thought to physiography, and was glad to find the subject now included among those with which he had to deal officially as Local Director responsible for editing his colleagues' reports. The Cork district is mainly composed of parallel ridges of Old Red Sandstone, separated by hollows floored with Carboniferous Limestone, or Carboniferous Slate. In keeping with the general practice of the day Jukes calls the rivers of the drainage pattern *transverse* (he more often says *lateral*) or *longitudinal,* according as they run *across* or *along* the strike of the geological formations. He argues that the drainage system started on a smooth tilted surface, originally planed by marine erosion ; and he interprets the geographical depressions along the outcrops of the limestone as due to subaerial erosion that kept pace with the downward cutting of the transverse ravines.

He recognises that some of the original transverse brooks have failed to deepen their courses as quickly as their neighbours, and so ' were eventually drawn down into the longitudinal valleys, and their water carried out to the ravines ' maintained by successful rivals. In fact he sketches in clear outline the *ideas* of consequent, subsequent and obsequent drainage, and of river capture, which have since been so brilliantly elaborated by American authors.

Jukes also naïvely rediscovers the importance of subaerial erosion—he seems never to have read Hutton's arguments, which led that great man to assert : ' We must conclude at least that all the valleys are the operation of running water in the course of time. If this is granted we have but to consider the mountains as formed by the hollowing out of the valleys.' Jukes also rediscovers the erosional connection which commonly exists between surface form and rock character, already epitomised in Hutton's statement : ' The height of the mountain depends upon the solidity and strength of the stone.'

These rediscoveries were valuable, since most, though not all, of Jukes' contemporaries had lost sight of the physiographic treasures stored in the writings of Guettard, Desmarest, and Hutton, and at a later date of Scrope (but see Col. Greenwood's *Rain and Rivers; or Hutton and Playfair defended against Lyell and all Comers,* 1857).

The most characteristic feature of Jukes' work lies, perhaps, in his approach to the problems of river development armed with a good geological map. In a postscript he asks ' whether it will not turn out to be a general law in all mountain ranges in the world, that the lateral [transverse] valleys are the first formed, running directly from the crests of the ranges down the steep slopes of the mountains, while the longitudinal valleys are of subsequent origin, gradually produced by atmospheric action on the softer and more easily eroded beds that strike along the chains.' He further states that, if later work shows that the Cork principles hold for the Weald of Kent and Surrey, it will be reasonable to suppose that they ' will ultimately be found applicable to all river-valleys in all parts of the world.'

6

The effect of Jukes' paper on Ramsay may be gathered from one of his letters written to Geikie : ' By the way, I think I have given up the marine denudation of the Weald. Atmosphere, rain and rivers must ha' done it. I'm coming to that, I fear and hope, and hoping, fearing, trembling, regretfully triumphant, and tearfully joyous with the balm of a truthful Gilead spread upon the struggling soul, bursting the bonds of antique prejudice, I yet expect to moor the tempest-tossed bark of Theory in the calm moral downs of Assurance.'

In the early spring of 1863 Ramsay gave one of his usual courses of six evening lectures to working men at the Museum, using material to a large extent based upon what he had seen during inspection tours of his colleagues' work in various districts. The lectures, taken down in shorthand, were published the same year in a small volume, *Physical Geology and Geography of Great Britain,* destined to reach a 4th edition by 1874. Ramsay now emphasised the breaching of escarpments in the Weald and other districts, where gentle downstream dips are characteristic. He attributed it to vertical downward erosion of the river concerned, a process that gives opportunity for subaerial development of escarpments and for their subsequent almost horizontal travel in the direction of dip. The new views were soon lucidly developed by C. le Neve Foster and W. Topley, who were responsible for mapping the Weald for the Geological Survey. Their famous *Remarks on the Denudation of the Weald* were read to the Geological Society in 1865. The same general story of the efficacy of subaerial (as well as submarine) erosion runs through Archibald Geikie's *Scenery of Scotland,* the first edition of which also appeared in 1865. Whitaker, following up in 1867 in the Geological Magazine, gives a masterly account of the position by that time reached. He is able to quote a personal letter from Lyell pointing out that the latter now considers two of the arguments for subaerial development of escarpments ' unanswerable.' After gathering together a formidable list of supporters, Whitaker adds ' a great number of these sub-aerialists are or have been employed on Government Geological Surveys, and therefore have been accustomed to be constantly in the field.' Of course, the obvious retort of history is : even geological surveyors make mistakes.

Glaciers.—Another immensely important physiographic advance of these days concerns the glacial erosion of many rock basins. Ramsay has recorded that the idea first came to him in Wales, in 1854. He put forward the suggestion to account for minor examples in an essay on *The Old Glaciers of Switzerland and North Wales*, 1859; but it attracted little attention until elaborated in a paper *On the Glacial Origin of certain Lakes in Switzerland, the Black Forest, Great Britain, Sweden, North America and elsewhere*, read to the Geological Society in 1862. Ramsay here tackles a problem that had always confronted students who relied upon running water for the sculpture of landscape. Hutton had only been able to suggest three possible explanations for lakes : landslip, earth movement and solution. He had indeed included glaciers among his agents of erosion ; but he knew far too little about them to connect them with overdeepening of valleys. Ramsay's contribution to the subject constitutes one of the brightest jewels in the crown of the Geological Survey. Its appearance brought down on its author's head criticisms reminiscent of the assault made on Agassiz and Buckland, 20 years previously. By chance Ramsay, like Buckland, spoke with the prestige of presidency ; otherwise, he used to assert, the Council would have voted against publication except in bare abstract.

Many of the younger men, Darwin, Hooker, Logan, and, on the Survey, Jukes, Geikie and Tyndall (with exaggeration) sided with Ramsay ; but the older men, prominent among them his own chief, Murchison, were hostile. Murchison's *Presidential Address* to the Royal Geographical Society, 1864, contains a detailed review of the whole subject of glaciated lands, based largely upon personal knowledge of the districts themselves and of the men who had worked on their problems. Reading this *Address* one realises that it is magnificent, but it is not true. For Murchison the results of floating ice and glaciers can only be distinguished by terminal moraines and common sense.

Floating ice, he says, cannot produce terminal moraines, and glaciers cannot travel over flat or uphill country. Rock basins are for him all products of earth movement. Here one may add that Murchison's various *Presidential Addresses* to the Geographical Society constitute a most important feature of his tenure of the Director-Generalship of the Geological Survey. He delivered no less than 13 during this period, full of inspiring information regarding current and prospective exploration and research. It is no exaggeration to say that Murchison came to be much more widely appreciated as the champion of men like Franklin and Livingstone than as the founder of the Silurian System.

One cannot but feel admiration for Murchison's decision to meet the supposed heresies of his staff with argument rather than closure. Geikie, speaking of his own *Scenery of Scotland,* says : 'The volume was dedicated to Murchison, to whose friendship I owed so much. Yet its main thesis [uniformitarian principles of erosion] was in such direct antagonism to his well-known cataclasmic opinions that I was prepared for a protest on his part, though he knew what my opinions were. But he accepted the compliment without demur.'

Glaciation by land-ice came to be much better understood in these years by Ramsay and Geikie and, largely through their influence, by many others. In a wonderful paper on the *Glacial Theory and its recent Progress,* published in the *Edinburgh New Philosophical Journal* for 1842, Agassiz had elaborated his contention that boulder clay in Scotland 'must have been transported under the ice.' In the spirit of compromise advocated by Buckland, this portion of Agassiz' theory was for some twenty years set aside by practically all British geologists—an amazing circumstance ! In 1859 Ramsay visited Geikie at work in Fife, and 'our conversation,' Geikie says, 'turned on the Boulder Clay and the mysteries of its origin. We both felt how unsatisfactory was the received explanation of iceberg action and submergence. I was thus led to study this deposit, and to reach thereby the conclusion, at which Ramsay also simultaneously and independently arrived from a consideration of other evidence

[distribution of rock basins], that the great glaciation was
the work of land-ice. This change of view was completed
before the summer of 1861.' One of Geikie's chief arguments
was the local nature of most of the debris found in boulder
clay.

In January, 1862, Geikie took over from Ramsay, who
was far from well, his course of evening lectures to working
men at the Museum, and explained to his audience his conversion to land-ice. In February T. F. Jamieson of Ellon,
factor, farmer and later agricultural lecturer, gave further
independent evidence leading to the same conclusion in a
paper read to the Geological Society (followed next year by
a vindication of Agassiz' glacier-barred lakes in Glen Roy).
In March came Ramsay's paper, already mentioned, on the
glacial erosion of rock basins. Truly British geologists were
beginning to consolidate Agassiz' conquests and to advance
on to new ground. Still, as one may judge from Geikie's
classic *On the Glacial Drift of Scotland* published by the
Geological Society of Glasgow in 1863, Ramsay, Jamieson
and Geikie at this date retained a great deal more submergence in their philosophy than is commonly admitted today.
They thought, for instance, that glacial sands, even if they
contained no marine shells, suggested the former presence
of the sea, so long as they lay 'far out of the reach of any
stream.' Geikie considered that the main submergence might
prove to have extended more than 2,000 ft. above present
sea level; and he pictured it as roughly intermediate in date
between the glaciation responsible for the boulder clay of
the lowlands and that which produced the valley moraines
among the mountains.

Devonian System.—From 1865 onwards for a few years,
Murchison was subjected to a rather futile crusade led by
Jukes, which virtually aimed at dispensing with the
Devonian System. Jukes based his judgment mainly on the
experience he had gained in Southern Ireland. He claimed
that the Old Red Sandstone of South Wales continued without serious modification into Devon, while above it the Carboniferous Limestone had changed over to a Carboniferous

Slate facies, miscalled Devonian. In all this, Jukes went much farther than Phillips and De la Beche, who twenty years previously, it will be remembered, had argued for a possible rectification of the line adopted by Sedgwick and Murchison as boundary between Devonian and Carboniferous.

Granitisation.—The Director General was probably much less ruffled by an announcement made next year by his other lieutenant in a Presidential Address to the Geological Section of the British Association, meeting at Nottingham. In it Ramsay avowed a long cherished view that granite is a metamorphic rock resulting from heat 'with the aid of alkaline waters.' This particular heresy for a time gained much support in Britain ; and after a long interval, during which it was more or less banished to France, it has recently returned to considerable favour. It is curious that in our country most of its present apostles, like Ramsay in his own day, have close connections with the Royal School of Mines. As regards immediate results, it is probably correct to trace Ramsay's influence (and less directly that of the Canadian, Sterry Hunt) in two papers published by James Geikie in 1866 : one in the *Quarterly Journal of the Geological Society,* the other in the *Geological Magazine.* Here Geikie sought to demonstrate that what we now know as Ordovician pillow lavas, serpentines, etc., near Ballantrae, and as Devonian granites in the Midland Valley and Southern Uplands of Scotland, are merely altered sediments. The challenge was at once (1867) taken up by David Forbes (brother of Edward) on general grounds, and at a later date (1878) by T. G. Bonney after examination of the Ballantrae exposures. Both these critics were early exponents of microscopic petrology. Geikie was not easy to convince ; but eventually in 1901 we find him joint author with J. S. Flett of a short note delivered at the Glasgow meeting of the British Association, in which one of the above-mentioned granites is spoken of as 'intrusive into Lower Old Red Sandstone' and surrounded by evidences of 'contact alteration.'

ROYAL COMMISSION ON COAL

In 1866 a great event happened in the history of governmental research. A Royal Commission was appointed under the Duke of Argyll 'to inquire into the several matters relative to *Coal* in the United Kingdom.' There had been much anxious questioning of the wisdom of exporting coal to foreign countries. The Commission was to take stock of the available resources in exposed and concealed fields, and to estimate probable dates for their ultimate exhaustion. Murchison, Hunt, Ramsay, Jukes and Hull were all included as members of the Commission, and several of their colleagues gave valuable assistance. The Commission continued to sit during the next four years, and did not draw up its Final Report till 1871, by which time Murchison was incapacitated by his last illness. The start of the Commission is mentioned here, because it marks the end of the first stage of the Murchison period. It enabled him and the Secretary of the Department of Science and Art to point to useful work completed, and at the same time to emphasise how much more was now in reach if staff facilities permitted. In Wales, South-West England and the Midlands the Survey had published maps and sections of the coalfields, sometimes accompanied by memoirs—but the field work had been carried out on the inadequate one-inch scale; in Lancashire and Yorkshire, six-inch mapping was in progress, but far from complete; in Durham, Northumberland and Cumberland, scarcely a start had been made; in Scotland only half the coalfield area was mapped; in Ireland, unfortunately, the coal resources were known to be very slight.

STAFF CHANGES DURING MURCHISON'S LAST FIVE YEARS

The urgency of closer coalfield survey appealed to the Government, as also did the importance of supplying adequate drift maps to agriculturists, civil engineers, medical authorities and town planners. It was clear that an increase of field staff was desirable, accompanied by considerable reorganisation. In 1867 the title of Local Director was abandoned. Ramsay, instead of continuing Local Director for Great Britain, now became, with increased salary, Senior Director for England and Wales. Jukes remained in charge of Ireland, but with his title abbreviated to Director. Geikie was promoted to be Director for Scotland, an altogether new position, with Headquarters in Edinburgh. More important still, an additional grade, District Surveyor (the District Geologist of later years), was instituted, with Aveline and Bristow appointed in England, Du Noyer in Ireland, and Hull in Scotland. Du Noyer died in 1869 and was succeeded by Kinahan. Twenty-one field geologists were recruited in 1867, and twelve in 1868. In the latter year Ramsay had a staff of 36, Jukes 13 and Geikie 8. As compared with 1866, the field force was a little more than doubled. On the other hand, it is rather sad that only one palæontologist was added to the existing five. In fact, Headquarter staff was actually reduced during Murchison's last five years, for John Tyndall resigned in 1868 and Robert Willis in 1869 from their respective lectureships in Physics and Applied Mechanics at the Royal School of Mines, and no successors were appointed.

Assimilation of a crowd of novices was a painful business for the old stagers among the field staff. Much time had to be given to training, and a depreciated standard had temporarily to be accepted in maps and memoirs. Moreover, the difficulties of the situation were intensified by continuous calls which the Royal Commission on Coal rightly made on the services of senior members.

While of necessity there were a few misfits among the newcomers, the upshot was much better than might have been anticipated. Many of the recruits were destined to make names for themselves by their contributions to geology, for instance: C. E. Fox-Strangways, J. G. Goodchild, W. Gunn, J. Horne, R. L. Jack, J. W. Judd, G. A. L. Lebour, J. Nolan, F. Rutley and H. B. Woodward, who joined in 1867, and W. A. Traill and W. A. E. Ussher, who followed in 1868. Two of the above, Horne and Woodward, eventually rose to be Assistants to the Director (an awkward term introduced in 1901, when the title Director was substituted for that of Director General). Horne came from Glasgow University and was sent for his training to Peach, thus starting an association which in later years won for them Albert Heim's happy designation of 'Investigator Twins.' Woodward, in choosing geology as a career, followed successfully in the footsteps of his father and grandfather. It seems natural that he is remembered today, not only as an original worker in, but also as a historian of his science.

James Croll is not mentioned in the foregoing list, because, though appointed in 1867, it was not as a field geologist, nor yet as one of the scientists of the Headquarter staff. Nevertheless, it is impossible to pass over his advent in silence, since he was the most remarkable man ever enrolled in the Geological Survey, in fact a prodigy. Croll was born in 1821, the son of a Perthshire stonemason and crofter. Poverty and ill-health dogged his footsteps; but in 1832 his mind was opened to what was for him a new world, through buying the first number of the *Penny Magazine*. Thereafter he took every chance of learning more, and soon was captivated by the 'beauty and simplicity' of 'Joyce's famous scientific dialogues.' Croll drifted from one occupation to another, compelled to give up work as a joiner by an accident to his elbow, and failing to make good as a shopkeeper through aggravation of the same injury. Physical ailments, affecting not only his elbow, but also his heart, eyes and hand, were enough in themselves to make existence precarious; but added to other difficulties was an 'almost irresistible propensity to study' the principles that underlie science, philosophy and religion. At last in 1859 he was appointed Curator of the Andersonian College and Museum at Glasgow. Here indeed was an opportunity, for, though the salary was a mere pittance, the duties were correspondingly light; and as Curator he had access to excellent libraries and could arrange a few hours daily for reading and study. His first publication, a book entitled *The Philosophy of Theism,* had already appeared in 1857; and now from 1861 onwards there followed a quiet steady stream of papers dealing with physical subjects, which he communicated to scientific journals, more particularly the *Philosophical Magazine*. To this latter in 1864 he contributed one of particular interest, *On the Physical Cause of the Change of Climate during Geolo-gical Epochs,* which took charge of his whole subsequent career. In it Croll connected glacial periods with recurrent combinations of different features of the planetary movement of the earth, coupled with such complications as the storage of cold, if one may use the phrase, in winter-made ice. His theory at once attracted very favourable notice from astrono-mers like Herschel, and from geologists like Lyell, Ramsay and Archibald Geikie. Thus it happened that in 1867 the latter was able to make a provisional offer to Croll of a post in the newly established Edinburgh office of the Geological Survey, as Secretary and Accountant. Croll agreed, and though he failed to pass the prescribed Civil Service entrance examination, he was on Murchison's strong recommendation eventually admitted at 7s. a day, rising to £350 a year. ' My Lords,' as Kelvin has put it, ' accepted his great calculations regarding the eccentricity of the earth's orbit, and the pre-cession of the equinoxes during the last 10,000,000 years as sufficient evidence of his arithmetical capacity.' Croll's offi-cial duties consisted in forwarding letters to geologists in the field, attending to their wants, ordering maps and keep-ing accounts. His unofficial occupation was mainly medita-tive country walks, pencil in one hand, paper in the other, jotting down new ideas to be elaborated on return before going to bed. By 1875, if we may look beyond the Murchi-son period that we are at present considering, Croll had published in book form his *Climate and Time.* This, in the following year, was acknowledged by St. Andrews with its Honorary Doctorate of Laws, by London with the Fellow-ship of its Royal Society and by New York with the Honorary Membership of its Academy of Science.

Up to this stage considerations of space have prevented mention of anyone who did not belong to the Scientific Staff, as that term is understood in the Civil Service—except per-haps Croll, whose classification is difficult. At all times, however, the work of the Geological Survey has depended very largely upon consummate skill developed among Assistants, more particularly Fossil Collectors, such as : R. Gibbs, 1843-72 ; A. McHenry, 1861, promoted 1877 ; A. I.

Macconochie, 1869-1913; J. Bennie, 1872-1901; D. Tait, 1897-1934; and J. Pringle, 1901, promoted 1913. Here we must also mention R. Lunn, 1861-1921, who made Survey photographs famous.

Jukes died in 1869, by which time the geological mapping of Ireland had been two-thirds completed. He was succeeded as Director in that country by Hull, whose place as District Surveyor in Scotland was taken by James Geikie. The two brothers Geikie, Archibald and James, were devoted friends of Ramsay, who until 1867 was their proximate chief. Both imbibed from him the fascination of glacial problems, but Archibald presently in large measure left this field to James, and devoted himself more particularly to a study of ancient volcanoes and of the Old Red Sandstone with its lake, or at at any rate continental, deposits—topics again to which Ramsay had made extremely valuable contributions. As we shall see in the sequel, close contact with Croll exercised a profound influence upon James Geikie, and also upon Peach and Horne.

PUBLICATION DURING MURCHISON'S LAST FIVE YEARS

During the last five years of Murchison's reign, one-inch map publication advanced quickly into the south-eastern and northern counties of England (*Fig.* 8). Thus by the end of 1871 the area covered by published maps came to include most of the country that lies south-west of a line drawn from Kendal in Westmorland to Southend on the Thames, with an isolated patch near Newcastle-on-Tyne. In Ireland the same five years saw good progress made in a belt reaching south-west from Belfast to Galway, south-east of which everything had already been published. In Scotland the published area was tripled; for, in the east, sheets covering the greater part of Fife and Peeblesshire were added to those standing for the Lothians; and, in the west, most of Ayrshire and Wigtownshire was overtaken.

Six-inch map publication, which had started in the Lancashire and Scottish coalfields in 1860 and 1861 respectively, began in Northumberland in 1867, Durham in 1868 and

Yorkshire in 1871. Sections, both vertical and horizontal, continued to appear.

One district memoir and a number of sheet memoirs were published, and there was no reason as yet to anticipate failure of descriptions either in the North of England or in Scotland. The district memoir was by Hull. It dealt with the Midland counties of England and established the classification of the Trias henceforward used on Geological Survey maps.

FIG. 9.—General Section : Shifnal, Shropshire. Keuper : e, Marl; d, Lower Sandstone with breccia at base. Bunter : c, Upper Mottled Sandstone; b, conglomerate; a, Lower Mottled Sandstone. Permian : Unconformably overlain by (a). (Quoted from Hull, *Trias and Permian, Midlands, Mem.*, 1869, p. 30.)

THE END

One November morning in 1870 Murchison's full life came well nigh to a close. While dressing himself he had a shock which paralysed his left side. He recovered sufficiently for a time to be able to drive out in his carriage; but he never again set foot in the Jermyn Street Office. Faithful Trenham Reeks, Curator of the Museum and Registrar of the Royal School of Mines, visited him daily and arranged for correspondence. In the spring of 1871 he dictated to his nephew his last Presidential Address to the Royal Geographical Society. In October he took a turn for the worse, and on the 22nd of the month passed quietly away at the age of seventy-nine.

Queen Victoria and the Prince of Wales sent their carriages to join the funeral procession. The Prime Minister, Gladstone, followed the bier to the grave. In Livingstone's journal we find a record of how that great explorer, still searching for the sources of the Nile, was affected when the news reached him within ten months of his own end : ' Alas ! Alas !,' he wrote, ' This is the only time in my life that I have felt inclined to use the word.' Few men have deserved such an epitaph.

1 8 7 2

RAMSAY, DIRECTOR GENERAL

IN 1872 Andrew Crombie Ramsay, 59 years old, succeeded Murchison as Director General of the Geological Survey of the British Isles, together with the Museum of Practical Geology and the Office of Mining Records. The governance, however, of the Royal School of Mines passed to a Council of Professors, with Warington Smyth as Chairman.

Thus dissolution started. Chemistry, Physics and Natural History left at once to form the nucleus of New Science Schools, built at South Kensington on ground acquired by the Commissioners of the 1851 Exhibition. In other respects the change was gradual. Huxley divided his allegiance, continuing to function as Naturalist to the Survey at Jermyn Street until 1881. Ramsay, as Professor of Geology, went on lecturing in the old quarters till 1876—when his successor, Judd, who had retired from the Survey in 1871, naturally started in the new buildings. Percy remained at Jermyn Street till his resignation in 1880; and Warington Smyth till his death in 1890. The separation might well have broken De la Beche's heart, if he had lived to see it; but viewed dispassionately it affords striking testimony to the greatness of the founder's success. It was growth and vigour that led to this departure from the parental home. Today the Geological Survey is happy to recognise in the Imperial College of Science a sturdy, independent offspring.

Bristow succeeded Ramsay as Director for England and Wales. Howell succeeded Bristow as District Geologist. Archibald Geikie and Hull remained Directors for Scotland and Ireland respectively. The field staff averaged 61 during Ramsay's ten years, maintaining for the time being the high numerical level reached in Murchison's last 4 years. On the

other hand, Headquarter Staff, owing to the transfer of the
Royal School of Mines, averaged 12 instead of 16.

The most interesting enlistments all fell to the English
Staff : Jukes-Browne, 1874, later to specialise in successive
British geographies; Clement Reid, 1874, to achieve fame
in the Pliocene and Pleistocene; A. Strahan, 1875, a future
Director; C. T. Clough, 1875, and G. Barrow, 1876,
eventual leaders in Scottish Highland research.

MAPS

Ramsay's period saw an approximation to modern standards of field work. Six-inch mapping was the rule, except
where, in some south-eastern counties of England, the one-
inch map was alone available. Much of the English and
Scottish work lay in coalfields and metalliferous districts.
Naturally, collection of underground, as well as surface,
information made progress relatively slow, now that there
was welcome map-space to record considerable detail. In
addition drift boundaries had to be traced. So it came about
that the hectic rush of former periods was temporarily
abandoned.

Publication rate of one-inch maps in England dropped
during the 70's to less than half of what it had been during
the 60's (*Fig.* 8). On the other hand, that of six-inch maps
rose to nearly three times its previous value. In Scotland,
where, it will be remembered, a separate staff had been
organised in 1876, the rate of publication of both one-inch
and six-inch maps was approximately doubled. In Ireland
one-inch publication continued much as in the 60's; while
six-inch publication remained a very minor proposition.

Without doubt much of the six-inch publication in the
North of England was justified; but some was excessive,
where it covered districts devoid of mining possibilities. It
is the easiest type of publication to extract from many a
fieldsman, who naturally welcomes quick, large-scale expression of his research; but such a one is only too apt to turn to
another area without troubling overmuch to complete the
corresponding one-inch map and its accompanying memoir.
Murchison's plan for routine provision of one-inch sheet-

explanations has, as we have already noted, only been successfully implemented in Ireland, where Jukes and Hull
deserve our special gratitude.

The *Annual Report* for 1881 contains a statement that:
' In accordance with directions issued by the Department last

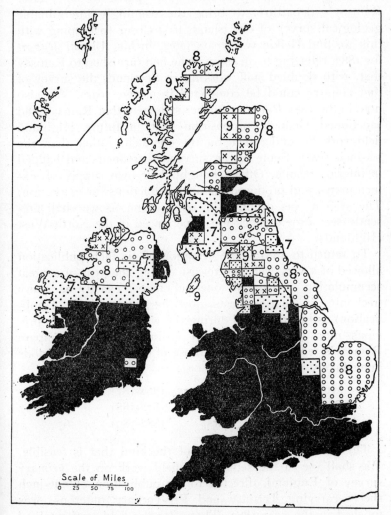

FIG. 10.—First-edition one-inch map publication in decades 1870-79 (7),
80-89 (8), 90-99 (9). (See *Figs.* 8, 28, pp. 62, 159.)

year the publication of the six-inch maps has been to a large extent suspended . . . in order that the publication of the one-inch maps may be more rapidly pushed forward.' There can be little doubt that these directions resulted from discussions in which the Department sounded Archibald Geikie regarding the steps he would be prepared to take, after Ramsay's departure, to bring the seemingly interminable geological survey of our islands to a close. In keeping with this we find Geikie two years later, in his *Annual Report* for 1883, referring to an estimate he had furnished to Ramsay that, with doubled staff working in Scotland, the survey of that country could be completed in eleven years. We also note in the 1881 *Report* a further statement that Ramsay had sanctioned Geikie's proposition that in future Highland field-work be undertaken on the one-inch, rather than the six-inch scale. Some of the surveyors groaned, and handed in inferior results. Others bought their own supply of six-inch maps, and produced one-inch reductions for inspection. The system was dropped in 1885, when, as we shall presently see, a great shock was experienced in the North-West Highlands.

To return to 1881 : The cessation of six-inch publication allowed of a very welcome release during the year of a great accumulation of English one-inch maps, exactly as many (reckoning in quarter-sheets, now the standard unit of publication) as had appeared during the whole of Ramsay's previous nine years of office. It is interesting to compare Ramsay's ten-year total with those of corresponding periods immediately before and after :—

> Murchison's last ten years, 1862-1871 ... 56
> Ramsay's ten years, 1872-1881 ... 34
> Geikie's first ten years 1882-1891 ... 67

This is the last comparison of the kind that is feasible. We shall see in the sequel that field work on the *primary* survey of England, directed to the publication of one-inch sheets carrying Tertiary and Pre-Tertiary outcrops, was finished in the year 1883. Thereafter the field staff retained in England was engaged on drift mapping and revision.

MEMOIRS AND UNDERGROUND WATER

We have said enough of the absence of descriptions of all too many areas published under Ramsay. If, for a change, we look at the memoirs actually produced, we are considerably cheered by a very fine assemblage indeed. Here we can note only a few outstanding examples.

1872. The fourth and last volume of the serial memoirs instituted by De la Beche deals with the *Chalk and Tertiaries of the London Basin.* The main author, W. Whitaker, fittingly acknowledges indebtedness to Joseph Prestwich—'for it would be presumptuous indeed for anyone to write on the Eocene Beds of the London district without studying his many papers.' A highly characteristic feature is the devotion of 150 pages to records of wells and bores. Whitaker had already in 1866 prevailed upon the Medical Officer of the Privy Council to allow him to publish an Appendix of this character. Records of underground exploration are of extreme value; but they are unpalatable to a general geological reader, so that it is difficult for an enthusiastic collector to find a publisher. It is said that Whitaker in after years, a venerable figure, bald on top, but with long white side locks and beard to match, beloved of all, willingly accepted the presidency of any local society which was prepared to reproduce a presidential address consisting largely of the details of well sections. With growing experience, as we shall see, the Geological Survey has got over the difficulty by adopting a policy of segregation. The Survey's usefulness in regard to all aspects of underground water has steadily grown, but the lion's share of the credit still belongs to Whitaker. His services continued officially till his retirement in 1896, and in actual fact till his death in 1925.

In this connexion it is proper to recall the activities of a British Association Committee appointed at the Belfast meeting of 1874 with the formal blessing of Ramsay and Bristow. Its Chairman and Secretary throughout were Survey men, Hull and C. E. de Rance, with Whitaker always on its list of members. Its original title was a 'Committee for investigating the circulation of the Underground Waters

7

in the New Red Sandstone and Permian Formations of England, and the quantity and character of the water supplied to various towns and districts from these formations'; but by 1882 its scope had been extended to cover water from all the permeable formations of the country. Its annual reports from 1875 to 1895 helped to emphasise the importance of England's underground water, especially in times of drought; and two bibliographies of the subject, presented by Whitaker in 1887 and 1895, include 695 items and will always remain valuable works of reference.

Having wandered so far from the London memoir of 1872, provoked by its high water content, we may perhaps transgress further still to note an unusual water inquiry which in 1876 took Ramsay and James Geikie to Gibraltar. A valuable official *Report* resulted, illustrated by a map and sections on the scale of 25 inches to the mile. This may seem excessive at a time when much of England was being geologically surveyed on the one-inch scale; but foot for foot Gibraltar is more important to England than most of the home countryside. As might be expected, Ramsay and Geikie during their visit found a great deal of scientific interest outside the water problem. This they communicated to the Geological Society.

In 1873 a large model showing the geology of the London basin was placed on exhibition in the Museum. It may be regarded as an illustration of the 1872 memoir.

1875. *The Geology of the Weald* is another famous memoir. Ramsay, in a foreword, points out that nine officers had been engaged in the mapping, during a period spread over 20 years; and of these, six had left and one had died. Even so, the author, W. Topley, had produced an 'eminently satisfactory' account. The succession, structure and topographic expression of the district are so marked that it is not surprising that Topley and Jordan had already in 1873 prepared a model to accompany that of London mentioned above. The Weald memoir contains all that it should, including adequate treatment of scenery, economics, water supply and health. Along with many other memoirs of the English branch it owes much of its bibliographical completeness to Whitaker's collecting instinct.

1875. *The Geology of Rutland* was written by J. W. Judd, gratuitously, to cover his researches while on the Geological Survey, 1867-1871. Judd had been mapping in Lincolnshire independently for 6 or 7 years, when he accepted an invitation from Ramsay to undertake the official

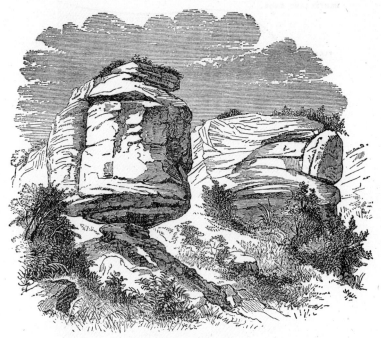

FIG. 11.—Weathering of Tunbridge Wells sandstone. (Quoted from Topley, *Weald Mem.*, 1875, p. 247.)

survey of Rutland on the zonal lines elaborated by Oppel, Quenstedt, Fraas, Marcou and others on the Continent. The local character of many of the Lower Oolite formations of the Midlands involved the necessity of a new stratigraphical classification. This is accompanied in the memoir by a clear statement of the ideas inherent in zonal research in a district complicated by contemporaneous differences of lithological and faunal facies. Little wonder that Ramsay expressed

deep regret that he had not been able to retain the services
of this gifted geologist.

1878. *The Geology of the Yorkshire Coalfield* by A. H.
Green and others is in the main an orderly account of the

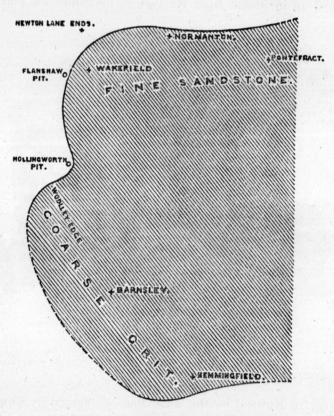

Fig. 12.—Depositional area of Woolley Edge Rock. Newton
Lane Ends to Hemmingfield is 14 miles. (Compare
Fig. 39, p. 244.) (Quoted from Green, *Yorkshire Coal-
field Mem.*, 1878, p. 433.)

stratigraphy of the Millstone Grit and Coal Measures of
Yorkshire, followed by a structural description under 38 district headings, the whole copiously illustrated. It is a great

achievement, 823 pages, the largest Survey memoir, I hope, for all time. A less grandiose style is more suitable, especially for coalfield publication, where mining operations are constantly affording new information that cries out for production of new editions. Moreover, the date this memoir carries, 1878, is four years later than that of its main author's resignation to become Professor at Leeds, showing how nearly it might have failed to materialise. Ramsay, in his preface, points to the advantage the Yorkshire Coalfield has gained through six-inch mapping; and hopes this advantage will soon be shared by coalfields to the south. His wish has taken some 70 years to fulfil.

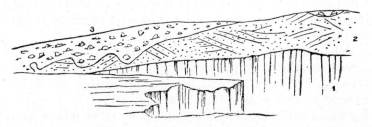

Fig. 13.—Moel Tryfan. 1, Cambrian slate; 2, sand and gravel, with sea shells; 3, Boulder beds. Ramsay's comment: 'He would be a bold man who could see the ground and still maintain that these well-bedded strata have all been shoved up 1,100ft. out the sea.' (Quoted from Ramsay, *Mem.*, vol. iii, 2nd ed., 1881, p. 277.)

1881. The second edition of vol. iii. of De la Beche's memoirs, which deals with *North Wales*, appeared in Ramsay's last year of office. The field section, written by Ramsay himself, shows in its Column of Succession a strong break between Arenig slates, above, and Tremadoc slates, below; but the Lower Silurian bracket is carried down to the base of Salter and Hicks' Menevian beds, below which comes the Survey's Cambrian, of Murchisonian scope. This does not, however, allow its author to continue his claim that the Cambrian strata, 'excepting annelid burrows, and a doubtful trilobite, have nowhere yielded in England and Wales well authenticated organic remains'—for owing to Hicks' discoveries Ramsay now knows of many pre-Menevian trilobites. The break at the base of the Arenig, Ramsay

points out, intensifies towards Anglesey, where ' the Arenig
and Llandeilo and Bala series lie directly and unconformably on Cambrian strata,' without intervention of Tremadoc
and Menevian. It is a matter of interest, rather than
criticism, that Ramsay here speaks of Cambrian in Anglesey, whereas Hicks and Callaway have already used the
word Precambrian for the same rocks—the difference seems
a trifle meaningless as no one yet had defined the basal
zone of the Cambrian.

Ramsay extended greatly his reference to glacial phenomena in this second edition, and introduced new physio-
graphical chapters on the history of the Menai Straits, the
Clwd and the Dee. This was in keeping with his heightened
interest in river development, as evidenced by his researches
on the Moselle, the Rhine and the Po.

Detailed discussion of stratigraphical classification is reserved for the long palæontological Appendix, which has
been greatly extended and brought up to date by Robert
Etheridge since Salter's death in 1869. It is full of interesting historical items, and contains among other things many
appreciative references to Charles Lapworth's recent work
in Scotland; though Etheridge does not think this has much
bearing upon North Wales' problems.

CHARLES LAPWORTH

In retrospect the years of Ramsay's Director-Generalship
are chiefly memorable in our Science as those in which
Lapworth, whom we have just mentioned, grew up to be,
perhaps, the greatest geologist who has ever lived. All the
same, Lapworth's contributions to knowledge, though accepted by Etheridge in 1881, did not produce much immediate effect upon the Geological Survey—as is evidenced,
for instance, by the fact that Archibald Geikie in his *Memoir
on Ramsay,* published in 1895, did not find occasion to
mention them at all. The feature which gives Lapworth a
unique position among geologists is his combination in one
person of qualities which are more often distributed among
a number of individuals. He had physical and mental
capacity for first class field work, with an eye for significant

minor features of lithology, a delight in large-scale mapping and a penetrating grasp of structure, even where badly exposed. He had the instinct of a connoisseur, who loved to find and extract his own fossils, and who appreciated them as works of natural art. He could reconstruct the living creatures which fossils represent, studying them as a zoologist, distinguishing them as a systematist, and dating them according to the principles of William Smith, applied with the utmost refinement. Then, too, he was a great reader in his own and foreign tongues, able to extract gold from among dross of a sadly muddled literature; and a wonderful correspondent, establishing an invigorating interchange of knowledge among contemporary workers engaged on cognate problems. Finally, he was a master of a lucid, logical style and fully realised that research is not completed till it is published for the benefit of others.

Among Survey men, the nearest comparison can be drawn with Peach; but Peach in matters geological could scarcely read or write; and in all directions found correspondence an anathema. Apart from his use of the picture books of palæontology, Peach depended for his knowledge of the work of other men upon his supreme power of conversation; and if he had not had companions like Archibald Geikie and John Horne to record his ideas he would today be little more than a tradition.

Lapworth was born in 1842. In 1864, after passing out of a training college in the South of England, he accepted a teaching post in Galashiels School, drawn thither by his interest in Sir Walter Scott's writings. He soon found friends among the intelligentsia of the town, such as James Wilson of the *Border Record*, and had his attention turned to geology. His progress was rapid, for in 1870 he read a paper to the Edinburgh Geological Society dividing by their graptolitic contents the rocks of his district into two great groups, the Galas, younger, and the Moffats, older. In this he did little more than develop in his own locality, and on evidence of his own finding, ideas of his friend-by-correspondence, Professor H. A. Nicholson; but soon he outstripped all competitors, except perhaps G. Linnarsson in

Sweden. By 1872 he had divided the Moffat 'Shales into three main divisions with several subsidiary zones; by 1878 he had published a great memoir in the *Quarterly Journal of the Geological Society* dealing comprehensively with this subject; and by 1882, the year after Ramsay's retirement, in another monumental paper, again in the *Quarterly Journal,* he had extended his conquest to the widely different facies of the Girvan district.

All this as here narrated may seem good work, but perhaps expectable. To realise its true value one must take count of the difficulties it surmounted, local and external. Among the local difficulties we find the following :—(1) Lithological distinctions, such as may in one part of the Southern Uplands allow of separation of formations, break down, as Lapworth discovered in the course of his researches, in a cross-strike direction, owing to amazing changes in the character and thickness of individual groups. (2) Most of the rock exposures are almost unfossiliferous. (3) Where fossil bands do occur, they often constitute parts of a series, so attenuated that their faunas, mixed on a scree slope or in the collector's bag, are apt to give a false impression of actual admixture in Nature. (4) The district has been subjected to close packing with development of steep isoclinal folds and accompanying faults. (5) Away from stream gorges, the hills are rounded and cloaked with grass or heather—there are no continuous exposures of key horizons, such as so often tie together outcrops in other complicated districts.

To these local difficulties was superadded an external difficulty of imposing magnitude : by far the greater number of the fossils of the region were graptolites, and graptolites had already been condemned by Joachim Barrande as transgressors against William Smith's law of faunal succession. Barrande was a confirmed disciple of Smith in regard to shelly fossils, such as brachiopods and trilobites—so much so that his protests against apparent anomalies reported from Quebec led Logan in 1861 to introduce large-scale overthrusting into Canadian interpretations; but graptolite faunas, Barrande imagined from his own misreading of

Bohemian tectonics, were capable of establishing a succession of temporary colonies in advance of their main entry into an area. Barrande's theory of colonies seems to have been adopted, to some extent at least, by all pre-Lapworthian British workers. Indeed, many of Lapworth's contemporaries, when speaking in public, deprecated the attention that he was paying to 'lowly organisms' and, in private, expressed more freely their contempt for his 'damned graptolites.' Nowadays, of course, Lapworth's graptolite zones in the Lower Palæozoic are as universally admired as the ammonite zones in the Jurassic worked out by Oppel and others some twenty years earlier. Graptolite zones, as soon as unravelled, have always been found to harmonise with trilobite zones, such as Salter and Hicks established in South Wales. Examples of this began to be realised in the latter district as early as 1872, by Hopkinson.

It must be admitted that the Geological Survey Staff in Southern Scotland under Archibald Geikie, working and publishing concurrently with Lapworth, were as slow as anybody else to accept the revolution of values introduced by the latter. Horne, a careful and diligent reader, first saw the light. Often he asked Peach whether, supposing Lapworth's fossil facts were dependable, one had any option but to accept his conclusions; and in after years he constantly congratulated himself on having been able to defer the publication of the Moffat and Loch Doon one-inch sheets for which he was largely responsible until, as we shall presently see, Lapworth's results came to be officially recognised.

Meanwhile, let us remember that Barrande's martialling of evidence in support of his colonies was not altogether labour lost. I feel certain that it helped Lapworth greatly both in his realisation and in his demonstration of the broad significance of the secrets he wrested from the uninviting exposures of Southern Scotland. To avoid misconception, let us add that no one questions the importance of migration in interpreting certain aspects of fossil sequence. For instance, shelly faunas, interbedded between graptolitic faunas, owe their position to migration, not, of course, to evolution *in*

situ. Equally certainly Birkhill graptolites replace Hartfell
graptolites towards the top of the Moffat Shales, by migration—unless one is prepared to invoke the aid of special creation. Where Barrande has been corrected is in regard to
particular misapplications which he made of the migration
concept.

MICROSCOPIC PETROLOGY

Lapworth, in his successful attack upon the graptolite
problem, inherited a wealth of experience not available to
William Smith, experience so full as to include detailed
palæontological descriptions by men such as Barrande of
Bohemia and Hall of New York; but his only instrumental
advantage over the Father of English Geology lay in his
possession of large-scale maps. Now let us turn to a totally
different field of research, modern petrology, the very inception of which depended upon the introduction of microscopic examination of thin slices of rocks, whereby much
that was formerly invisible came clearly into view. It was
in Ramsay's Director-Generalship that microscopic petrology began to figure somewhat prominently in Survey work,
though Ramsay himself was quite unimpressed by its possibilities.

Hutton, it may be noted, had employed a ' microscope '
(the word may perhaps mean no more than a lens) to examine
surfaces of fine-grained rocks for evidence of origin; and
others, from about the same early date, had similarly
studied rock powders and residues. The real foundations,
however, of microscopic petrology were not laid till the
1820's, when William Nicol, soon to become inventor of the
nicol prism, began to grind thin slices for mineralogical and
palæobotanical research. Henry Clifton Sorby, apprised of
Nicol's technique, turned it to more direct geological advantage. In 1850 (published 1851) he communicated to the
Geological Society a paper on the Calcareous Grit of Yorkshire, in which he gives an account of the microscopic appearance of thin slices as well as of acid-resistant concen-
trates. Sorby continued to publish at intervals, always with
some definite point of view. We may note, for instance, in

1858 a particularly thoughtful micropetrological discussion, supported by experimental detail, in which he extracted much information from the cavity-fillings of rock-forming minerals. Another skilful pioneer was the far-travelled chemist, mineralogist and geologist, David Forbes, whose best known writing on the subject, *The Microscope in Geology,* appeared in 1867 as a guide to beginners. In this excellent work, which is beautifully illustrated, little mention is made of polarised light. On the other hand, S. Allport, a business man of Birmingham, produced a stream of important papers, starting in 1869, all of which benefited conspicuously from the use of crossed nicols. A characteristic feature of Allport's researches is his conviction of the essential identity of ancient igneous rocks in Britain with much more modern lavas of the Rhine and Central France, ' another proof,' he said in 1870, ' of the doctrine long taught by Lyell—the uniformity and continuity of the laws of Nature.'

By this time Germany had become the main focus of petrological research. Zirkel, whom Sorby had initiated into his methods in 1862, Vogelsang and Rosenbusch advanced our knowledge by leaps and bounds. At home a few members of the Survey took a hand in the general progress. Geikie recalls how Zirkel, on first meeting him in 1868 at Largs, where he was investigating the Carboniferous lavas of the Clyde, was surprised to find a microscope and thin slices among his household goods. Others of like mind were Clifton Ward and Rutley in England, and Hull in Ireland. Ramsay's lack of enthusiasm for minutiæ did not prevent Ward's memoir on *The Northern Part of the Lake District,* 1876, and Rutley's on *The Eruptive Rocks of Brent Tor,* 1878, from carrying coloured illustrations of microslices; nor did it hinder Geikie from establishing primitive chemical and slicing departments at his Edinburgh headquarters—a most valuable innovation. Rutley also started a petrographical laboratory in London.

Hull, in the *Geological Magazine* for 1873, pointed to appreciable differences between the Irish Carboniferous basalts (Limerick) and their Tertiary compeers (Antrim).

This observation holds good for the British area as a whole;
but it allows us still to subscribe to Allport's broad generali-
sation regarding magmatic uniformity and continuity for the
world, a much larger whole. Further experience has shown
that, *if no attention be paid to locality,* the total possibilities
of magma seem to be essentially the same today as in all
preceding geological periods.

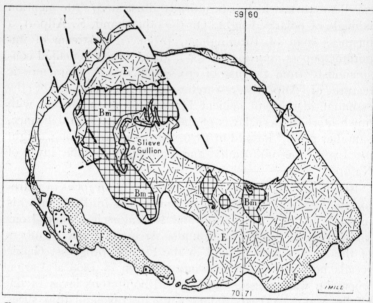

FIG. 14.—Slieve Gullion Ring-Dyke Complex, 55 m. N. of Dublin, as
  mapped on one-inch sheets 59, 60, 70, 71 (1874), slightly simplified for
  reduction. The complex was thought to be Late Palæozoic. It is now
  known to be Tertiary. Country-Rock (Silurian Greywacke and Newry
  Granite), left blank; Bm, Micaceous Dolerite; E, Elvanite (Quartz-
  Porphyry); F, Felstone; Fs, Agglomerate; Broken Lines, Faults.

VOLCANOES AND GLACIERS

Apart from microscopic research one of the most interesting steps taken about this time in the study of vulcanology
was the publication, 1875-6, of four Irish one-inch sheets
showing a Tertiary ring-dyke complex at Slieve Gullion.
The authors responsible, F. W. Egan, J. Nolan and W. A.
Traill, did their work well; but do not seem to have realised
that they were introducing a new idea into igneous tectonics.

It was 30 years before much more was to be heard on the subject.

Here a few words may be added in regard to Archibald Geikie's outstanding contributions to the history of vulcanicity in the British Isles. His interest in the subject antedated his entry into the Survey in 1855. His publications are many, and among them his share in the official memoirs on Mid and East Lothian, 1861 and 1866, show great skill in dealing with field relations of lavas, ashes and intrusions. In 1866 he announced a new point in Scottish geology : the discovery of Permian eruptions and associated necks in Ayrshire. In 1867, in a Sectional Presidential Address to the British Association at Dundee, he was able to offer a complete review of British vulcanicity. All this was before Ramsay became Director General, and even before Zirkel in 1870 and 1871 began publishing microscopic descriptions of Scottish rocks.

In 1874, Judd opened a new chapter. He had come to Scotland to study the Mesozoic sediments of the country, and now he startled the Geological Society with a long field and microscope account of the Tertiary volcanic rocks, which in the West have sheltered so many occurrences of their frail predecessors from destruction by erosion. As in Geikie's own early work there was much in Judd's account that was crude and mistaken, largely because of the poor maps available at the time; but subsequent criticism has left a great deal more of permanent value than at one time seemed likely. We shall return later to the Judd-Geikie controversy, which had its origins in this 1874 paper. Meanwhile, we may note that Judd administered a substantial additional pinprick nearer home, when in 1875, he corrected an interpretation of the Carboniferous volcano of Arthur's Seat, Edinburgh, which Geikie had adopted in his boyhood from Charles Maclaren. Geikie's next great volcanic paper was published by the Royal Society of Edinburgh in 1880, and deals with *The Carboniferous Volcanic Rocks of the Basin of the Firth of Forth—their Structure in the Field and under the Microcope.*

Glaciation figures prominently as a subject among outside papers by the staff in England, Scotland and Ireland. For

instance, in 1870 Croll had published on ' The Boulder-clay
of Caithness a Product of Land-ice.' He argued from available information, gathered by others, that Caithness, the
Orkneys and Shetlands had been glaciated by a confluent
Scotto-Scandinavian ice-sheet. This grand conception Peach
and Horne confirmed in 1879 and 1880 as a result of holiday
excursions. Their holiday work arose largely from an idea,
which Archibald Geikie held in common with a number of
others similarly situated, that the head of a research institute
should act as mouthpiece for any extra-official announcement
of results obtained by its members in the course of their
duties. It is refreshing to think of the curious circumstances
from which good has sometimes resulted.

Perhaps the most important extra-official publication of
the period by a Survey man was James Geikie's book, *The
Great Ice Age,* which first appeared in 1874. It produced a
profound impression on glacial investigation, both at home
and abroad.

RAMSAY, HUXLEY AND CROLL RETIRE

In 1881 Ramsay retired at the age of 65. Worn out by his
long and fruitful service, he had not the strength to contribute further serious work before his death in 1891. He was
knighted in 1881, and had received the Royal Medal of the
Royal Society in 1879 and the Wollaston of the Geological
in 1871. The Royal Medal has been awarded to nine (including Ramsay) whose names figure on the Geological
Survey roll, four of them geologists.

The same year, 1881, saw the virtual severance of Huxley's
long and honourable connection with the Geological Survey.
He left to become Dean of the Royal College of Science.
It was also marked by the resignation of James Croll. Poor
Croll's infirmities had increased, and for a time he lost the
power of intelligible speech. The Civil Service authorities
allotted him the minimum pension corresponding with his
years of service; so that he found his income reduced from
£350 to £75 16s. 8d. Encouraged by friends, he made three
applications for a further pension on the Civil List, two
during Gladstone's premiership, and one during Salisbury's

His sad fate aroused almost as much sympathy as if he had been convicted of a romantic murder. One of his appeals, for instance, carried the signatures of 4 Dukes, 1 Marquis, 14 M.P.'s, The President, 3 Vice-Presidents and 62 other Fellows of the Royal Society, the Poet Laureate and 39 others holding distinguished places in academic and ecclesiastic life. The net result was disappointing, merely £100 from the Queen's Bounty. Croll's friends, however, made life livable, and with ameliorated health he continued working to the end, giving all the time he could spare to his dearest love, Philosophy. In 1889 and 1890, unable to write, he dictated *The Philosophical Basis of Evolution*, which he had the great satisfaction of seeing in print in the autumn of the latter year, before he himself closed his eyes for the last time on this world of struggle.

1882

GEIKIE'S ACCESSION

ARCHIBALD GEIKIE took office as Director General on 1st February, 1882. His ability, energy and attainments marked him out as proper successor to Andrew Ramsay. His broad grasp of his subject was emphasised before the year was out by the publication of the first edition of his *Textbook of Geology,* written with the declared intention of widening the international outlook of British geologists. The fourth edition, which appeared in 1903, is still indispensable.

Geikie had been born in 1835, the same year as the Geological Survey which was now placed in his charge. There is no doubt that he was extremely gratified by his new appointment. Still his task was humanly difficult, and cannot have been altogether congenial. He had more or less undertaken to wind up most of the activities of his office. The great institution, over which he presided with an affection almost equal to that of the founder himself, would soon celebrate its jubilee. It had grown in strength with well-doing through the years. It now stood within striking distance of its original objective : the last one-inch map of the primary survey of Wales had been published in 1852 ; the corresponding last maps of Ireland, England and the Isle of Man have followed in 1890, 1893 and 1898—though one must admit that, with two wartime interruptions, a not inconsiderable fraction of Scotland remains untouched even to this day.

Bristow continued Senior Director for England and Wales till his retirement in 1888. Similarly Hull remained Director for Ireland until his post and that of District Surveyor Kinahan were dispensed with in 1890—when Nolan was left as Senior Geologist in charge of three fieldsmen and J. S. Hyland, the latter a pupil of Zirkel appointed in 1888.

Howell, who will always be remembered for having recognised the equivalents in Scotland of the three major divisions of the Carboniferous of England, was nominally promoted to fill Geikie's place in Scotland before the close of 1882, and presently, in 1888, to become Director for Great Britain—a throwback to early Murchisonian days. It is necessary to qualify these two appointments as ' nominal,' since, so far as field supervision was concerned, Geikie limited Howell's activities as though he were still a District Surveyor, holding him responsible only for the North of England with its vanishing staff. Howell continued to live in Newcastle till 1884, and then migrated to Edinburgh. Geikie, in becoming Director General, did not wish to cease functioning as Director; and, when Howell left in 1899, no successor was appointed.

Aveline's retirement in 1882 from the English service, and James Geikie's from the Scottish, allowed the promotion of Whitaker and Peach as District Surveyors; but the vacancy created by Howell's elevation remained unfilled. Robert Etheridge's transfer to the British Museum (Natural History), which had occurred in 1881, made room for the advance of G. Sharman and E. T. Newton jointly, as Palæontologists and Curators of the Fossil-Collection in London. Baily and Peach continued as Palæontologist and Acting Palæontologist respectively in Dublin and Edinburgh. Close co-operation of the eminent palæobotanist, Robert Kidston, was secured in 1884, though he never became a regular member of staff. Rudler remained Curator of the Museum and Librarian.

James Geikie's retirement practically marked the end, for Survey purposes, of a Government custom which had permitted multiple employment in the higher ranks. In early days of organised Science, an outstanding personality, such as Huxley, might simultaneously give the benefit of his powers to a number of offices, and receive corresponding remuneration. The practice is quite understandable; and is, of course, still continued in business circles, where a capable administrator may simultaneously act as paid director to several independent companies. In the scientific field, however, opinion gradually hardened against its continuance. Hull, for instance, when he went to Ireland in 1869 as Local Director for the Survey, found great difficulty in persuading Government authorities to allow him to follow Jukes as Professor of Geology at the Royal College of Science, Dublin. Archibald Geikie, too, was only very reluctantly permitted in 1871 to accept the newly founded Murchison Chair of Geology at the University of Edinburgh. By 1882 the segregationists had so far established their case that James Geikie was bluntly told that he must choose between the proffered succession to the Murchison Chair and retention of his place on the Survey. He chose the former. Since those days there have been a few minor departures from the rule of undivided employment, mostly in Dublin; but the only really important exception was afforded by the introduction of Alfred Harker (1895-1905) as a member of the Scottish field staff while he still retained a lectureship at Cambridge. We shall have more to say of this special case in the sequel.

Unprecedented activity was shown during 1882 in the Mining Records Office, which it will be remembered was established under De la Beche's care in 1840, primarily as a precaution against loss of life consequent upon loss of information regarding abandoned underground workings liable to flooding. Robert Hunt, Keeper of the Records, visited Cornwall, Devon, the Midlands and Yorkshire to gather plans and statistics from coal, iron and lead mines. He claimed, probably correctly, that the collection under his charge was now more perfect than that of any other country in the world. It was a final effort. Next year, at the age of 76, Hunt retired; and the Mining Records Office was transferred to the Department of Inspectors of Mines at the Home Office. This was a natural rearrangement from the point of view of safety; and the mining plans can still be readily consulted at any time by the staff of the Geological Survey, a very important consideration. The last copy of *Mineral Statistics* issued by the Geological Survey covers 1881. Since then the publication has been continued by the Home Office, though until 1920 not in so complete and useful a form as previously.

This devolution of De la Beche's responsibilities was, of course, in keeping with the previous separation of the Royal School of Mines from the Geological Survey. The most lively reminder of the old state of affairs was afforded by Warington Smyth, working and lecturing at Jermyn Street till his death in 1890. Another redistribution dating from 1883 involved the transfer of many non-geological publications from Jermyn Street to South Kensington, to supply a nucleus for the new Science Library that was there established.

One naturally turns to the *Annual Report* for 1882 to see how Archibald Geikie felt after his first year in the saddle. We find him expecting that field-work in relation to the original survey of England and Wales would be finished the next year, 1883; and contemplating corresponding transfers of staff, some to drift-mapping in the South and Midlands of England, others to augment the meagre forces already engaged in the Highlands of Scotland. As regards progress in this latter region we read : ' The field-work has been prosecuted upon the one-inch scale, and I have every reason to be satisfied with the result.'

Geikie's very proper ambition to speed the completion of the primary survey of the British Isles led, as expected, to transfer to Scotland of five Surveyors from England during 1884 and 1885, and of two from Ireland, 1889. The Englishmen included :—

> Gunn, whose main monument is his splendid work in Arran—started in 1892.
> Clough, impeccable mapper, gratefully remembered for his researches on : (1) the Dalradian Schists of Cowal in Argyll—started in 1884; (2) the Lewisian of Loch Maree, which among other claims to attention is traversed by flint-like veins of crush-rock semifused by frictional heat—started in 1889; (3) the Kishorn, Tarskavaig and Moine Nappes in Skye and Glenelg—started in 1892 (*Fig.* 15).
> Barrow, brilliant but uncertain, who (1) established a world reputation for his observations on granitic permeation with associated zonal development of index

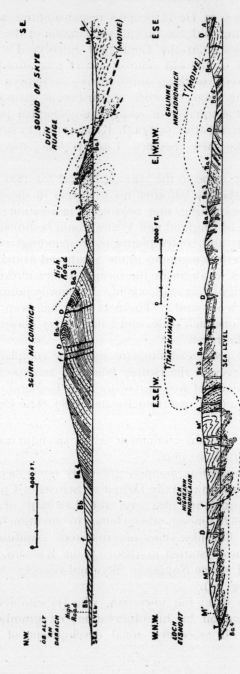

FIG. 15.—Sections across Sleat of Skye. A, Lewisian of Moine Nappe (above T') and of Tarskavaig Nappe (above T); M, Moine Schists of Moine Nappe; M', Tarskavaig Moine Schists of Tarskavaig Nappe; Ba 1-4, Lower Torridonian, and Bb, Middle Torridonian, of Kishorn Nappe; f, faults; D, Tertiary dykes and sill. (Quoted from Clough, *N.W. Highland Mem.*, 1907, pp. 575, 589.)

minerals in the metamorphism of the Dalradian Schists of the Central Highlands—first published in the *Annual Report* for 1892; and who (2) did more than anyone else to unravel the stratigraphical sequence of these last-named difficult rocks.

The movement of staff from England to Scotland was coupled with resignations, the occlusion of Woodward and Fox-Strangways through preparation of a monograph on *The Jurassic Rocks of Britain,* and the withdrawal of Goodchild to the Jermyn Street office. The result was a virtual halving of the number of Surveyors employed in England in 1885 as compared with 1881.

	1881	1885
England	23	12
Scotland	10	13
Ireland	10	9

Goodchild never went back to actual surveying. In 1889 the Science and Art Museum in Edinburgh, later renamed Royal Scottish Museum, assigned a gallery for exhibit of specimens and maps of the Scottish branch of the Geological Survey. Goodchild was appointed Curator and was brilliantly successful, winning disciples who have done much research of permanent value. He died in harness, 1906.

Apart from R. H. Tiddeman, who revised the Burnley coalfield, the 12 Surveyors in England during 1885 were engaged on drift-mapping and concomitant revision in non-mining areas. They worked on the six-inch scale, a circumstance which, we shall presently see, was closely connected with recent happenings in Scotland.

GOOD INTENTIONS

No one could have had a clearer idea than Geikie of what was required in England and Wales after the completion of the general map. He outlines his programme in his *Report* for 1883 briefly as follows:—

1. Preparation of the maps for the engraver with corresponding horizontal sections and sheet-explanations.
2. 'The resumption of the Drift Survey to complete the general Agricultural-Geological Map of the country.'

3. Resumption of ' resurvey of the Coal and other Mineral Districts.'
4. Preparation of sheet-explanations where none has yet been published.
5. Preparation of full Stratigraphical Monographs dealing with individual systems.

Of these five items, the first four amount to a recognition of the virtue of established ideals, including, as we note in (4), a determination to catch up on arrears in the carrying out of Murchison's plan for routine publication of sheet-explanations. Obviously the spirit was willing, but the temptation to rush forward to further and further achievements of area surveyed proved irresistible. In his *Report* for 1885, after referring to the strengthening of the Scottish, at the expense of the English, staff, he makes the following ominously optimistic admission : ' In order to push on the mapping in Scotland, these officers were transferred before the completion of the indoor work connected with English maps, sections and memoirs. But in intervals of wet weather throughout the year, and during the winter, this work has been carried on by them, so that much of it has been cleared off.'

No wonder, with such a weakness, Geikie, instead of eradicating the outstanding shortcoming of the Ramsay period, confirmed and extended it. Many of the one-inch maps of Northern England and Southern Scotland are even now unaccompanied by explanatory text. The ill-treated area includes the great coalfields of Durham, Northumberland and, until comparatively recently, Whitehaven.

It must not be imagined that it is easy for the Chief of the Survey to arrange compliance with Murchison's maxim. Altitude, weather, agriculture and sport often make it wise to station a fieldsman in more than one area during a single season. It is sometimes absurd to insist that a Surveyor should spend a summer indoors to free himself of old entanglements, if this will entail his having nothing on hand during the following winter. Moreover, a one-inch map is generally covered by a team, rather than by a single man ; and publication by a team is determined by the pace of the hindmost. Controversies, too, are inevitable, especially if isolation is chosen in preference to team association. Inspection and discussion may remove most of them at early stages; but others are likely to persist and to handicap co-operation. In addition, the fieldsmen are dependent, not only on one another, but also in many cases on overloaded experts at Headquarters for determination of fossils, minerals and rocks, and the writing of appropriate chapters. They are hindered, too, by the fact that superior officers may often, owing to pressure of work, have to delay editorial reading of their texts when at last these have been submitted. Over and above all this, the Ordnance Survey and Stationery Office, responsible for actual publication of maps and memoirs respectively, take their time over the process, and as likely as not supply proofs when the staff concerned is in the field under conditions that may make proof-reading impossible.

So the years pass with the men growing older and approaching the age limit, which admittedly is foreseeable; but then any one of them may unexpectedly die, leave the country or accept a professorship. Some of the best observers, too, have no aptitude for writing, and are delighted if they can skip on to new districts before the material they have accumulated is put in order for presentation. Others again, having saturated themselves for years with the detail of a particular area, feel that they should spend the rest of their lives revising and revising. Some, too, cannot realise the balance that is expected of an official memoir. They may want to write in full detail of a discovery they have made the day before yesterday; and to leave unrepeated some much more important fact, discovered perhaps a hundred years ago. Then there are those, perhaps the majority, who feel it is their duty to record *all* they have observed, instead of accepting responsibility for making selection. For them the kindest treatment is to institute an efficient filing system that allows of ready disinterment of information in case of need.

I am certain that those in authority should aim at encouraging the research worker concurrently to prepare two different kinds of report : (1) a concentrated specialised account, dealing with new discoveries; and (2) a balanced general account, combining new knowledge with old in a form suitable for a sheet explanation. Many specialised accounts find their most useful home in the pages of unofficial scientific periodicals.

What has been said above about the desirability of avoiding over-emphasis of new discoveries in Survey Memoirs does not apply to such memoirs as deal with rapidly developing coal or other mineral fields. In their case memoirs should be written with the intention of frequent revision; and facts likely to guide exploitation in the near future should be given high priority.

For the moment we shall postpone consideration of Geikie's new plan for Stratigraphical Monographs. It embodied a great conception and led to important results; but it is obvious that such memoirs cannot be regarded as a convenient alternative for sheet-explanations. It is not reasonable to expect a man to buy three volumes of *The Cretaceous Rocks of Britain* because he happens to live at Eastbourne and wants guidance as to the local geology. Even if he does buy them, he will find in them no mention of the Quaternary features of his district.

NORTH-WEST HIGHLANDS AND SIX-INCH MAPPING

When Geikie proudly entered upon his duties as Director General in 1882, he little thought that the greatest disaster of his scientific career lurked just round the corner. Two years later he met his trouble face to face, if not with generosity, at least with dignity and courage. Undismayed, he supported with all the powers at his disposal the new researches which followed in its wake, thus bringing great honour to the British Survey and to British Science in general. Many a man would have behaved very differently under the trying circumstances.

The story is poignant, to those who understand, and is best told told in Geikie's own words quoted from his *Annual Reports* for 1883 and 1884. In the first instalment he was quite unconscious of the possibility that in the second he would be recanting what had been for more than twenty years his dearest geological conviction.

Before, however, we turn to this contemporary record, let us step backward through history. In the first place let us recall how Murchison in 1860 took Geikie, then only five and twenty years of age, on a long excursion through the Highlands. During the trip the leader confirmed his own belief that the crystalline schists forming the main mass of the Highlands *overlie* non-metamorphic fossiliferous Ordovician rocks exposed along the north-western fringe of the region, *and are therefore* younger than the latter. It would have been truly marvellous if Geikie, in such company and under the conditions holding during the expedition, had not been satisfied that his Chief was right. It is, however, a little strange that in after years no uncertainty assailed him. There was a great difficulty inherent in Murchison's interpretation, which James Nicol continually emphasised. The supposedly earlier non-metamorphic rocks lie cheek by jowl with the supposedly younger metamorphic rocks. Murchison accepted this as a fact upon which to build; but he did not explain how it had come to pass. Nicol reviewed the problem from its foundations. He postulated as geological common sense that metamorphic rocks must be older than adjacent non-metamorphic rocks; and he disposed of the contrary age-argument, which Murchison based upon superposition, by *disputing the superposition* and invoking instead hypothetical steep junctions determined by faulting. Geikie, in common with many other competent observers, found in the field that Murchison's superposition is a plain fact of observation. He accordingly dismissed Nicol's alternative statement, unfortunately in all particulars, and accepted Murchison's views in their entirety. This, of course, was illogical; but after all it was very much in accordance with human nature.

Murchison died in 1871; Nicol in 1879. In 1880 a composite obituary note concerning the latter appeared in the *Quarterly Journal of the Geological Society*. It was largely furnished by Lapworth and includes the following pregnant statement: 'His opinions upon the Highland succession were shared by very few geologists in his day; but there is every probability that the whole question will soon be re-opened by those who believe that an opinion held by such a modest and patient investigator as Nicol is certain to have been founded on solid grounds.'

Charles Callaway was one of the 'very few geologists' influenced by Nicol. He was still at work on the subject in 1882, when Lapworth decided to see for himself what could be learnt at Durness and Eriboll in the far north of Suther-land. In 1883 the two of them, Callaway and Lapworth, quite independently, announced a new solution, to which we have already briefly referred. In considerable measure it affords a compromise between Murchison's and Nicol's hitherto apparently irreconcilable interpretations. Superposi-tion of metamorphic rocks on non-metamorphic is a reality, but is tectonic, not stratigraphic; dislocations do in fact separate the two sets of rocks, but they are low-angled, not steep.

Callaway's announcement appeared in the March number of the *Geological Magazine*; Lapworth's followed in May. They agree in all essentials, except that, while Lapworth left the age of the 'Eastern Gneiss' an open question, Callaway continued to maintain Nicol's pre-Torridonian view without qualification. This comparatively minor difference was due to Callaway's remaining unconscious of the fact that he had swept away the grounds upon which Nicol had built his proposition of relative age, as soon as he had demonstrated that Nicol's dislocations involve immense *horizontal* rather than *vertical* transport of rock masses.

Callaway's summary reads as follows :—

1. The Eastern Gneiss has been brought over the [Cambro-Ordo-vician] Quartzo-dolomitic group by earth-movements subsequent to the deposition of the latter.
2. The Quartzo-dolomitic series is frequently, at its junction with the Eastern Gneiss, folded back upon itself.
3. The 'Upper Quartzite' of Murchison is the 'Lower' Quartzite repeated by either faulting or folding, and the 'Upper Lime-stone' is either the Dolomite repeated by faulting or a part of the Eastern Gneiss.
4. The 'igneous rock' of authors ('Logan Rock' of Professor Heddle) is usually the Hebridean Gneiss [now commonly called Lewisian] brought over the Quartzo-dolomitic group by enor-mous overthrows,

In 1883 Geikie dispatched his two best field geologists, Peach and Horne, to Durness. The mission is very reminiscent of the biblical story of Balaam. In fact, in conversation, Horne used to claim that he had acted the part of the sage's famous ass, when together he and Peach first encountered the apparently concordant succession of schist on fossiliferous limestone characteristic of the Durness basin. That it was an old succession was clear enough, for it was cut by numerous faults, large and small; but Horne realised the danger of drawing too rapid a conclusion. 'Wait,' he cautioned, 'till we see what it is Lapworth has got at Eriboll.'

Here now is Geikie's record taken from the *Annual Report* for 1883. He had pointed out therein that the field-work on the original one-inch sheets of England had been completed 'within the time estimated in the summer of 1881,' and that 'every fit and available man will be employed' henceforward in Scotland.

As the true key to the Geological structure of the Highlands is not to be found in any of the areas now in course of examination by the Survey, but along the Western borders of the counties of Sutherland and Ross, of which the Ordnance maps are now available, and as it is of great importance to have the base lines of the Survey-work accurately determined, I resolved to begin the survey of the extreme North-West Highlands during the early part of the Summer.

Accordingly Messrs. Peach and Horne, with the assistance of Mr. Hinxman, stationed themselves at Durness in Sutherland, where the order of succession of the rocks was established by my predecessor, the late Sir R. I. Murchison. During the three months when these officers were at work in that district an area of 113¾ square miles with 166¾ miles of boundary was surveyed. As the ground is complicated in structure and will serve as the base from which all our sections across the Highlands will run, I considered it desirable to have this survey made on maps of the scale of six inches to a mile, but as soon as this typical area is completed the mapping will be continued on the one-inch scale. Whilst the work was in progress I visited the district and, after inspecting what had been done, took the officers over a series of important sections further south, where I had in previous years established the order of succession, and which will, I trust, expedite the progress of the work this year [that is during 1884].

Here next is the second instalment written only twelve months later by the same author in his *Annual Report* for

1884. Peach, Horne and L. W. Hinxman had now been joined by Clough, transferred from England, and H. M. Cadell, who, like Hinxman, had been recruited the previous year.

> Their work contains some of the most important results obtained by the Geological Survey for many years. The transference of a portion of the staff into the extreme north-west of Scotland was designed to obtain a proper base-line for the prosecution of the survey of the Highlands, as stated in my previous Report. Hitherto the stratigraphical succession in that region, as determined by the late Sir Roderick Murchison, has been accepted by the Geological Survey in the mapping of the southern parts of the Highlands, but it must now be abandoned. At the close of the season, I went into Sutherland and Ross-shire with Messrs. Peach and Horne for the purpose of critically inspecting their work. I found their surveys to have been done with remarkable skill and accuracy. After fully examining the ground with every disposition to support the view of my predecessor, Sir R. I. Murchison, I am compelled by the evidence to admit that these views can no longer be sustained, and that an entirely new basis has been laid for the Geological Survey of the Highlands.

As soon as he was satisfied with the correctness of Peach and Horne's findings, Geikie decided on the fullest publicity. He instructed his two lieutenants to furnish a report to the November number of *Nature,* to which he himself supplied an illuminating preface. In this he candidly acknowledged that he had been driven to jettison the Murchisonian interpretation and to accept in its place one involving ' prodigious terrestrial displacements,' so large in fact that ' overlying schists have certainly been thrust westward across all the other rocks for at least ten miles.'

The effect upon the outside world was electrical. The new discoveries were received with acclamation ; and many recognised the support they afforded to earlier descriptions of large-scale thrusting in Switzerland, Quebec and Belgium.

Big-hearted Lapworth two years later, in commenting upon the *Close of the Highland Controversy,* pointed out that the laborious task of tracing the thrust-belt south to Skye is ' a work which can only be accomplished speedily and in its entirety by the Geological Survey.' Geikie saw to it that this vast task was not only fittingly carried out in the field, but also properly supported by petrographical

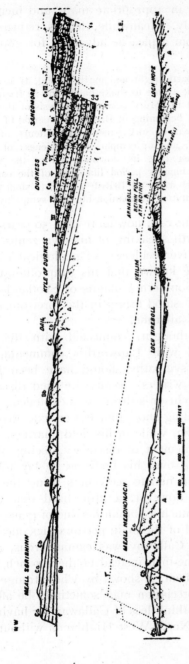

FIG. 16.—Section (continued in two parts) passing by Durness and Eireboll. A, Lewisian gneiss; Bb, Torridonian sandstone; Ca-d, Cambrian Quartzites, etc.; Ce i-vii, Cambrian and Ordovician limestone and dolomite; M' mylonite; M, Moine Schists; λ, marble; x, quartz-schist; T, Thrusts; T', Moine Thrust; f, faults. (Quoted from Peach and Horne, *N.W. Highland Mem.*, 1907, p. 479.)

study and presented in appropriate maps and memoirs—of which more presently. Meanwhile, let us return to Lapworth, and quote from a plea he advanced for good fellowship :

> We have all been partly right and partly wrong. It is time for a hearty laugh all round, a time to shake hands and be friends.
>
> The inauguration of the Murchisonian hypothesis of the Highland succession marked the beginning in Britain of a period of bitter controversy, of estrangement of Survey men and amateurs, of decline in geological enthusiasm, and of comparative feebleness of geological research. Let us trust that its downfall marks the commencement of a new and happier period like that of the earlier years of the present century, when all British geologists shall meet upon an equal footing, in mutual companionship and sympathy.

Looking back to this call, now more than 50 years old, one is amazed at Lapworth speaking of his own zenithal period as one of ' comparative feebleness of geological research ' ! Surely he must have known that his graptolite-guided investigations in the Southern Uplands of Scotland—in spite of tardy recognition—stood firmly in the forefront of geological achievement of all time.

Here is another thought, connected with the subject, though unconnected with Lapworth's commentary. It is natural that special sympathy should have been bestowed upon Nicol by later writers, because he died discredited a few years before Murchison's theory was exploded. It is also natural that a like feeling should have been extended to Lapworth, because in 1883, while in his field quarters, he broke down under the excitement of discovery, feeling the great Moine Nappe grating over his body as he lay tossing on his bed at night; and had to see others bring the work to full fruition. It is, however, a little hard that Callaway should as a rule get much less than his due of general approbation; a close friend of the main personalities once offered, as explanation, that Callaway was cantankerous, and that he mapped on the one-inch instead of the six-inch scale. If this be a true assessment, it shows by what strange circumstances scientific appreciation may sometimes be affected.

Whether or no we think less of Callaway for having made his discovery in the North-West Highlands without the aid of six-inch maps, we shall probably all agree that the Geological Survey of the time ought to have been equipped with these well-tried instruments of research, not only here as was the case, but also in every other district in which they were engaged. Fortunately the events of 1884 led to a return to the Ramsay tradition that six-inch maps should be used wherever available. Thus the *Annual Report* for 1885 remarks that six-inch mapping had been found of great advantage for drift and revision work in Southern England; while that for 1887 speaks of clean copies of six-inch maps of the counties of Banff and Elgin, which adjoin the East Highland block of one-inch mapping started in 1880—the only important patch of the kind in the whole of Scotland. The results were so good that we find Geikie writing in 1897 : ' It is impossible to over-estimate the gain, both in completeness and accuracy.'

MICROSCOPIC PETROLOGY ESTABLISHED

Geikie continued to foster microscopic petrology. His own assumption of additional duties in 1882, coupled with Rutley's resignation from the English staff the same year (following upon that of Clifton Ward in 1878) and Hull's retirement from the Irish service in 1890, greatly weakened the Survey's petrological position. To meet the urgent needs of the case Geikie made a series of special appointments as follows (in London except where Dublin is stated) : 1886-1892, F. H. Hatch, who left to undertake consultant mining work ; 1888-1914, J. J. H. Teall, who succeeded Geikie as Chief in 1901 ; 1888-1891, J. S. Hyland, in Dublin ; 1891-1892, W. W. Watts, following Hyland in Dublin, and then 1893-1897, following Hatch in London—until he himself resigned to become Assistant Professor of Geology under Lapworth at Mason College, Birmingham ; 1893-1897, W. J. Sollas in Dublin ; 1898-1901, W. Pollard, a chemist, to fill the vacancy due to Watts's resignation and to give much needed analytical support to Teall. After Pollard's appointment Grant Wilson ceased to act as part-time Chemist in Edinburgh and confined his attention to field-work. A small chemical laboratory had been fitted up at Jermyn Street as early as 1886. For several years most of the slicing was done in Edinburgh, as was natural from the relative abundance of crystalline rocks in Scotland as compared with England.

Of the fieldsmen, Barrow, as already indicated, took full advantage of his petrological opportunities among the intrusions and metamorphic rocks of the Central Highlands. He owed much to Teall's guidance, but more still to the education and encouragement he received from Allan B. Dick, who in past years, 1851-1856, had been Assistant to Percy at Jermyn Street, and still took a keen interest in Survey welfare. In the field Barrow often had recourse to powders, supplemented by thin slices. Clough, too, in unobtrusive fashion and with much discussion with Teall, derived great benefit from microscope slices in his struggles to understand some of the mysteries of metamorphism.

The enlistment of petrological specialists for London and Dublin did not add to the numerical strength of the Survey. There were never more than three at one time. Hatch's appointment was made following a reduction of staff in Great Britain, Hyland's followed the death of Baily, the Palæontologist in Dublin. All except Teall ranked as Temporary Assistant, or Assistant, Geologists—grades which we have not hitherto differentiated from that of Geologists. Teall, however, was introduced as full-ranking Geologist (Petrographer) on the proceeds of an economy effected after Bristow's retirement, through amalgamation of the Directorships of England, Wales and Scotland.

Hatch and Hyland had both received their training in Germany; but Teall, Watts and Sollas were brilliant examples of the amazing Cambridge school of Geology for which Bonney in the latter days of Sedgwick's professorship was mainly responsible. Other Survey men from the same source were Jukes-Browne, Clough and Strahan.

Teall was undoubtedly the outstanding acquisition among the gifted petrological recruits secured at this stage by Geikie. In his subject there are only two other British workers who may, perhaps, be compared with him, Harker and Flett—of whom more later on. After graduating, Teall undertook for a time valuable work as a Cambridge University Extension Lecturer, which brought him into contact with Allport and other amateurs away from the main seats of learning. Presently, however, he retired to devote himself more continuously to research and the publication of his classic *British Petrography,* which was completed, so far as igneous rocks are concerned, just before he accepted his post on the Survey.

Teall's first important petrological paper appeared in three parts in the *Geological Magazine* for 1883. He had frequent recourse in it, as in all subsequent publications, to chemical analysis, in part performed by himself. His microscopic methods were such as are employed today, though, of course, at that date discrimination of felspars was laborious and sometimes impossible. His main conclusion, when he first wrote his article, was that the 'porphyrites' of Lower Old Red Sandstone age in the Cheviots should be called andesites or altered andesites, if one is prepared in Allport fashion to name igneous rocks without reference to date of eruption. He further showed that they are quite different from what had been 'described as porphyrites by Professor Geikie in his paper on the Carboniferous Volcanic Rocks of the Firth of Forth.' He strengthened this contrast by furnishing a detailed account of one such Carboniferous 'porphyrite' from a lava outcrop near Jedburgh, adjoining the Cheviots. He found it to be 'a representative of the basaltic family,' similar to that of Dunsapie crag, Arthur's Seat, Edinburgh. In all we see the seeds of much of the petrological literature that has grown up in after years around the Late Palæozoic igneous products of Scotland.

As luck would have it this paper, excellent in itself, blossomed out in entirely unexpected fashion as it passed through the Press. In Part i Teall mentions that much of the pyroxene of his andesites gives straight extinction and adds: 'It is possible of course that the pyroxenic constituents of the rock may comprise more than one species of the mineral.' In an appendix added to this part he is able to go much further. Rosenbusch by this time had examined slices and had identified the straight-extinguishing pyroxene as hypersthene, and the rock itself as 'the porphyritic equivalent of the ancient norites and directly equivalent to the recent hypersthene-andesites '—which latter, we may add, were little known at the time except at Santorin. In Part ii, entirely rewritten, Teall points out that by strange coincidence Whitman Cross had published a paper *On Hypersthene-Andesite,* on the other side of the Atlantic just a month before his own Part i had appeared. In it Whitman Cross had announced that in very many so-called augite-andesites of America and Europe ' augite is decidedly subordinate to a rhombic pyroxene which is presumably hypersthene.' Teall followed up in Parts ii and iii, and in a sequel *On Hypersthene-Andesite* published in the August number of the *Geological Magazine* for the same year, 1883. Altogether he gave over a dozen new localities for hypersthene-andesite, occurring in widely separated parts of the world. ' It is not a little interesting,' he adds, that, ' just as the true character and wide distribution in space of this rock type is beginning to be recognised, evidence of its existence as far back in geological time as the Lower Old Red Sandstone period should be forthcoming.' If he had been a prophet he might have continued that it is not a little interesting that it was Judd who first drew his attention to Whitman Cross's paper, and that it was Judd who supplied him with several of the specimens from localities such as Stromboli and Mt. Ararat, in which he identified hypersthene. I say this because of a second remarkable coincidence, Teall's article *On Hypersthene-Andesite,* August, 1883, synchronised with the famous explosion of hypersthene-andesite magma at Krakatoa, and it was Judd who was destined to investigate this marvel for the Royal Society. Thoughts of this kind were probably present in Judd's mind when he confirmed the origin of the world-wide Krakatoan sunsets by identifying hypersthene among the dust that settled on the roofs of London.

We cannot, of course, review Teall's other pre-Survey publications at similar length. From 1884 to 1887 he was responsible for twelve papers on very varied subjects, extending geographically from Sutherland to the Lizard. One of them, which gave him particular pleasure, appeared in 1885 describing *The Metamorphosis of Dolerite into Hornblende-*

schist. The metamorphosis concerned was of pre-Cambrian date, but it so happened that Teall was keyed up for its discovery, in 1883, through having been shown by Lapworth, only a few days previously, post-Cambrian mylonisation along the Moine Thrust at nearby Eriboll.

Then in 1888 came *British Petrography,* a large octavo volume, which no one who aims at advancing knowledge in this domain should fail to consult in advance. Its first 68 pages deal with the constituents, chemical and physical characters, and classification of igneous rocks in general. Then follow 293 pages on ultrabasic, basic, intermediate and acid igneous rocks, with separate treatment for mica-traps and felspathoidal rocks. In every case Teall devotes a section to illustrative British examples—of which in the last-mentioned class only one at that time was known, the nosean-phonolite of the Wolf Rock described by Allport in 1871. The final 64 pages are given over to metamorphism which igneous rocks either produce or endure; and to what he entitles 'The Origin of Igneous Rocks.' The whole is illustrated by 67 lovely plates in colour, some of them drawn by other workers, including his talented wife. Bonney, in a review, has said : ' We have now a book in our own language which is comparable in its illustrations with that of Fouqué and Lévy, and in its erudition with the treatise of Rosenbusch. . . . Knowing well Mr. Teall's abilities and learning, we had expected much, but we have found more.'

For ' convenience of description ' Teall adopts a classification ' essentially based on the systems of ' the authors whom Bonney has named above; ' but of course no distinction is made between rocks of the same composition and texture merely because they have been produced at different periods.' In regard to texture he often distinguishes three grades : granitic, intermediate and trachytic, or, as many say today, plutonic, hypabyssal and volcanic. As regards age he remarks : ' The dominant school of petrography on the Continent proposes to make geological age a primary factor in the classification of igneous rocks,' but ' English, and, to a certain extent, also American petrographers, do not accept this principle.'

Teall's physico-chemical outlook may be gathered from the attention he pays to H. Vogelsang's observations and experiments, and to Sorby's on inclusions within minerals—though with the caution that it is essential to be able to distinguish between primary and secondary inclusions. He also emphasises the lessons to be learnt from zonal structures, and warmly accepts R. W. Bunsen's claim that magmas are solutions. He quotes with similar approval recently published conclusions drawn by A. Lagorio from chemical segregation that accompanies devitrification of artificial glasses and crystallisation of magmas. One of his own most important suggestions is that micrographic and spherulitic intergrowths of quartz and felspar are essentially eutectic. This word has been introduced by F. Guthrie as a result of experiments carried out on relatively fusible non-silicate mixtures, 1875-1884; and it is proper to recall that Guthrie himself all along expected geological applications of his laboratory work. Of less permanent value may be mentioned Teall's sympathy for Soret's principle of concentration by diffusion of near-saturation products within regions of relatively low temperature.

After Teall joined the Survey he devoted most of his energies to problems arising in the North-West Highlands : the nature of the Lewisian Complex ; the effects of dynamic metamorphism on various rocks below the Moine Thrust ; the wonderful alkali intrusions of Assynt, including borolanite with its garnets and pseudoleucites ; and the contact-alteration produced by these intrusions upon adjacent, somewhat siliceous Durness Dolomite. Other contributions from the West Highlands farther south include his detailed treatment with Dakyns, 1892, of a peridotite-to-granite complex called after Garabal Hill. In this he clearly showed that the earlier members of the complex are composed of the earlier crystallisation products of the magmatic assemblage ; while the last member of all is quite likely a quartz-felspar eutectic. This would be easy to understand if the story were one of differentiation *in situ* of a crystallising magma—but Teall knew that such was not always the case. Barrow, in the discussion which followed, indicated his own outlook on the *succession* of events : (1) gravitational differentiation through crystal-lisation of a parent magma to give a stratified mass, in which basic rock came to be overlain by acid; (2) remelting from below with production of successive partial magmas liable to upward intrusion, among which basic was followed by acid.

Another specially important contribution made by Teall to West Highland geology was his description of contact-altera-tion produced by the Cruachan Granite with development of corundum and other minerals in neighbouring Dalradian Schists. Another, again, his account of regional develop-ment in appropriate members of the Dalradian of albite-schists, similar to examples described from the Alps, Saxony and Massachusetts—in all his work Teall thought inter-nationally. Then, in the Southern Uplands, we find him giv-ing a splendid account of the Galloway granites and their attendant contact-alteration.

Administratively Teall gradually strengthened rock-slicing activities at Jermyn Street operated by John Rhodes; but in 1900, we learn, only 216 slices were made here as against nearly 1,000 in Edinburgh. The serially numbered slices of Great Britain as a whole were grouped by Teall, for ready geographical reference, in catalogues corresponding with in-dividual one-inch sheets.

Hatch's most important single contribution to British geology is an altogether admirable account of the Carboni-ferous basalts and trachytes of East Lothian, 1892. In it he records limburgite for the first time in our isles; and, much more important, he recognises the clink-stone of Traprain Law as a nepheline-phonolite. Hatch's discovery of this Car-boniferous nepheline-phonolite finally broke down the de-fences of the Continental school which advocated significant differences between Cainozoic and pre-Cainozoic igneous rocks. In their latter days they had whittled down their claim to little more than that nepheline-phonolite at any rate is exclusively Cainozoic.

Watts left his mark on Irish geology by his *Handbook of the Rocks and Minerals exhibited in the Dublin Museum;* and in later years firmly established himself as Interpreter-in-Chief of the Precambrian of Charnwood Forest, romantically draped in desert deposits of Triassic age.

INTERNATIONAL GEOLOGICAL CONGRESS

The meeting of the International Geological Congress in London, 1888, under the presidency of Joseph Prestwich, allowed of welcome interchange of opinion between home and overseas geologists. The Congress owed its origin to the Philadelphia Exposition of 1876, when a committee was formed to arrange for a first meeting in Paris, 1878. A second meeting followed at Bologna, 1881; and a third at Berlin, 1885. The 1888 meeting in London, unlike its successor in the same city sixty years later, was an English, rather than British, function. It was, of course, largely organised by Survey men, with Archibald Geikie as one of the Vice-Presidents, and Topley one of the Secretaries. Two aspects may be touched upon as particularly important to the Survey: one a debate undertaken by a commission asked to report on Cambro-Silurian nomenclature; the other a description of the Carboniferous of the North of England, preparatory to an excursion to be held after the meeting.

Barrande had early distinguished three faunas in his expansive Silurian as developed in Bohemia, and had shown all three could be recognised in other countries. Hicks, for Britain, had drawn the two dividing lines separating these three faunas, beneath the Arenig and the Llandovery respectively. Lyell fully agreed in the 1865 edition of his *Elements*, calling the earliest division Cambrian and the two later Lower and Upper Silurian. This Hicks-Lyell procedure only went part way to mollify McKenny Hughes and others at Cambridge, who claimed that Sedgwick's priority of partial investigation was being slighted. They accepted the three divisions, but named them Lower and Upper Cambrian followed by Silurian. In 1879 Lapworth, to clear away confusion and to do justice to fossils rather than to men, proposed a terminology 'which imitates Nature herself in placing the three grand members of the Lower Palæozoic Rocks upon an equal footing,' with the three titles Cambrian, Ordovician and Silurian. Now, at the Congress, he tried to win

formal confirmation of his innovation. He did indeed receive strong support from Hicks, and also from John E.
Marr—the latter destined to be Hughes' successor to the
Cambridge chair, and easily the most fruitful worker on
Lower Palæozoic classification connected with that University since the days of Sedgwick and Salter. On the other
hand, so much difference of opinion was expressed that the
motion was never put to the vote. Geikie, who in his 1882
Textbook had followed Lyell, continued on the same lines
to the end; but after his retirement Ordovician has been
freely used in Survey publications.

The other matter of special Survey importance, which was
broached at the Congress, was of very different character. E.
Dupont in 1881 had described what he called ' coral islands '
in the Devonian of Belgium, and attributed them to localised
organic growth during subsidence, very much according to
Darwin's 1842 interpretation of modern atolls. Tiddeman explained at the Congress that he adopted a similar interpretation for certain ' reef knolls,' 300-400 feet high, which he
had discovered in the Carboniferous of the Craven district of
Yorkshire. He also correlated abrupt associated changes of
facies with contemporaneous operation of faults affecting the
sea bottom. Few communications have left so noteworthy a
train of worth-while controversy, extending even to the present day. There seems to me, however, little doubt that
Tiddeman was substantially correct.

STRATIGRAPHICAL, DISTRICT AND WATER MEMOIRS

In England the dominant Survey publications of Geikie's
period were the Stratigraphical Monographs, which he early
planned. They were all extremely fine works :—

> The Pliocene Deposits of Britain, 1890, by Clement Reid, with
> Vertebrata, 1891, by E. T. Newton.
> The Cretaceous Rocks of Britain, vols. i-iii, 1900-1904, by A. J.
> Jukes-Browne, with contributions by W. Hill.
> The Jurassic Rocks of Britain, vols. i, ii, Yorkshire, 1892, by C.
> Fox-Strangways, vols. iii-v, England and Wales, except York-
> shire, 1893-95, by H. B. Woodward.
> The Silurian Rocks of Britain, vol. i, Scotland, 1899, by B. N.
> Peach and J. Horne, with Petrology by J. J. H. Teall.

The importance which Geikie attached to these great memoirs is shown by his dispatching Clement Reid to Belgium in 1886 and to Italy in 1887 for comparative study.

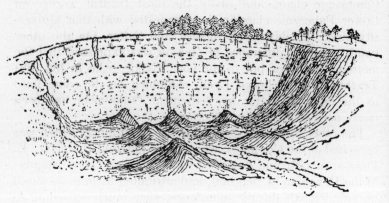

Fig. 17.—Chalk pit at Lenham, Kent. The pipe material in quarry face and collected in spoil heaps contains fragments of Lower Pliocene Lenham Beds. (Quoted from Reid, *Pliocene Mem.*, 1890, p. 44.)

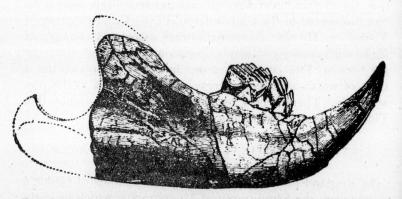

Fig. 18.—Jaw of Purbeck mammal, *Plagiaulax becklesi*, Falc. (The fossil is 1in. long.) (Quoted from Woodward, *Jurassic Mem.*, 1895, p. 237.)

The Silurian Rocks of Great Britain was an indirect product of the work in the North-West Highlands. Horne, as we have seen, managed to delay publication of the Moffat and Loch Doon one-inch sheets, because he was convinced that Lapworth had supplied corrections which ought to be adopted by the Survey. With their hands strengthened by

the North-West *debacle,* he and Peach were eventually able
to persuade Geikie to allow them, with the skilled Fossil
Collector, A. Macconochie, to undertake a revision of these
sheets—the excuse offered in print was the death of one of
the surveyors concerned in their production. Starting in
1888, the result was, in Geikie's words, ' to reconcile the dis-
crepancies.' So it came about that the Moffat sheet appeared
in 1889, and the Loch Doon in 1893; but field-work was
continued till 1898 for the sake of the Stratigraphical Mono-

W.   E.

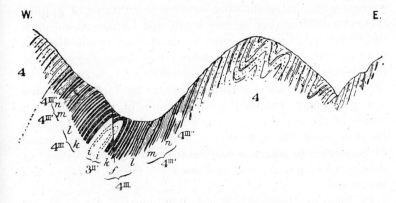

FIG. 19.—Section in Dobb's Linn.
Tarannon : 4, Greywackes and Shales.
Llandovery : { 4ᴵᴵᴵ'' and 4ᴵᴵᴵ', Upper Birkhill Shales.
              { 4ᴵᴵᴵ   , Lower Birkhill Shales.
Caradoc : 3ᴵᴵ', Barren Mudstones of Hartfell Shales.
The letters i-n denote particular graptolite zones. (Quoted from Peach
and Horne, *Silurian Mem.,* 1899, p. 94.)

graph. Throughout most of the eleven years, 1888 to 1898,
this revision was relegated to the winter, when the North-
West Highlands were out of the question; and, taken in
conjunction with the quality maintained, it stands as a monument to endurance and perseverance of a kind seldom encountered in peacetime outside of polar exploration. Among
entirely new discoveries we may instance Peach's detection
of minute organisms in cherts of very wide distribution. The
matter was taken up by H. A. Nicholson, and more especially by G. J. Hinde, both publishing in 1890. The latter

described from Peach's material no fewer than twenty-three new species of radiolaria.

Geikie's general acceptance of Lapworth's discoveries about this time is further shown by his sanctioning revision of the surrounds of the Warwickshire coalfield in 1886. The underlying cause was a habit, which Lapworth developed after coming to Birmingham in 1881, of finding Early Palæozoic and Precambrian rocks in unexpected places. It is pleasant also to note Geikie thanking Lapworth in the *Annual Report* for 1887 for kindly furnishing the Kendal memoir with a table showing the time distribution of graptolites. Apart from this we may recall that Lapworth, through his experiences in the English Midlands and Welsh Borders coupled with his universal reading, was led to suggest that the Durness Quartzite of the North-West Highlands might prove to be Lower Cambrian, instead of Ordovician—the age previously assigned to it because of the Ordovician fossils of the upper part of the Durness Limestone. Inspired by this guess, as one may call it, Horne in 1891 asked Macconochie to search a particular shale bed that seemed of promising character, and as a result an *Olenellus* fauna was unearthed.

Of District Memoirs, six were published in England and two in Scotland during Geikie's regime. The English included *The Geology of London,* 1889, by Whitaker. It was planned as a replacement and extension of the same author's memoir of 1872—a replacement in so far as descriptions of Mesozoic and Tertiary rocks are concerned, and an extension in its inclusion of a detailed account of Quaternary deposits. Its records of wells and bores, now expanded to 352 pages, is conveniently presented as a separate volume.

Ten years later, 1899, saw the inauguration of the *County Water Supply Memoirs* of the Survey. The first volume, by Whitaker and Clement Reid, is entitled *The Water Supply of Sussex from Underground Sources.* All this bespeaks the Survey's healthy appreciation of its responsibilities in applied Geology, beyond the very obvious fields of mining and quarrying. A little volume by Woodward on *Soils and Subsoils from a Sanitary Point of View: with especial reference*

to London and its Neighbourhood, 1897, is a further reminder on the same lines. It soon sold out.

Two other very important English District Memoirs are a
second edition covering the *Isle of Wight,* 1889, by Clement
Reid and Strahan, and the *Isle of Purbeck and Weymouth,*
1898, by Strahan. Both districts had now been mapped for
the first time on the six-inch scale. The revision of the Isle

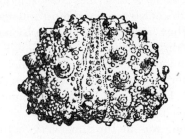

FIG. 20.—Corallian sea urchin, *Hemicidaris intermedia,* Flem.
(1½in. across) and Purbeck tree, *Mantella (Cycadeoidea)
microphylla,* Buckl. (6in. across). (Quoted from Strahan,
Purbeck Mem., 1898, pp. 27, 88.)

of Wight was undertaken in 1886 and completed in 1887;
and the one-inch reduction published next year. Bristow,
who had shared in the original field work 1848-56, furnished
a *Notice* for the new memoir; but died before it actually
appeared. It is interesting to find that Reid made no fewer

than 358 bores, ranging from 10 to 33 feet, in his investigation of the Tertiary outcrops of the Isle of Wight. He had just been to Belgium in connection with his Pliocene memoir, and Dupont, as Director of the Royal Museum at Brussels, had supplied him with boring apparatus such as had been largely used by the Belgian Survey in their areas of soft rock. At the present day Geological Surveyors in the South of England constantly make use of hand-augers.

The Purbeck memoir describes Mesozoic exposures, which from many points of view are the most interesting in Britain. For one thing they have been overtaken by an advance guard of the Alpine disturbances. In 1889 Geikie examined with Strahan the famous Purbeck Fault, which the latter had rightly connected with the Alpine tectonics. Geikie also, the same year, with Huxley and Reid, saw some very interesting thrusting, which the latter had found at the foot of Beachy Head. This, too, was at the time very naturally correlated with the Alpine disturbance; but it is more probably evidence of recent escape of Gault Clay from under the load of the Chalk, which rises abruptly above it for 500 feet in the sea cliff.

Of the two Scottish District Memoirs, one by Geikie on West Fife will be returned to later in connexion with coal. The other, by Clough on the Cowal district of Argyll, was of particular scientific importance. It puts forward wonderful suggestions of large-scale recumbent folding in the Dalradian Schists with subsequent refolding, and also discusses successive stages of metamorphism.

COALFIELD REVISION

Of Coalfield Memoirs we find the first two of thirteen parts which eventually covered the South Wales Coalfield. Part i was by Strahan, 1899, and Part ii by Strahan and Gibson, 1900. Strahan had been sent in 1891 to start the revision, that is to start the original six-inch mapping of this great coalfield. He had already obtained coalfield experience in North Wales and Cumberland. Now he was to take up a task which was to occupy the rest of his time as a field-geologist. By 1909, the year he was appointed Assistant Director for England, he had with others published ten parts. In 1914, the year he became Director of the whole Survey, he published Part xi. The remaining Parts xii and xiii followed later, when he was no longer an author. Strahan's record of high-class publication in the Isles of Wight and Purbeck, and the coalfields of North, and especially of South Wales, is one of which the Survey is justly proud.

At first Strahan was alone in South Wales, but in 1893 he was joined by Walcot Gibson; and later by others, making a very strong field unit. Gibson was Lapworth's first student at Birmingham. Before joining the Survey in 1893 he had spent four or five years at mining geology in South Africa. We shall hear of him later as one of the great Coal Measure geologists of the Survey. His first move from South Wales was to North Staffordshire in 1897. Revision of this coalfield had been started in 1894, along with that of Leicestershire; to be followed by Warwickshire in 1895 and Derbyshire in 1897. Fox-Strangways did much of this Midland work, and in 1897 was put in charge. Little publication resulted during Geikie's period, except for a map and memoir by Fox-Strangways and Watts on *Atherstone and Charnwood Forest* in Leicestershire, 1899 and 1900; and a very important paper on the divisions of the Upper Coal Measures of the Midlands, communicated by Gibson to the Geological Society in 1901.

Incomplete coalfield revision by Grant Wilson in Scotland north of the Forth found expression in revised editions of two one-inch maps, and in District Memoirs written by Geikie on *Central and Western Fife and Kinross* and on *Eastern Fife*. The West Fife memoir appeared a little before Geikie's retirement; the East Fife a little after. The latter, in addition to its valuable coalfield data, reproduces an exemplary measured section with palæontological data, detailing a great thickness of Carboniferous sediments exposed in truly wonderful coastal exposures. This section represents long years of close observation by J. W. Kirkby, a local colliery manager. The memoir also contains Geikie's own account of various volcanic rocks, especially the numerous necks dissected on the shore, today the best known of their kind in the world.

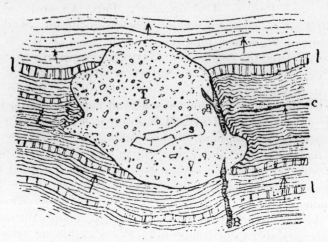

FIG. 21.—Plan of neck, 60 yards long, St. Monans Shore, East Fife. l, limestone; c, coal in shale; B, basalt; T, agglomerate; s, sandstone block. Quoted from Geikie, *East Fife Mem.*, 1902, p. 236.)

OIL-SHALE

Oil-shale, unlike coal, was worthless until industrial chemistry had reached a high degree of development. So far as Britain is concerned, the oil industry started with James Young, who had been a companion of Lyon Playfair in Professor Graham's chemistry class at Glasgow. In 1847 Playfair, by this time on De la Beche's staff, wrote to Young telling him of a petroleum spring in a Derbyshire coal pit and suggesting that he should erect works and refine it. Next year Young established on the site what was probably the first petroleum works on modern lines to be set up anywhere in the world.

The Derbyshire spring, however, showed signs of failure, and Young tried the effects of low-temperature distillation on many English and Scottish coals. He finally selected for development the famous 'Torbanehill Mineral,' a gas coal of very special character lying near the base of the Coal Measures and restricted to a small area near Bathgate in West Lothian. He took out a patent in 1850 for low-temperature distillation of *coal*, and had his first retorts working almost at once. At the Great Exhibition the following year he was awarded a medal for his achievement; though he did not stand alone, for a Prussian and two French scientists were decorated at the same time for somewhat similar successes. Young prospered, and so did the lawyers. Was the Torbanehill Mineral a coal? Did distillation of shale infringe the patent? One great result was that light flooded the homes of the people, out of reach in many localities of supplies of coal gas—for now a modern lamp could replace candle and cruse. Till 1859, when petroleum was discovered commercially in Pennsylvania, Scotland supplied almost all the world-wide demand for mineral-lubricant and lighting oils, and paraffin wax. Since then competition has been severe; and Scottish oil continued to be profitable only because of the manurial value of its by-product, ammonium sulphate.

The Torbanehill Mineral was exhausted in 1862. Before this happened, Young had turned to oil-shale outcropping in the Lower Carboniferous farther east. In 1858 he found a suitable seam near Broxburn, much poorer in oil, but by way of compensation much more abundant and much cheaper to work—and endowed with what proved in the future to be the saving grace of ammonia. Geikie has given the following very interesting account of the initial stages of the hunt for oil-shale :—

In mapping the western part of Midlothian and the eastern part of Linlithgowshire or West Lothian I traced certain bands of black shale which appeared to occur on definite horizons in the lower division of the Carboniferous series. They had never apparently been worked for any purpose, though some of them were so bituminous as to be easily kindled into flame. Mr. James Young, afterwards known as ' Paraffin Young,' consulted me as to the extent of these shales, and accompanied me on the ground. I was able to show him many localities where their outcrop could be seen, and to indicate to him roughly the area under which they extended. He did not say anything about the purport of his enquiry. But in a short while, having secured the right to work these and other shales over a con-

siderable tract of ground, he began active operations for the extraction of mineral oil from them. He thus founded the oil-shale industry
of Scotland from which so much wealth has since been obtained.

The above quotation illustrates the *unpublished* help that
is constantly given to inquirers by the Geological Survey.
Examination of the *published* record of Geikie's field-work,
which appeared in one-inch map and memoir, 1859 and 1861,
further shows that the early seekers after oil-shale were provided with an excellent rough and ready guide. Many besides Young entered the field : in 1865 there were no fewer
than 120 works distilling oil in Scotland, mostly from the
shales of the Lothians. Naturally the intensive search, justified by the economic reward and conducted to a large extent
by boring, soon put the Survey publications out of date.
The first official revision was carried out by H. M. Cadell,
1885-1887, and a new edition of the one-inch map appeared
in 1892. Cadell retired from the Survey in 1888, and his full
account of the stratigraphy of the Oil-Shale Measures was
not given till 1900, when he made it the subject of a Presidential Address to the Geological Society of Edinburgh. It
is obvious that, after laying a satisfactory foundation, the
Geological Survey, with its small staff and uncompleted
primary survey, for a time did less than it would have wished
to help the industry. It must, however, be remembered that
in those days the Survey had no compulsory rights to
examine mining plans of working companies or to learn the
results of exploratory bores; and, with so many companies
staking out claims, attempts to help by governmental research might have been more resented than welcomed. On
the non-geological side we are told that in the competitive
days : ' Oil-works chemists were not generally permitted to
publish the results of their experience, and with their death
their knowledge was lost.' Since Geikie's day it has been
possible to give a comprehensive treatment of the subject in
a Geological Survey Memoir entitled *The Oil Shales of the
Lothians*. This has gone through three editions, 1906, 1912
and 1927, and has probably a wider international reading
public than any other economic memoir published by the
Survey.

EAST ANGLIA AND THE ISLE OF MAN

In spite of what has been said above of publication of maps without memoirs, many excellent memoirs did, of course, appear in Geikie's time, in addition to those which have been specifically mentioned. There were good patches and bad. Perhaps, the best covered East Anglia and Lincolnshire, where much of the work was done under the guidance of Whitaker and Woodward. Whitaker retired in 1898 as District Surveyor and was succeeded by Woodward.

An unusual type of recruit may be mentioned at this stage, G. W. Lamplugh. He joined in 1892, and was destined, like Woodward, one day to be Assistant Director for England

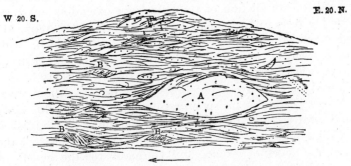

W 20. S.   E. 20. N.

FIG. 22.—Crush-conglomerate in Manx Slates. (Quoted from Lamplugh, *Isle of Man Mem.*, 1903, p. 57.)

and Wales. He was some 33 years old, married and with children, when he signed on as Temporary Assistant Geologist, to receive a pay that has been described as on a level with that of a dock labourer. Previously he had been a wheat merchant of substantial position; but all the time an incorrigible geologist. He first made his name by researches on the Lower Cretaceous rocks and Glacial drifts of Yorkshire; and it is typical of the man that in 1884 he took part in the Yukon gold-rush, not for the fashionable reason, but to study large-scale glaciation still in operation. On joining the Survey he was given the task of completing the geological mapping of the Isle of Man, which had been started in 1889. He finished the field-work with petrological help from Watts

10

in 1897. The one-inch map followed next year, and the
memoir in 1903, after Geikie's retirement.

NORTH-WEST HIGHLANDS AGAIN

The North-West Highland Memoir is another District
Memoir, which, though it did not appear till 1907, is naturally considered at this stage, since Geikie served as its
editor. He had already done all he could to foster the great
research recorded in its pages. He had persuaded Teall, as
we have seen, to join the team. He had seen to it that one-
inch sheets along the line were duly completed to their margins and published. At half-time he had arranged for a very
fine report presented to the Geological Society. He had
pressed for completion of the field-work extending in space
from Durness to Skye, and in time from 1883 to 1897. He
had provided adequate staff working under Peach, with
Horne always close at hand. He had sent in 1885 other members of the Scottish staff to benefit by the lessons learnt;
followed in 1888 by their fellows from Ireland—there have,
of course, been constant spontaneous pilgrimages to this Holy
Land of tectonics. Of these latter the most distinguished
in Geikie's day was arranged in 1892 at the request of the
Foreign Offices of France and Germany for the benefit of
Marcel Bertrand, De Margerie and von Richtofen (accompanied by Hughes, Sollas, Harker and Watts) with Peach
as leader.

The greatest change of opinion that came during the course
of the North-West Highland investigation concerned the
nature of the Moine Schists. To begin with, Lapworth,
Peach and Horne thought that these Moine Schists were in
large measure a ground-down mixture of Cambrian Quartzite
and Lewisian Gneiss—that, in fact, they were dynamic in
origin as well as in metamorphism, if this latter term were,
under such conditions, applicable. Eventually, however, in
1892 Peach suggested that the Moines were Torridonian
sediments metamorphosed in post-Cambrian time; while
Horne about the same date reverted to Callaway's variety of
Nicol's interpretation, that they were pre-Torridonian sediments metamorphosed in pre-Torridonian times. The evi-

dence is so difficult to interpret that agreement has not yet
been reached; but this in no way affects the main tectonic
story, where Peach, Horne and everyone else are at one.

GEIKIE'S ANCIENT VOLCANOES

Another great memoir claims attention, though, from its
treatment of the subject, it was not issued as an official
publication. I refer to Geikie's masterpiece, *The Ancient
Volcanoes of Great Britain,* 1897. In the breadth of its geographical scope it surpasses even the Stratigraphical Monographs.

Geikie had felt the call of the volcanoes from the days of
his boyhood, when he absorbed the studies of Charles
Maclaren in the neighbourhood of Edinburgh, or roamed
Arran with Ramsay's pamphlet in his pocket, or took
steamer from Glasgow to Skye fortified with a copy of
Macculloch's *Western Isles.* We have already caught a
glimpse of his progress during Survey days before he
migrated to London. We have also sensed a cloud which
came to darken his horizon cast by Judd when the latter
turned from Scotland's Mesozoic sediments to her igneous
rocks, especially to those of the Tertiary West. Much of
what Judd said seemed to Geikie ill-considered or untrue;
but there could be no doubt of the attractiveness of his claim
that the plutonic rocks of St. Kilda, Skye, Rhum, Ardnamurchan and Mull mark the cores of mighty central volcanoes which had supplied the nearby lavas.

Geikie had at this time seen a number of volcanic fields
abroad; and in 1879 was privileged to add the great experience of travelling across the lava-plain of Idaho, deeply
trenched by the Snake River and its tributaries. The impression it made upon him is best conveyed in his own
words:—

The lavas ' were not emitted from central volcanic cones of the
type of Etna or Vesuvius, but from numerous longitudinal fissures in
the crust of the earth, many of which are now revealed as dykes of
basalt running for miles through all the other rocks. The region was
a magnificent example of the colossal volcanic type of massive or
fissure eruptions, so well diagnosed by my old friend Baron F. von
Richtofen. It was in this ride over the vast Snake River volcanic

plain that the mists fell from my eyes as to the origin of the Tertiary basalt-plateaux of Scotland, Ireland, the Faroe Islands and Iceland. The problem with which they had puzzled me for many years was here solved. They were now recognised to be an older and more wasted example of the same type of fissure eruptions. It may be imagined with what satisfaction my volcanic studies in Western America came to a close, and how I longed to be able to return to the plateaux of Antrim and the Inner Hebrides, in order to apply to those familiar areas the lesson which had now been learnt.'

On his return Geikie visited his old haunts and wrote to *Nature,* 1880, proclaiming, as quoted above, the new idea which he had brought home with him. Thus started a very heated controversy as to whether the Hebridean eruptions came from central volcanoes or fissures; and, in addition, as to whether the main magma sequence were from acid to basic (Judd) or from basic to acid (Geikie). In a preface to the *Skye* memoir issued in 1904, Teall supplies the following commentary :—

On account of the exceptional interest of the Tertiary Volcanic area of the West of Scotland, 'Sir A. Geikie determined that a typical portion of the region should be mapped and described in great detail. The district comprising the central mountain group of Skye was selected by him in 1895, and the services of Mr. Harker were secured in order that the actual survey and the petrographical work might be carried out by the same officer.' Then follows a statement of Judd's and Geikie's rival views, much as outlined above; and with reference to Geikie's the verdict is given : ' These conclusions have been confirmed by Mr. Harker.'

Later work by others, especially in Mull, has tended to revive the volcanoes, and has shown that there are so many recurrences of basic and acid magmas that the ' main magma sequence ' is too hypothetical a conception to be worth a quarrel. On the other hand, Judd did accept the contact of Cuillin gabbro with Red Hill granophyre in Skye as representative; and here all who go to see realise that his acid-followed-by-basic claim is utterly untenable. This last fact coupled with respect for Harker's impartiality, care and ability, blinded geologists for many years to all the good in

Judd's Hebridean volcanic study, apart from its petrological aspects. It was very hard on Judd. It was also very hard on British geology, which had a long wait ahead of it for rediscovery of the great volcanoes, not to mention the pneumatolysis of Mull and the upheaval of Rhum. On the other hand, if Geikie at this time had been discredited in Skye, the consequences might have been even more disastrous. We have spoken already of reverses which he suffered in the North-West Highlands and Southern Uplands; and there were various other big matters in which his interpreta-

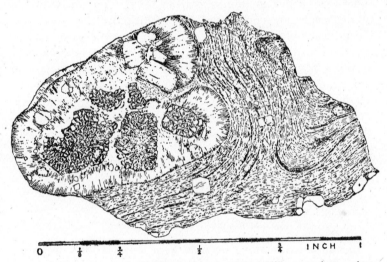

FIG. 23.—Thin slice from rhyolite apophysis of Red Hill granophyre, where it cuts Cuillin gabbro. (Quoted from Harker, *Skye Mem.*, 1904, p. 285.)

tions were being rightly questioned. The five great volcanoes might well have pulled him down and broken his apparently indomitable spirit. As it was, he escaped this trial, and gave the world his *Ancient Volcanoes,* one of the most helpful of classics in geological literature.

It may be noted before we go on that Geikie's transference to London put him in the way of acquiring considerable supplementary knowledge of these volcanoes. He made a point of keeping in personal touch with all aspects of his colleagues' field-work, and naturally visited any igneous subject they happened to be investigating. In addition, he made 'preliminary traverses with a view to the future field-work of the staff. In Cumberland and Westmorland,' he tells us, speaking of 1890, 'I was accompanied by Dr. Hatch; in Carnarvonshire and Merionethshire I had the assistance of Mr. B. N. Peach from the staff of Scotland. In some later traverses in Anglesey I was accompanied by Mr. Teall'— the last-mentioned, it may be added, joined with Geikie later in an important paper on banded structure in the Cuillin gabbro. Much help was also received from Watts, and in some cases from amateurs, as from H. H. Arnold-Bembrose in the toadstone country of Derbyshire. In his leave, too, Geikie was able to extend his knowledge of the west coast of Scotland to include St. Kilda and the Faroes. Henry Evans, a sportsman still legendary in the island of Jura where he stalked deer on his pony for years after losing a leg as a result of a gun accident, provided the transport. Evans was as keen a yachtsman and field-naturalist as he was a sportsman, and on several occasions got Alfred Newton, the celebrated ornithologist, and Archibald Geikie to pilot his voyages 'to every cliff,' as Geikie recalls, 'that I wished to observe or to examine from a small boat.'

SUMMARY OF PROGRESS

In another direction, we may here note Geikie's influence upon the *Annual Report,* an uninviting publication into which we have already often dipped for dated information. In 1892 a new Vice-President of the Committee of the Council on Education was appointed, and in a long conversation he asked Geikie whether he were satisfied with the present form of these *Reports*. Geikie replied, as was expected, that he was far from satisfied. Accordingly in the *Annual Report* for 1892 we find for the first time a special section headed *Record of Geological Work*. This was presently expanded to give a separate publication, the first number of which appeared under the title *Summary of Progress of the Geological Survey for* 1897. The innovation proved of great assistance to the Service, more than repaying the time taken each year in the process of preparation. It makes Survey results immediately available. It is also excellent discipline in a research to have to issue interim reports. In many cases, too, these reports, written by men who afterwards became casualties through death, resignation or other causes, have helped those left behind in their task of memoir writing.

SMALL-SCALE MAPS

Publication of an official four miles to the inch geological map of England and Wales, in several sheets, was recommenced by Geikie in 1889. Murchison, as we have already seen, had made a good beginning on these lines as early as 1858, but had then desisted. Geikie adopted colour-printing, an innovation for Geological Survey maps. Four-mile maps did not begin to appear for Scotland and Ireland until after his time—for Scotland in 1907, and for Ireland 1914.

The four-mile map took much time to prepare, when Murchison started with it, for his staff had not only to draw geological lines, but also those of the topographic reduction. He seems to have stopped, because he thought it more sensible to support the third edition of Greenough's eleven-mile map, published by the Geological Society, 1865. Geikie's four-mile map was based on an Ordnance Survey reduction, but the colour-printing of it had to be handed over to the Stationery Office. All smaller-scale maps until after Geikie's day were entrusted to private publishers; but they did much to synthesise the work of the Geological Survey for the benefit of the public. Such maps include (with their scale stated in miles to the inch): Murchison and Geikie's Scotland, 25 miles, 1861, 1862; Ramsay's England and Wales, 11 miles, 1859, 1866, 1879; Geikie's British Isles, 14 miles, 1864, 1896; Jukes's Ireland, 8 miles, 1867, 1870; Geikie's Scotland, 10 miles, 1876, 1892, 1910; Hull's Ireland, 8 miles, 1878; Geikie's England and Wales, 10 miles, 1897; Geikie's Ireland, 10 miles, 1907.

Progress in publication of sheets on the scale of one inch to the mile has already been referred to on p. 100, and is summarised in *Fig.* 10, p. 83.

THE INQUEST

Six months of Geikie's last year on the Survey were largely occupied with a Committee appointed by the President of the Board of Education. It had as terms of reference :—

> To enquire into the Organization and Staff of the Geological Survey and Museum of Practical Geology; to report on the progress of the Survey since 1881; to suggest the changes in staff and the arrangements necessary for bringing the Survey in its more general features to a speedy and satisfactory termination, having regard especially to its economic importance; and further to report on the desirability or otherwise of transferring the Survey to another public department.

The Chairman was the Rt. Hon. J. L. Wharton, M.P., and under him sat four distinguished Civil Servants, together with W. T. Blanford, formerly Director of the Geological Survey of India, and Charles Lapworth.

The Committee owed its origin to a memorial presented by the staff. There were ample grounds for dissatisfaction, including the following :—

1. As we have already noticed, the sudden expansion of the field staff to more than double its former strength through Murchison's recruitment of 33 field geologists in 1867 and 1868 introduced immediate difficulties of assimilation. As time passed it became more and more apparent that it had drastically reduced prospects of promotion. It is true that senior posts were concomitantly doubled, with four District Surveyors added to the previously existing Director General and his three Directors; but the new higher grade was of lower rank than the Directorship and, in addition, with half the staff of practically uniform seniority, a time was bound to come when there would be a block in promotion from Geologist to District Surveyor.

2. Such prospects of promotion as survived from Murchison's period into Ramsay's wilted sadly during Geikie's term of office. The Director General remained, but other changes can be gathered from a statement of successive roll calls :—

	Director.	District Surveyor.	Senior Geologist.
1881	... 3	4	0
1882	... 3	3	0
1888	... 2	3	0
1890	... 1	2	1
1899	... 0	2	1

The decline in the above figures should be compared with the contemporary trifling change in the numbers of Geologists,

Assistant Geologists and Temporary Assistant Geologists. These three grades totalled 38 (three employed indoors) in 1881, and 35 (six employed indoors) in 1899.

3. The field staff were normally appointed as Assistant Geologists or, since 1879, as Temporary Assistant Geologists. The glut of 1867-1868 led to subsequent great delay in reaching even the Geologist rank, in one case as much as 35 years—a Temporary appointment with no certainty of pension had been known to last for more than 25 years.

4. Most of the staff felt that the Geological Survey's opportunities for valuable scientific and economic work were greater now than ever before, and that the policy of over-centralisation and retrenchment, which had been pursued since 1881, was as detrimental to the public interest as to their own. The output of work during the Geikie period had been extremely creditable in amount and quality; but the failure to accompany many of the one-inch sheets with explanations, especially in the coalfields of the North of England, and the omission to publish any six-inch maps of coalfield areas since 1881 had produced a very painful impression.

It is, of course, possible to let partial failure obscure the good that an institute has done. The Wharton Committee did not make this mistake :—

> With regard to the practical uses of the work of the Survey, they reported, there is no doubt that, apart from the scientific and educational aspects, it has been of great practical service to the country. It has been shown to us that great benefit has been found to be obtainable from the results of the Survey in the matter of mining, agriculture, water-supply and sanitation; and we believe that the cost of the Survey has been more than justified by the practical services rendered to the country at large.

The Committee recommended that the completion of the primary geological survey on the scale of six inches to the mile should be made the first duty of the institution. They did not repeat the folly of trying to rush in recruits to finish what remained to be done—in addition to the troubles mentioned above, such a course is sure to introduce an undue proportion of misfits, in spite of probationary precautions, and also to defeat any attempt at planning of supply on the part of Universities. Rather it aimed at an establishment destined for piecemeal replacement. It recommended that the title of Director General should, for Geikie's successor, be changed to Director; that England (with Wales) and

Scotland should each have an Assistant to the Director;
that seven so-called District Geologists should be appointed,
five in charge of field-units, the two others, indoor specialists,
namely, the Palæontologist and Petrographer; that the lower
grades of the Scientific Staff, numbering 31, should all rank
as Geologists, with automatic annual increments of pay leading to a maximum; that the Curatorship of the Museum and
Library (still held by Rudler) should remain, with two supporting posts of Geologist rank; and that a substantial increase should be made in pay and travelling allowances.

Finally, it proposed that a Consultative Committee (later
called a Committee of Advice) should be set up by the Board
of Education, with members drawn from scientific institutions, universities and industries. This Committee met
yearly, from 1900 to 1919, to consider a report and programme submitted by the Director. In the latter year its
functions were taken over by a Geological Survey Board,
part of the machinery of the Department of Scientific and
Industrial Research, a new department created in 1916.

Geikie recognised that 'the recommendations of the Committee's Report, if carried out [and such has been the case]
would put the Geological Survey on a firmer footing than
ever; the justifiable discontent of the younger members of
the staff would be removed, and the status of the seniors
improved.'

RETIREMENT

Shortly afterwards, very reluctantly, at the end of
February, 1901, Geikie retired, but not to rest. He had been
knighted in 1891, and had received the Wollaston and Royal
Medals in 1895 and 1896. Now in his retirement he served
as one of the two Secretaries of the Royal Society, 1903-
1908. In 1907 he was awarded the K.C.B., and presided over
the notable Centenary Meeting of the Geological Society.
In 1908 he was elected President of the Royal Society, re-
tiring in 1913, when he received the further distinction of
the Order of Merit. Until his death in 1924 he continued to
write and publish. In the eyes of the world, British Geology
had come to be identified with his name. This was partly

due to the care he bestowed upon elementary as well as advanced education. Perhaps his achievement of most permanent value is his successful demonstration that many of the profound lessons of geology can be accurately and effectively conveyed in simple, non-technical language.

NATIONAL PHYSICAL LABORATORY

On the 1st January, 1900, an event occurred, which was destined in after years to have a considerable indirect effect upon the Geological Survey. The National Physical Laboratory was established with the avowed object of testing instruments, constructing and observing standards and measuring constants. It arose from a widespread desire to reproduce in Britain something in the nature of the Physikalisch-Technische Reichsanstalt, founded in Berlin through the joint labours of Werner von Siemens and von Helmholtz. Here we find a limited resurgence of the same ideal as actuated De la Beche and the Prince Consort in the early days of the Geological Survey. R. T. Glazebrook, on appointment as Director, soon put it on record that : ' The first aim of the Laboratory is to bring home to all ' the important fact that science can help industry.

The National Physical Laboratory did not spring into being out of nothing. There was already a meagrely endowed Standards Office at the Board of Trade, and arrangements were made for future liaison between this Office and the new Laboratory. There was also the Kew Observatory, which since 1867, under the guidance of a committee of the Royal Society, had busied itself in a comparatively small way with tests and measurements. Its activities were now incorporated with those of its successor ; and it was decided that the whole should remain under a Royal Society committee responsible directly to H.M. Treasury without the intervention of any of the specialised Government Departments. It was further laid down that the controlling body nominated by the Royal Society should contain a stipulated proportion of representatives of industry, and that its members need not be Fellows of the Society.

1 9 0 1

TEALL'S DIRECTORATE STARTS

JETHRO JUSTINIAN HARRIS TEALL took office as Geikie's successor, March, 1901, though with the diminished title of Director in accordance with one of the recommendations of the Wharton Committee. I do not know whether this titular reduction was wholly due to the completion of the first official geological maps of England, Ireland and Wales; or whether it was influenced to some extent by the presence on the Committte of an ex-Director of the Geological Survey of India. Be this as it may, it has caused no real inconvenience. On the other hand, the correlative renaming of the local chiefs in England and Wales and in Scotland as Assistants to the Director for their particular realms did give rise to some misunderstandings outside the service, and has since been rectified. The officers concerned are now called Assistant Directors.

Apart from such trifles the findings of the Wharton Committee produced an excellent effect. Through them it had been publicly announced that the Geological Survey was not approaching the day when it would have outlived its utility. A bright future seemed assured, and Teall's taking over marked, as it were, a rebirth of the institution. As Marr has put it: 'His honesty and uprightness were transparent to all, and he was universally trusted.'

Along with a majority of his colleagues Teall felt that a stage had been reached when the Survey could and should apply more of its limited resources to economic aspects of Geology; but this did not prevent his stating in a Presidential Address to the Geological Society the same year as he became Director of the Geological Survey that: 'The chief glory of science is not that it produces an amelioration in the conditions under which we live, but that it continually enlarges our view, introduces new ideas, new ways of looking at things, and thus contributes in no small degree to the intellectual development of the human race.'

It is not surprising that with such an understanding of the importance of both applied and pure science Teall made an inspiring leader. Among his many delightful characteristics was an enthusiastic recognition of the work of certain distinguished amateurs, who at the time were developing special lines of zonal palæontology, for instance, A. W. Rowe in the Chalk, and R. Kidston and A. Vaughan in the Carboniferous. In his heart, perhaps, he sometimes doubted whether he ought not to rejoin the amateur ranks and thus find time to complete his *British Petrography* in regard to sedimentary and metamorphic rocks.

Woodward and Horne were appointed Assistant Directors, the former for England and Wales, the latter for Scotland. Of the first seven District Geologists all except Newton, the Palæontologist, were fieldsmen. They were Fox-Strangways, Clement Reid and Strahan, under Woodward; Peach and Gunn under Horne; and Lamplugh in charge of Ireland.

J. S. Flett, who had been first Lecturer in Petrology in Edinburgh University, was introduced as Petrographer; but until 1903 he ranked as Geologist, not District-Geologist. Coming from Orkney, he had already published on the fossil fish and igneous dykes of his native islands. His paper on the latter had impressed Teall very favourably, especially on learning that the young author had acquired his petrological knowledge and skill in Edinburgh without personal instruction from Germany or elsewhere. The quality was excellent, and the treatment of lamprophyres incidentally involved a minor correction of Teall's own writings. On appointment to the Survey, Flett visited the field geologists both in the Highlands and in Cornwall, and so soon found his legs that he contributed a six-page review of his first impressions of Southern Highland petrology to the *Summary of Progress* for 1901. He also immediately improved the standard of preparation of rock slices for the Survey collection; so that, since his arrival, these have been as thinly cut and cleanly mounted as any produced on the Continent.

By this time the Universities, especially Cambridge, where Harker was in charge, were turning out graduates with sufficient petrological knowledge to be definitely useful with a microscope as soon as enrolled. H. Kynaston, for instance, had been a valuable recruit to the Scottish staff in 1895, but was destined to leave in 1903 to become first Director of the Geological Survey of the Transvaal. In 1901, H. H. Thomas, who followed Flett as Petrographer in 1911, and H. B. Muff (Maufe), who left to be first Director of the Geological Survey of Southern Rhodesia in 1910, were additional examples; and others followed. Flett, as a born teacher, gathered younger members of the staff into his laboratory in Jermyn Street for a few weeks each winter, and parcelled out among them with great and wise generosity attractive portions of the superabundance that sometimes threatened to overwhelm him.

Here we may briefly list the changes that occurred among senior officers during Teall's reign :—

Woodward retired as Assistant Director for England and Wales in 1908, and Strahan took his place, starting 1909.

Horne retired as Assistant Director for Scotland in 1911, and Flett was promoted to the post. Flett had already in 1903 been upgraded to District Geologist rank (still Petrographer) in anticipation of Fox-Strangway's retirement in 1904—Fox-Strangway's field duties were taken over in 1905 by Lamplugh, returned from Ireland.

Flett, as already noticed, was succeeded as Petrographer (District Geologist) in 1911 by H. H. Thomas.

Newton as Palæontologist (District Geologist) gave place in 1905 to F. L. Kitchin, who had joined the staff in 1898 after doing valuable research under Zittel at Munich. Kitchin was an indefatigable worker, and is as gratefully remembered for his writings on the fossil faunas of India and South Africa as on those of Britain.

Gunn in 1902, Peach in 1905, Strahan in 1909 and Reid in 1913 were followed as District Geologists in charge of field units by Clough, Hinxman, Barrow and Gibson respectively.

Rudler was succeeded as Curator and Librarian in 1902 by J. A. Howe, who had joined the staff with considerable experience the previous year.

PROGRAMME FOR GREAT BRITAIN

Teall's directorate introduced no startling innovations, but one is sensible of a change of emphasis and of a selection and development of such alternative procedures as had in the past proved of special value.

The determination to give economic geology a first place in annual programmes has been maintained ever since. It received a great stimulus from the work of a Royal Commission appointed at the end of 1901 to inquire into 'the extent and available resources of the coalfields of Great Britain.' Teall, Hull, Lapworth and Strahan, the latter added to good purpose in 1903, represented geology. Much work was specially undertaken by other members of staff to supply information. In addition, Survey publications proved of great value, though many were long out of date. The contrast between six-inch and one-inch mapping was, of course, clear to all.

The Royal Commission submitted its final report in 1905. Next year its members laid before the Home Secretary certain suggestions for the improvement and extension of the service which the Survey should give in matters relating to coal supplies; but the proposals for additional staff required for these purposes were not at the time adopted. In 1909, however, the Board of Education consented to Teall's request to undertake revision of certain coalfields excluded by too rigorous application of the Wharton Committee's priority in favour of primary six-inch mapping. The date is a little amusing for, as we shall soon see, wholehearted revision of the Scottish coalfields, already mapped on the six-inch scale, had been started in 1902, seven years earlier.

In England and Wales, primary six-inch survey of coalfields gave plenty of scope for the time being. It will be remembered how Ramsay had hoped that the coalfields south of Lancashire and Yorkshire, mapped by the Survey on the one-inch scale, would some day be remapped on the six-inch; and how Geikie had initiated the necessary work in South Wales in 1891 and in the Midlands in 1894. Strahan and Fox-Strangways had been in charge of these two districts, though merely ranking as Geologists. Now as District Geologists under Woodward their hands were strengthened, and both proved extremely capable. Experience led to progressive improvement of coalfield technique. Moreover, the one-inch maps containing the coalfields were revised up to their margins; and the South Wales ' surrounds,' in particular, gave plenty of scope for palæontological and petrological research in the Lower Palæozoic by O. T. Jones and H. H. Thomas, and in the Carboniferous Limestone by E. E. L. Dixon.

Among his colleagues Walcot Gibson became specially identified with coalfield research. He took a particular interest in lithological and palæontological divisions which he did much to establish in the Midlands both in the Productive Coal Measures and in overlying pre-Triassic Barren Red Measures. The latter in many cases he transferred from the Permian of earlier authors to the Carboniferous. For help with fossils he relied mainly upon two outside specialists, Kidston for plants and Wheelton Hind for non-marine lamellibranchs. He also laid great stress upon intercalated marine bands which furnished widespread index horizons. His researches thus had special value for surface and underground exploration of concealed coalfields adjacent to those in actual operation. In later years, 1920, he was to publish the first edition of his book *Coal in Great Britain*, reminiscent in a way of Hull's *Coalfields of Great Britain*, of which the first of five editions had appeared in 1861.

Since De la Beche's day the Survey had done little in relation to coal quality. In 1901, however, Pollard started an elaborate chemical examination of the coals of South Wales, already planned in Geikie's time; and this eventually led to a joint memoir by himself and Strahan on : *The Coals of South Wales, with special reference to the Origin and Distribution of Anthracite*, 1908. The investigation

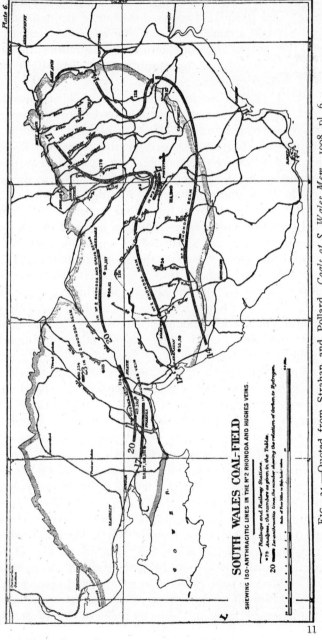

FIG. 24.—Quoted from Strahan and Pollard, *Coals of S. Wales Mem.*, 1908, pl. 6.

SOUTH WALES COAL-FIELD

SHEWING ISO-ANTHRACITIC LINES IN THE N°2 RHONDDA AND HUGHES VEINS.

greatly increased our knowledge of the subject, and its value is recognised by all. There is, however, a disinclination to accept Strahan's conclusion that the essential contrast between the anthracitic and bituminous qualities in South Wales was determined by conditions of deposition rather than of metamorphism.

A third district under Woodward was organised by Clement Reid in charge of the Devon-Cornwall peninsula, where Ussher and two others were already at work. The determination to push forward in this province is easily understood when one remembers the mineral resources of the counties and the little that had been added to the maps since De la Beche's survey. A mining geologist, D. A. MacAlister, was employed from 1902 to 1911. He often recorded the information he collected on maps of the 25 inches to the mile scale; and he furnished important contributions to several memoirs, especially those on Falmouth and Camborne, 1906, and Land's End, 1907. Flett, too, proved of great service throughout the attack upon this region of diversified petrology. In particular he was entrusted with both field and microscopic examination of the famous igneous complex of the Lizard with its attendant metamorphic problems.

Returning to 1901, we may note as a sample of the first year's achievement two results announced by Reid in the corresponding *Summary of Progress:* (1) The Land's End granite is a complex with two distinct members; and (2) a Pliocene coast line can be clearly recognised in Cornish scenery 420 ft. above present sea level.

The resurvey proceeded so rapidly in the South-West that by 1913, the year of Reid's retirement, eighteen one-inch maps with corresponding memoirs had appeared. They extended continuously from the Scilly Isles and Trevose Head to Lyme Regis, but did not include North Devon. Ussher, it should be explained, had already published five of these maps; but until Teall's day he had produced no memoir.

In Scotland in 1901 Horne divided the staff among Peach, Gunn and himself to carry forward or complete work already started among schists and igneous rocks of the West, North

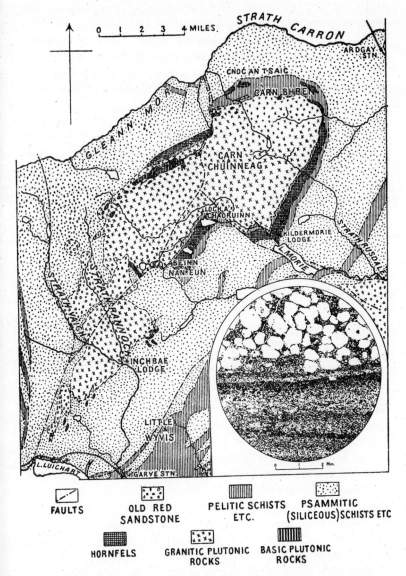

FAULTS

OLD RED
SANDSTONE

PELITIC SCHISTS
ETC.

PSAMMITIC
(SILICEOUS)SCHISTS ETC

HORNFELS

GRANITIC PLUTONIC
ROCKS

BASIC PLUTONIC
ROCKS

FIG. 25.—Map of hornfels area, and microslice of garnetiferous biotite-quartz-hornfels, pseudomorphing original sedimentary texture, Inchbae, Northern Highlands. (Quoted from Crampton, Clough and Flett, *Ben Wyvis Mem.*, 1912, pls. ix, xii.)

and Central Highlands. The *Summary of Progress* for the year contains references to a discovery near Inchbae in Ross by C. B. Crampton. It relates to a belt, two miles wide, consisting of hornfelsed sediments which, indurated by adjacent granite, had escaped the general Moine-Schist-making metamorphism of the region. Full descriptions, published later in the *Geological Magazine,* 1910, and the official memoir, 1912, have rendered this occurrence one of the outstanding treasures of Scottish geology (*Fig.* 25).

Peach, in addition to his mainland responsibilities, was placed in nominal charge of the final mapping in Skye, where Harker was still at work. Harker's memoir on the *Tertiary Igneous Rocks of Skye* appeared in 1904, and is one of the most important ever published by the Survey.

Fig. 26.—Scenic contact of gabbro of Cuillins, to left, and granite of the Red Hills, to right. (Quoted from Harker, *Skye Mem.,* 1904, p. 449.)

Together with the apposite parts of two one-inch maps, it represents in splendid fashion the main achievement of its gifted author, appointed, it will be remembered, with one object in view. Accurate mapping and close correlation of field work with microscopic petrology, combined with clear thinking and expression, won immediate world-wide recognition. As a specially original contribution to igneous tectonics one may perhaps single out his separation, from other intrusions, of a group of centrally inclined sheets, which have since come to be descriptively entitled cone-sheets.

Naturally some of Harker's propositions have been questioned, even by those who feel most admiration and gratitude for his work as a whole. A widely criticised departure from Geikie's position concerns his claim that the basalt lavas of

Skye have been almost everywhere flooded by sills of substantially later date—it is generally thought that most of
these supposed sills are nothing more than the hard interior
portions of the lavas themselves.

Harker retired in 1905, after having extended his Skye
mapping into Rhum and Eigg.

It might seem from the above narration that Scotland had
been forgotten in the planning of economic research, but the
programme for 1902 shows that such was not the case. As
a general rule Highland geology can only be effectively carried on during the summer, and it is a great advantage for
Scottish members of staff to have a Lowland campaign to
occupy their attention in spring and autumn. Double-deck
programmes were launched by Teall and they proved highly
successful. It is interesting to recall that Gibson was, for
the winter of 1902-1903, transferred to Scotland to assist his
northern colleagues with his experience of recent coalfield
procedure.

GOODBYE TO IRELAND

In Ireland Teall at first adopted an experimental attitude.
It was decided to aim at closer contact with the overwhelm-
ingly agricultural interest of the country. No Assistant
Director was appointed, but Lamplugh, as District Geologist, was entrusted with a limited objective : the preparation
of one-inch drift maps and corresponding memoirs covering
the neighbourhood of Dublin, Belfast, Cork and Limerick.
For this Lamplugh's experience of the glaciation of the Isle
of Man in the centre of the Irish Sea basin afforded an excellent introduction.

While the field work was essentially confined to the tracing and examination of Quaternary deposits, hitherto treated
in generalised fashion, the memoirs aimed at furnishing an
effective guide to the geology as a whole. Full advantage
was taken of pre-existing publications, and the result was
excellent.

The last of the memoirs, that on *The Geology of the
country around Limerick,* is dated 1907. Its preface is signed
by J. J. H. Teall at Jermyn Street, London, and Grenville

A. J. Cole at Hume Street, Dublin, and its final paragraph
reads as follows :—

On April 1st, 1905, after the main part of this memoir had been
prepared, the work of the Geological Survey in Ireland was transferred to the charge of the Department of Agriculture and Technical
Instruction in Dublin. The responsibility for the final revision and
issue of the memoir, and of the map which it describes, has thus
become shared between two public bodies. This fact, however, which
marks a transition rather than a break of continuity, may be regarded
as of pleasant augury, and as typical of the free intercommunication
and interchange of ideas that will, it is hoped, always subsist between
the Geological Surveys of Great Britain and Ireland.

The tales of four cities unfolded during the Lamplugh
episode had much more than local interest. They took their
place among contending theories as a clear exposition of
land-ice glaciation, and greatly extended our knowledge of
the shelly boulder clay of Eastern Ireland with its Ailsa
Craig and associated erratics. In regard to other glacial
phenomena, an exposure of water-eroded limestone at the
base of an esker near Dublin told that the stream responsible
for this particular gravel ridge flowed at the actual bottom
of the containing glacier; while deserted gorges, elsewhere
eroded across spurs by rivers in what now seem impossible
situations, provided additional instances of interplay of
vanished ice and water. Most of these dry gorges had clearly
resulted from marginal diversion, by remaining ice, of water
gathering in streams on the land surface, as this was pro-
gressively re-exposed during the melting away of the
glaciers.

The interpretation of such glacially controlled spillways
and the lessons to be learnt from their distribution were at
the time exciting special interest among British geologists
led by P. F. Kendall, Professor at Leeds. American and
Scandinavian geologists had long been familiar with the subject as exemplified in their own lands; but British geologists
had lagged behind. Whether we islanders should be proud or
ashamed of the fact, Kendall's revelation came direct from
Nature. He told me himself that, on returning home one
day from the Cleveland Hills, aglow with discovery, his wife
saw that something wonderful had happened; and to her inquiry he replied: 'I have met God upon the mountain.'

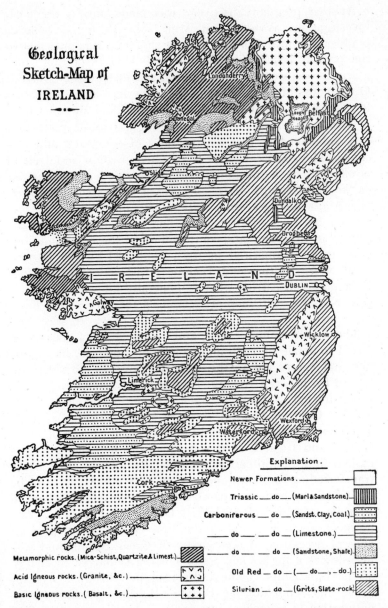

Geological
Sketch-Map of
IRELAND

Explanation.

Newer Formations. _____

Triassic ___ do ___ (Marl & Sandstone).

Carboniferous ___ do ___ (Sandst. Clay, Coal.)

_____ do _____ do ___ (Limestone.) ___

_____ do _____ do ___ (Sandstone, Shale.)

Old Red ___ do ___ (___ do ___ , _ do.)

Silurian ___ do ___ (Grits, Slate-rock.)

Metamorphic rocks. (Mica-Schist, Quartzite & Limest.)

Acid Igneous rocks. (Granite, &c.)

Basic Igneous rocks. (Basalt, &c.)

FIG. 27.—Quoted from Kilroe, *Soil Geology of Ireland,* 1907, frontispiece.

Another pregnant discovery was made during the Irish investigation. Wright and Muff (Maufe) found beneath boulder clay near Cork an ancient shoreline very little above the present beach. The feature and deposits of this 'preglacial' coast were soon recognised as widespread in Ireland. Occurrences of what is supposed to be the same beach had long been known bordering the English and Bristol Channels and, since 1891, near Flamborough Head in Yorkshire.

A valuable link between the days of connected and disconnected geological surveys of Great Britain and Ireland is afforded by a substantial volume entitled *A Description of the Soil-Geology of Ireland, based upon Geological Survey Maps and Records, with Notes on Climate*. It was written by J. R. Kilroe, who had been appointed to the Survey in 1874, and who continued under the new conditions until 1913. It appeared in 1907, published by the Department of Agriculture and Technical Instruction for Ireland. In a pocket it carries what is generally known as Geikie's colour-printed drift map of Ireland on the scale of ten miles to an inch.

The 'intercommunication and interchange of ideas,' referred to above in Teall and Cole's joint preface, has found personal expression in the wanderings of W. B. Wright, to and fro between Ireland, England and Scotland. Wright was attracted to Geology as a student of mathematics at Trinity College, Dublin, through reading Croll's *Climate and Time*. In 1901 he joined the Geological Survey of Great Britain and Ireland, as it was then, and had the unforgettable delight of apprenticeship under Lamplugh. In 1904 he transferred to England, and in 1905 to Scotland. In 1910 he went back to the now separated Survey of Ireland, where in 1921 he was promoted District Geologist. The same year, however, on the advent of the Free State, he accepted an offer of accession to the Survey of Great Britain and was installed as a highly successful District Geologist in charge of the Lancashire coalfield. In 1914 he had already established his reputation as Britain's leading glaciologist by publication of a book of international standing entitled *The Quaternary Ice Age*.

CONCENTRATION

Teall was a great upholder of the District Geologist organisation. He favoured team concentration to obtain results in reasonable time with adequate concomitant discussion. It is symptomatic of his outlook that he recast the *Summary of Progress* so as to present the findings of the year in the form of a series of district reports. Geikie had arranged his successive *Summaries* primarily on a stratigraphical basis— which incidentally was not appreciated by English contributors as it tended to put Scottish topics in the forefront. Teall, of course, still retained stratigraphical order within each individual district report, and also in his general introductory section.

Another innovation introduced by Teall, and one that continued from 1902 to 1936, was to accept as appendices to the *Summaries* a number of subject-papers contributed by members of staff, and occasionally by outsiders. Previously, appendices had been reserved for catalogues of type fossils belonging to the Survey collections.

Teall's preference for concentration and collaboration was further shown in his ruling that everyone must henceforward spend the winter at Headquarters in London, Edinburgh or Dublin as the case might be. In Geikie's day and earlier it had been common practice for a surveyor to take a house for himself in a region in which he was likely to be employed for many years to come, as Horne at Inverness, Clough at Dunoon and Howell at Newcastle.

BARROW RETURNS TO ENGLAND

Partly as a result of Teall's new ruling about winter quarters, Barrow returned to England in 1903. Since his transfer to Scotland in 1884 Barrow had always maintained a home in London, and had done his indoor work at Jermyn Street. The arrangement had greatly helped his acquisition of petrographical technique, but it had made it specially hard for him to keep in touch with his field colleagues.

Controversies had arisen, as too often in geology, and to straighten them out so far as possible Teall in 1903 arranged a joint excursion to Perthshire of Horne, Peach, Barrow,

Cunningham Craig and Flett. The party did not reach positive conclusions on all the semi-independent issues investigated, but Horne did furnish a report which was in the main adverse to Barrow's theories.

Several of the views then held by Barrow and his companions, whether in opposition or in agreement, have since had to be modified or abandoned; so that it is difficult to offer a fair comment upon the verdict resulting from this inquiry. It is, however, a fact that most attention was given to the question as to whether the Perthshire Quartzite, anywhere in the district examined, exhibited both its stratigraphical margins, or only its base—whether, in other words, it functioned as an intercalation in the local Highland succession or was an end term restricted at outcrop to a series of isoclinal synclines. Barrow maintained the former view, his opponents the latter. Barrow, all now admit, was right in this matter; but with total assurance he accepted as a test locality one in which Cunningham Craig had correctly interpreted the local evidence on the single margin hypothesis. It was clear in *this particular case,* to other members of the party, that Barrow's double-margin alternative was untenable; and as Barrow himself remained obdurate, his colleagues came to the conclusion (quite wrongly) that his *general proposition* was mistaken.

It is probable enough that Barrow's removal at this time was good for Highland geology. It gave other workers a breathing space in which to reconsider the problems, and separate so far as in them lay the wheat from the chaff. It is at any rate satisfactory to recall that Barrow was encouraged from Headquarters to explain his views in official and unofficial publications—where, quite properly, readers were informed that different conclusions had been reached by colleagues.

Barrow remained true to himself in his altered geological environment, stirring up keen inquiry into the origin of the high-level gravels so common in South-East England. It is also pleasant to read the *Colliery Guardian* for 1904 congratulating him on having foretold the finding of a particular coal seam near Cheadle, North Staffordshire, where the 'old miners' had declared that it did not exist.

PUBLICATION

Teall introduced various reforms that increased the time given to indoor work as compared with field work. We have seen how Ramsay and Geikie both failed somewhat lamentably to implement Murchison's plan that each published

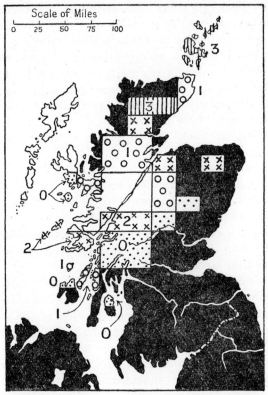

FIG. 28.—First-edition one-inch map publication in decades 1900-09 (O), 10-19 (1), 20-29 (2), 30-39 (3). (See *Figs.* 8, 10, pp. 62, 83.)

one-inch map should have its own explanatory memoir. Teall met the difficulty with a simplicity that suggests administrative genius. He laid down that the issue of map and memoir must be simultaneous; and by this both-or-nothing policy succeeded in enlisting co-operation at all levels, and in replacing good intentions by planned achievements; but, of course, more memoirs, fewer maps—though actually the output was extremely satisfactory (*Fig.* 28).

Teall at the same time did much to improve map publication. He decided upon the issue of a colour-printed 25-miles-to-the-inch geological map of the British Isles. This appeared in 1906, after the administrative separation of the Irish Survey. It has been maintained ever since, and has been of great scientific and educational value.

Teall also introduced colour-printing of one-inch maps, starting with the sheet covering Stoke-on-Trent. The innovation has proved a boon, because it has greatly reduced prices to the public. He soon earned further gratitude by embellishment of these colour-printed maps with horizontal and vertical sections to supplement their unmeasured indexes.

Colour-printing eliminates the need for individual check of sale copies, and in practice has reduced colourist errors to a minimum. It also enables maps to be handled out of doors in showery weather. It is, however, necessary for economy's sake to issue a considerable number of copies at one printing, and not to look forward to making even minor changes for a long time to come.

Besides new editions since 1901, Teall wisely published in colour-print several selected one-inch sheets of older date.

Teall also introduced routine publication of six-inch maps of regions of special economic importance, mainly the coalfields. The maps in this case were not colour-printed, but could be purchased either hand-painted or uncoloured. The earliest of this revived suite came from the Staffordshire coalfield, 1903. During Geikie's period, publication of six-inch maps had been all but discontinued, and had totally disregarded the coalfields. The few examples issued covered some of the non-ferrous metalliferous fields of the North of England, as at Alston and Atherstone Moor, the ironstone field of Cleveland, the city site of Liverpool and certain choice localities illustrating overthrusting in the North-West Highlands. Teall, it may be added, included some of Harker's six-inch maps of the Tertiary igneous rocks of Skye in his publication programme for 1905.

CHANGES AT HEADQUARTERS

Reorganisation at Jermyn Street, accompanied by some interior rebuilding, greatly improved working and exhibition conditions. Concentration of purpose is again evident. De la Beche's ideal to assemble as complete an illustration as possible of geological applications to industry and the arts had largely been fulfilled by the birth and growth of extraneous institutions. Meanwhile, the fundamental geological needs of the Survey called aloud for more space and attention. Thus, in accordance with one of the recommendations of the Wharton Committee, the pottery collection which Murchison had discussed with the Prince Consort was dispersed. Some of its best specimens went to the Victoria and Albert Museum. Other valuable possessions shared in the exodus, among them 12,000 additional volumes handed over to the Science Library.

From very early days efforts had been made to file for reference boring information that could not find space either in memoirs or vertical sections. The task is heavy, for in the books of a mining company or well driller the journals or logs, as they are called, may be very vaguely located, and the items recorded may need much comparative study for identification. In Teall's *Annual Report* for 1901 we read: ' Some attempt has been made to carry on the work of registering all records of Borings and Well-sinkings which was commenced in 1895 ; but much remains to be done.' Filing systems evolved during Teall's period by junior members of staff engaged in coalfield revision immensely strengthened the handling of mining information ; but well records remained fairly chaotic, in spite of the publication of many Water Supply memoirs. Success was delayed in this matter until the development of a Water Unit and of a second World War.

HAPPENINGS OVERSEAS

The main geological event of 1902 was the almost simultaneous eruption of the Soufrière in St. Vincent and Mont Pelée in Martinique. The effects were so devastating and impressive that various national parties were sent out to in-

vestigate. On the suggestion of the Colonial Office the Royal
Society despatched a commission of two. The choice fell
upon Tempest Anderson, above all things an experienced
photographer of volcanoes, and Flett, who was accordingly
given leave of absence from May to August. Their reports,
speedily furnished and full of detail both petrographical and
otherwise, were mainly composed by Flett, and rank as a
great achievement. In them is to be found the origin of what
is now a very generally accepted theory that the down-
valley rush of the black cloud (or *nuée ardente* to use its
alternative rather contradictory title) characteristic of these
eruptions was determined by gravity. The matter is still
under debate, for A. Lacroix claimed, at least in relation to
Mont Pelée, effective co-operation of sideways-directed ex-
plosive blast. Indeed, a week before his death, Flett told me
he thought there was some evidence in favour of Lacroix's
interpretation, and that a final decision should await further
observations at some repeat performance.

Teall was rather disposed at this time to permit members
of staff to undertake special tasks abroad. Thus, in 1903,
Cunningham Craig was lent for two years to Trinidad, and
Scrivenor for three years to the Malay States. Similarly, in
1905, Maufe was allowed to look for water along the Uganda
railway, and Lamplugh to prepare the way for a British
Association visit to the Victoria Falls and Zambezi Gorge.
Even as late as 1908 Reid spent two months in Cyprus, with
water again as objective. Such occasional help had been
given before Teall's day; but presently it became less necessary owing to the development of Colonial Geological
Surveys.

Two other widely different overseas events may be included here on account of their interaction with Survey life
at home. In 1904 the United States celebrated the centenary
of the purchase of Louisiana by mounting a Universal Exposition at St. Louis on an unprecedented scale—it occupied
a site of 1,240 acres as compared with the 21 acres allotted
to the Great Exhibition of 1851 in Hyde Park. On our side
a Royal Commission was appointed to help ensure success
for British representation, though it proved difficult to in-

PLATE III.

PEACH (back), HORNE (left), CLOUGH (front).

[*To face page* 163

terest manufacturers who at the time were finding American tariffs prohibitive. Peach and Strahan were entrusted by Teall with the production of large-scale coloured models of the tectonically interesting districts of Assynt in the North-West Highlands of Scotland and Purbeck in the South of England. Copies of these models, furnished with descriptive pamphlets, find place today in a number of museums.

Then again there was the twelfth session of the International Geological Congress assembled in 1913 at Toronto. Its main publication was a three-volume quarto monograph on *The Coal Resources of the World*. Strahan, who had played a particularly active part in helping to prepare the 1905 report of the Royal Commission on our own coal supplies, was given the task of furnishing the British contribution.

EDINBURGH, 1902 AND LATER

In 1902 I had the great good fortune to join the Survey and to be sent to Scotland. Edinburgh in those days was as invigorating a geological centre as when the followers of Hutton and Werner contended for supremacy. Peach and Horne were in the ascendant, intensely interested in all aspects of their subject and flood-lit by the glory of the North-West Highlands—the great memoir on which, as already mentioned, duly appeared in 1907. Clough, much less conspicuous, had amazing discoveries and hypotheses to impart. Goodchild, at the Museum, was deservedly winning and maintaining popular interest. R. H. Traquair, also at the Museum though not a Survey colleague, and Robert Kidston were acknowledged masters of the fishes and plants of the Old Red Sandstone and Carboniferous. Their recognition of a 'break' in the Carboniferous succession of freshwater fish and land plants afforded a special incentive during the Survey revision of the Scottish coalfields, which started in 1902. Sir John Murray, of the Challenger Office, was much in evidence, mainly engaged in directing a comprehensive survey of Scottish lakes as they exist today. Kendall, too, was coming across the Border to investigate other lakes, which had vanished with the melting of the glaciers, but which in many cases had left tell-tale eroded spillways. James Geikie also must not be forgotten, though by now his local influence, outside the University, was felt more in geographical than geological circles. No wonder a new-comer soon realised that he moved among a jostling crowd of problems awaiting solution.

Horne's attitude to recruits was partly determined by his experiences under Archibald Geikie. For years he had suf-fered from frustration owing to the latter's objection to sub-ordinates publishing results obtained during official service, except in official memoirs—which latter, all too often, failed to materialise. Horne had promised himself that if ever the power came into his hands he would treat others as he him-self had longed to be treated. *Mirabile dictu,* he kept his pro-mise! He encouraged research to the uttermost, and if results followed he urged publication, within or without offi-cial covers according to the special circumstances. The public interest was never better served.

The whole question of outside publication by publicly em-ployed scientists presents matters of great difficulty, which of late years have increasingly exercised the minds of poli-ticians responsible for expenditure of public money. It is impossible to draw a hard and fast line between what may be called the public and the private thinking of a civil-ser-vant scientist. Accordingly, it seems to some, I think to the majority, that a scientist who has become a civil servant should accept a discipline controlling his right to publish on almost any subject. I do not agree. Instead, I should limit censorship to:—strategic matters, involving the safety of the realm; economic matters, where among other things sug-gestion of corruption may arise; and fair dealing, for it is important that a civil-servant scientist should not improperly anticipate or criticise a colleague (inferior or superior) or indeed anyone else in the world. If some such standard were officially adopted it would probably be found workable. What is most dreaded by a scientist is a comprehenisve power of veto, which may prevent his offering a theory for publication just because a superior officer thinks the theory wrong. Publicly maintained research-institutes must aim at a reputation for sensibly administered freedom, or else they must accept the alternative of trying to do their work with second-rate recruits. Pay without opportunity is not enough to attract a real scientist.

When Flett replaced Horne in 1911 a great change came over the Scottish Survey. In part this was due to the fact that the new Assistant Director was deaf, which tended to isolation of thought. On the publication question he unfortunately went even further than Geikie, though from different motives. He claimed universal veto, whereas Geikie had admitted that unofficial work lay outside his jurisdiction. I have no doubt that Flett's object was to purge the writings of his subordinates of error; but it is difficult to understand how an important officer of the Survey could want to extend his official power of censorship, since, as a matter of history, the names of almost all high-ranking Geological Surveyors are linked with theories that have come to be discarded.

FURTHER DEVELOPMENTS IN ENGLAND AND WALES

A few words will suffice to complete our outline sketch of happenings in England and Wales during Teall's highly successful term of office.

The field work planned for the three original operative districts, namely, South Wales, the Midlands, and Cornwall-to-Lyme Regis, was finished by 1909; by which time also a special map and memoir of the Oxford district had appeared for the convenience of the University at its centre. Accordingly, in 1910 field-work was transferred to the Denbighshire coalfield under Lamplugh, to a further Midland group of coalfields under Barrow, and to London and South-East England under Reid. On Reid's retirement in 1913, Barrow was put in charge of the London district and Gibson took over in the Midlands.

The choice of London and South-East England as a successor to Cornwall and the West was determined by density of population. Detailed information in regard to the solid and drift geology of the Metropolis and its surrounds is in everyday demand.

12

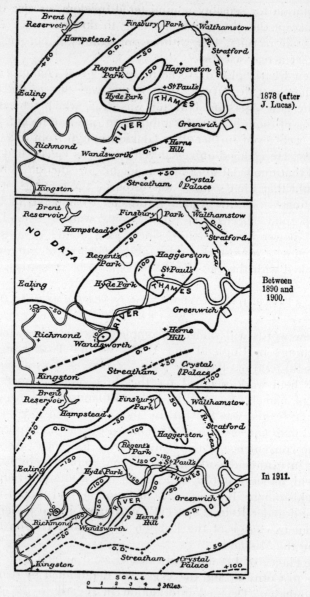

FIG. 29.—Contours of upper surface of underground water at various dates. (Quoted from Barrow and Wills, *London Wells Mem.*, 1913, p. 19.)

UNDERGROUND WATER

Underground water constitutes one of the main economic interests of South-East England. Mention has already been made of *County Water Supply* memoirs started by Geikie in 1899. Under Teall eleven examples appeared, covering much of the south-eastern area and extending north into the East Riding of Yorkshire. The work of producing these memoirs fell mostly outside the district organisation of the Survey, and much of it was entrusted to Whitaker (retired), with the co-operation in regard to rainfall statistics of the famous meteorologist Hugh Robert Mill. In four cases, however, including *Records of London Wells*, Whitaker's name does not appear on the title page. The production of the London volume, for instance, fitted comfortably into the programme of the London and South-East district, and both its authors, G. Barrow and L. J. Wills, were drawn from the active list of the Survey. This memoir was particularly important owing to the progressive drop which pumping causes in the water-level established in wells sunk to the Chalk under the Metropolis, a feature well illustrated in contour-maps.

It may come as a surprise to readers to learn that the Water Supply memoirs of the Survey are well worth attention, even from those who are not in search of a new source of the essential fluid, or of some obscure stratigraphical detail. Admittedly the serried ranks of well journals are as dull as they are useful; but with them is combined introductory material that appeals strongly to the imagination. The London memoir probably takes first place in this respect. It is, however, closely followed by Whitaker's *Water Supply of Kent*, where 68 pages are devoted to such matters as shafts and galleries, geological succession, rainfall (Mill), springs, swallow holes and intermittent streams. The whole county depends upon underground sources, apart from widespread household storage of rain. Even so, it may interest our transatlantic friends to learn that the Kent Water Company, now forming part of the Metropolitan Water Board, operated at the time of publication the world's largest supply of water drawn solely from wells.

PROGRESS IN SCOTLAND

In the Highlands of Scotland Clough, after finishing with
the early granite and resistant hornfels of Inchbae in Ross,
changed places with Peach, taking over in the West instead

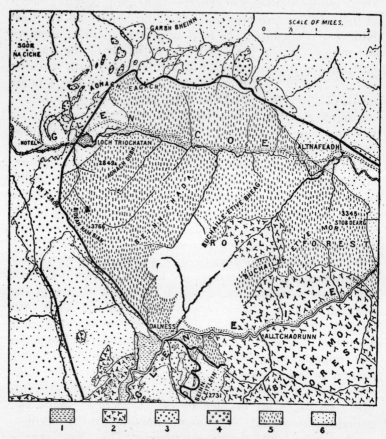

FIG. 30.—Cauldron Subsidence of Glen Coe, Lower Old Red Sandstone age.
1, River Terraces; 2, Ben Cruachan Granite; 3 and 4, main and earlier
granitoid intrusions accompanying Boundary Fault; 5, Lavas and
Ashes; 6, old Schists. Thick lines show Boundary Fault with branches.
(Quoted from Bailey, *Sum. Prog. for* 1905, p. 98.)

of the North. Peach asked for the transfer to enable him to
guide current research on Lewisian ' inliers ' and associated
Moines. Much new information was gathered on this sub-

ject, but the interpretation is still regarded as debatable. Presently, after Peach's retirement, the Northern 'Gang' under Hinxman included the Central as well as the Northern Highlands in their scope. Thus, in the Rannoch district, they came in contact with recent work of their Western fellows, with consequences to which further reference will be made in a moment.

Meanwhile, the Western 'Gang' developed in Glen Coe, Ben Nevis and Mull many novel or semi-novel ideas on igneous tectonics, including cauldron-subsidences, both subaerial and subterranean, ring-dykes, cone-schists, dyke-swarms and peripheral folding. At the same time in the schists of the Ballachulish and Fort William district they established the presence of recumbent folds of amazing horizontal extent, accompanied by fold-faults, or slides, that cut out great thicknesses of strata. The first important announcements in regard to the cauldron subsidence of Glen Coe and the recumbent fold of Ballachulish were made in the *Summary of Progress* for 1905. A much fuller account of the tectonics followed in the *Summary* for 1908; while Ben Nevis was described in that for 1909. Maufe played a great part in these stirring days, in which I had the good fortune to assist.

Thanks to R. G. Carruthers of the Northern 'Gang' a very important modification of detail was soon demanded in that part of the Ballachulish district, which includes the upper reaches of Loch Leven. I had wrongly thought that there was enough evidence to assign all the local rocks to one quartzite and one mica-schist, repeated by folding, whereas there are really three of each. The circumstances are so complex that I could not for a long time decide whether or no to accept Carruthers' correction—and here I must record my thanks to Flett for full facilities for re-examination. Eventually, however, a visit of three young graduates from overseas, trained to the use of current bedding, supplied the means to settle the dispute. The direct and indirect results have constituted a major advance in our appreciation of Highland structures. For instance, at the head of Loch Leven, a tyro in geology can now *see*, by examining current bedding, that all the rocks are upside down for a distance of six miles across strike. The main stages in this welcome development of knowledge can be followed on consulting the *Summary of Progress* for 1912, the *Geological Magazine* for 1930 and the *Quarterly Journal of the Geological Society* for 1934. (It has since been found that Patrick Ganly, one of Sir Richard Griffith's men in Ireland, was using current bedding to demonstrate inversion as long ago as 1838!)

In the Scottish coalfield revision, undertaken under Teall, much stratigraphical, palæontological, petrographical and

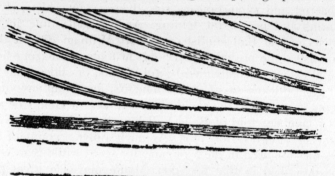

FIG. 31.—Uninverted current-bedding in Glen Coe Quartzite, × 1/5. (Quoted from T. Vogt, *Geol. Mag.*, 1930, p. 70.)

glacial progress was made, with work first centred about Edinburgh and later Glasgow. At the same time closer and more continual co-operation was established with the mining world than anywhere else in Britain.

TEALL RETIRES

Teall's retirement came at the beginning of 1914. By this time he had firmly established as a Survey ideal :—

The provision of a reasonably up-to-date colour-printed geological map covering the whole country on the one-inch scale, each sheet to be accompanied by an explanatory memoir.

This one-inch map is to be based everywhere on six-inch field-mapping. In the case of districts of special economic importance, the fundamental six-inch maps must themselves be published. In other districts they must be held available for reference.

In view of his circumscribed man-power Teall had made a full contribution towards the attainment of this ideal. He was knighted in 1916, by this time a spectator of the First World War. By strange coincidence he died in 1924, the same year as his predecessor in office, Archibald Geikie. We may quote again from Marr : 'A beautiful life is ended, but its effects will be long felt for good in the future.'

1914

STRAHAN PROMOTED DIRECTOR

AUBREY STRAHAN followed Teall on the 6th of January, 1914. His record of fieldwork, administration and publication furnished a fitting guarantee of competence. Lamplugh succeeded him as Assistant Director for England and Wales, with Gibson, Barrow and Cantrill (promoted to fill Lamplugh's place) as Director Geologists. Flett remained Assistant Director for Scotland, with Clough and Hinxman as District Geologists.

Pollard had retired as Chemist (ranking geologist) in 1913. It was necessary for the Survey to have at least one chemist at work all the time in its own laboratories on its own specialised problems; and yet it was difficult to offer such a one proper prospects of pecuniary advancement. The dilemma was circumvented in 1914 by the seconding of a chemist from the Government Laboratory, an organisation concerned with chemical work and analyses required by Government Departments. The procedure proved satisfactory; and, ever since, the Survey laboratories have been manned by one or two chemists drawn from this source. Such collaboration became all the more interesting in after years, when the newly formed Department of Scientific and Industrial Research absorbed the Geological Survey, but not the Government Laboratory, whose normal function involves comparatively little research.

FIRST WAR DIRECTORATE

At the start of Strahan's term of office it seemed as if he would have little more to do than persevere on the lines laid down by his predecessor, painfully conscious that with the limited staff available the completion of the primary six-inch survey of Britain lay far below his horizon. Outbreak of war on the 4th August, 1914, sank the accomplishment of this primary six-inch survey still further out of sight.

The 1914 War was a comparatively happy one for juniors on the staff, with very little talk of reserved occupations. By the end of 1914 six Geologists had been allowed to join the army, with corresponding numbers from Assistants, Draughtsmen and other ranks. Before long these six Geologists were increased to fourteen, of whom four presently came to be employed on geological tasks, such as water supply, on the Western and Gallipoli Fronts. Among them, W. B. R. King, today Sedgwick Professor at Cambridge, was attached to the Engineer-in-Chief at General Headquarters in the West. He was so well remembered by brother officers that the Second War brought an immediate call for a renewal of his association. So now he can look back on two tours of duty as Geologist to the Army during his country's recent major struggles for existence.

The 1914 War was less expected than that of 1939. The Survey did not have war plans laid in advance, and had to discover by experience what was required of it. There was no paper famine, so that *Annual Reports* and *Summaries of Progress* appeared much as in peace-time; and we can follow in them to some extent the course of events. A few normal sheet memoirs already in hand were published; but they had to appear without the maps which they purported to describe —the Ordnance Survey was far too busy to supply the deficiency. Thus Teall's rule of simultaneous appearance of memoir and map was temporarily broken, under circumstances never contemplated by its author. Two *County Water Supply* memoirs were also produced. One of them, on Nottinghamshire, was prepared by Lamplugh and Bernard Smith. Nottinghamshire, like Kent, drinks from underground. It does so, however, not because of the rarity of its streams, but because of their prevailing dirtiness. The other water memoir covered Essex, and was written by Whitaker and J. C. Thresh, the latter for many years County Medical Officer of Health.

SPECIAL WAR PUBLICATIONS

The first war-inspired publication of the Survey appeared in 1914, a useful twopenny pamphlet entitled : *Sources of Temporary Water Supply in the South of England and the Neighbouring Parts of the Continent*. It followed naturally on unpublished *Notes* furnished to the Army telling how to obtain drinking water at short notice from the Chalk and Tertiary strata of the Western Front. Another early war publication, put through under Survey guidance, was a geological map of Belgium, on the scale of 1 : 160,000—based, of course, on official Belgian sources.

Many inquiries were coming in at the time in regard to minerals. These were at the start especially concerned with localities for sand suitable for glass manufacture, since delivery of glass sand from the Continent had been immediately upset. Thus the Survey's attention came to be restricted more and more to economic subjects, with the coasts of Britain as the usual geographical limit. In spite of this a certain amount of mapping and description of districts already in hand at the declaration of war did linger on, largely to minimise loss of unpublished pre-war results in case authors did not return after doing their bit. Strangely enough this precaution proved unnecessary. There were no fatal casualties, though six out of the fourteen Geologists, turned soldiers, were wounded in action. In one direction the war of course made little difference. It was still necessary, so far as possible, to watch deep bores put down in search of minerals, water and, presently, oil.

In 1915, with Barrow's retirement at the age of 62, the London and South-Eastern district was definitely suspended, and a series of *Special Reports on the Mineral Resources of Great Britain* was commenced. These *Reports* soon made subject, rather than locality, the guide to Survey war-time organisation. Thus the *Summary of Progress* for 1916 is essentially given over to refractories; and that for 1917, to reserves of iron ore.

The *Special Reports* constitute Strahan's outstanding achievement as Director. They are a modern Domesday Book dealing with the country's resources of minerals, other than coal. They were published as volumes numbered according to order of issue. In 1915 the first three appeared: 1, *Tungsten and Manganese Ores;* 2, *Barytes and Witherite;* and 3, *Gypsum and Anhyrite.* By 1918 seven had materialised, and for five of these second editions had been issued. Their preparation was continued after peace returned, and in the 1936 *List of Memoirs, etc.,* of the Geological Survey the *Special Reports* total thirty-one, with, in nine cases, second or third editions.

All remaining members of staff, supplemented by temporary recruits from the Universities, threw themselves whole-heartedly into the preparation of the *Special Reports.* The incentive, as Strahan tells us, was not only the 'shortage of some materials as a result of the War,' but also an expectation of 'fuller utilisation of home-sources after the War.' Compilation was in many cases rushed, and authors had sometimes to be content with a much lower standard of inquiry than that to which they were accustomed; but all in all the series is infinitely preferable to the scattered literature with yawning gaps that previously existed. Moreover, the *Reports* were drawn up by geologists who visited the localities at a time when many temporary wartime excavations were still available for inspection, or regarding which it was at least possible to gather first-hand information that would otherwise have been lost. Apart altogether from this last consideration, it is probably right to say that the production of these *Special Reports* would have constituted a justifiable short-term deviation from the Survey's normal objective, even if it had been undertaken in peace time.

Here it seems apposite to notice in passing two entirely new economic developments of the war period that arose out of Survey discoveries:—

(1) *Raasay Ironstone.*—A Liassic ironstone had been discovered by Woodward in 1893 in the course of routine geological survey in the Hebrides. As a result its economic possibilities had been investigated by a Scottish iron-master, Wallace Thorneycroft, starting in 1909. During the war the ore was extensively wrought by German prisoners and

shipped through comparatively safe waters to foundries on
the Clyde.

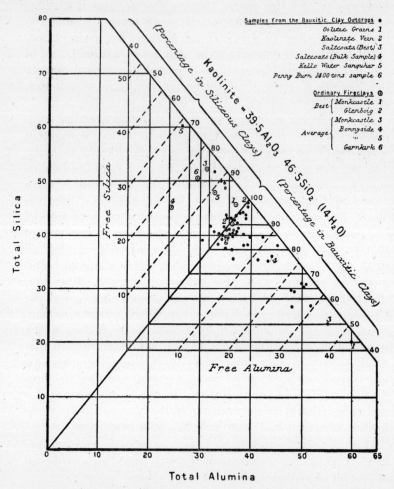

FIG. 32.—Composition of bauxitic and ordinary fireclays. (Quoted from
Wilson, *Ayrshire Bauxitic Clay Mem.*, 1922, p. 7.)

(2) *Ayrshire Bauxitic Clay.*—A specially valuable refrac-
tory of lateritic origin occurs at the weathered top of a series
of basalt lavas of Millstone Grit age in Ayrshire. E. M.
Anderson first established its importance in 1915, when he

had a sample analysed which contained 47.6 per cent. alumina. G. V. Wilson soon succeeded in interesting industrialists; and exploitation was started in 1917, to be continued ever since.

Following quick upon the initiation of the *Special Reports* came another experiment in presentation, entitled *The Economic Geology of the Central Coalfield of Scotland*. The first of nine areal parts was issued in 1916, and has provided a pattern for all subsequent Scottish coalfield publication. The unit selected for description in each part is not a whole coalfield or a one-inch map, but a group of adjacent six-inch maps. Attention throughout is focused upon economic subjects, viewed, of course, in relation to their geological setting. This treatment has proved extremely convenient.

OIL IN BRITAIN

A novel geological exploration of Britain was started in 1918 as a result of perilously low reserves of oil held by the navy at certain critical stages of the War. On the 15th October the first drilling ever undertaken in this country in search of free oil was begun under the provisions of the Defence of the Realm Act.

Lord Cowdray, head of an oil company called Messrs. Pearson and Sons, Ltd., had previously offered to place his geological staff at the Government's disposal, free of all charge; but the venture was eventually financed by a grant of £1,000,000 voted by Parliament. Lord Cowdray's firm was appointed Petroleum Development Managers acting for a newly constituted Mineral Oil Production Department of the Ministry of Munitions. (In May, 1919, this department was handed over to H.M. Petroleum Executive, later called the Petroleum Department of the Board of Trade.)

The first Petroleum (Production) Act was passed in November, 1918, and provided for compulsory notification to the Director of the Geological Survey of intention to sink a shaft or bore-hole for petroleum, and for free access for officers of the Geological Survey to the site of any such shaft or bore during operation, and to specimens and journals relating thereto.

The Geological Survey did not undertake the responsibility of search; but its published maps and memoirs and unpublished records, together with assistance in such matters as the determination of fossils, have been cordially acknowledged by the companies concerned. After the exhaustion of the first million pounds activity waited for the passing of a second Petroleum (Production) Act, 1934, which nationalised any oil that might be discovered, thus immensely simplifying the legal position. Under it companies with approved resources can secure from the Petroleum Department exploration rights, coupled with duties, covering some specified area.

The prospect of finding oil in Britain, in amount that would repay costs, has always seemed to Survey geologists remote, or at best highly speculative. It is in the day's work for a powerful oil company to include in its exploration programme a certain proportion of highly speculative areas in the expectation that profit on one or other will more than recompense loss on the remainder. The shareholders in the companies which have tried their luck in Britain have no cause for complaint, even though altogether only one field of minor importance — Eakring in Nottinghamshire, very welcome in the Second World War—has been discovered. If the taxpayers of Britain had had to foot the bill, they might have felt distinctly worried.

Finally, it must be realised that exploration for oil is not only very expensive, but is also dependent—apart from wild cat gambling—upon a combination of extremely high technical skills. Geology and geophysics are very important, and so also are engineering, chemistry and the handling of labour. The efficiency of the companies concerned has won universal admiration; and the deep bores put down in many parts of the country have vastly extended our knowledge of the underground geology of Britain. It is possible that this extension of knowledge, which comes as a windfall to the State, may eventually repay the monetary cost incurred— though the benefit is not likely to accrue to the companies concerned.

Geophysics has been mentioned above. Oil companies,

especially, have utilised various developments of this science, which enable a prospector to test the properties of what lies out of sight beneath his feet through the aid of magnetism, electricity, gravity or artificial earthquakes. The findings are often very hard and uncertain to interpret; but they do sometimes furnish suggestions even where geology, unaided, has frankly to admit incompetence. The recognised procedure is to couple geophysical exploration with boring, so that suggestions can be tested at once if they seem to point in a favourable direction. The Geological Survey took a first short wartime step towards use of geophysics in 1917. It co-operated with an Iron Ore Committee of the Conjoint Scientific Societies in an investigation of magnetic anomalies, known since 1890, near Melton Mowbray and Irthlingborough further south. The result was inconclusive. A. H. Cox temporarily attached to the Survey, suggested that the anomalies were due to basic dykes or sills such as are known in the Leicestershire coalfields; but, as we shall presently see, the matter was reinvestigated during Flett's directorate and a somewhat different interpretation advanced.

VARIOUS ITEMS

From March, 1916, the Museum at Jermyn Street was closed to the general public on account of danger from air raids. It remained shut until the 1st April, 1919, though meanwhile it functioned continuously as part of the inquiry service maintained by the Survey. Among the many problems attacked, one of the most interesting fell to H. H. Thomas. It concerned the quality of quartz employed on account of its piedzo-electric properties in submarine detectors.

Strahan, at the conclusion of hostilities on the 11th November, 1918, published in his *Summary of Progress* for the year a list of over seventy important services rendered to other Government Departments arising out of the War. It makes interesting and instructive reading, though definitely of a modest character.

It will be readily understood that during the war years pure science made little appeal, except as regards its emergency applications. Many, however, remember how the intensive working of a glass sand of Cretaceous age near Leighton Buzzard in Hertfordshire helped to fan the embers of an important, though unnecessarily heated, controversy between two Survey colleagues. The affair was not confined to the Strahan period (1914 to 1920). In fact it had its origin as far back in 1903 and continues today. It was started by a paper of Lamplugh's describing a small patch of fossiliferous limestone exposed in one of the Leighton Buzzard pits. The fauna of this limestone and of adjacent beds suggested to Kitchin that the succession had been tampered with by glacial disturbance. This interpretation he publicly announced in 1920. Lamplugh, however, disagreed, and said so plainly and at great length in 1922. At the time most onlookers sided with Kitchin; but fresh fossil finds, after the death of both protagonists, have produced a strong reaction. When fully published the story should prove of great educational value to geologists.

CLOUGH KILLED

In retrospect one event in the Survey's First War Directorate stands out for me beyond all others. In 1916, in the days of the Somme carnage, Clough, while undertaking official work along a Scottish railway line, was caught unaware by a shunting wagon. It passed across his legs above the knees. When friends rushed to his assistance he was able to do little more than assure them that it was not the engine driver's fault. Thus passed one of the greatest, and at the same time least assuming, of Survey men.

The vacancies left by Barrow's retirement and Clough's death were not filled till 1919, when, with Hinxman also gone on the score of his 64 years, E. B. Bailey, R. G. Carruthers and M. Macgregor were promoted District Geologists. The two former were among the returned combatants. Macgregor, much to his sorrow, had failed repeatedly on medical grounds when he offered himself for service in the Army. He had spent his time at home to good purpose, and by now had established himself as the leading authority on the Scottish coalfields. Carruthers went to London; the other two remained in Scotland.

STRAHAN RETIRES

Sir Aubrey Strahan, as he had become in 1919, retired on the 20th July, 1920. All acknowledge that he had met the abnormal conditions of his term in high office with conspicuous success. In spite of greatly reduced staff he had supplied the fighting forces, industry and commerce with a wonderful amount of information in acceptable form. He had thus greatly widened the contacts of the Survey in the world of practical affairs. He was able in after years to see this valuable relationship maintained and extended. He died in 1928.

DEPARTMENT OF SCIENTIFIC AND INDUSTRIAL RESEARCH

In May, 1915, the President of the Board of Education presented to Parliament a scheme for official organisation and development of scientific and industrial research in fields other than medicine and agriculture. A Committee of the Privy Council was established in July of the same year, together with an Advisory Council composed of leading scientists and industrialists, particularly those prominently concerned with industrial research. By December, 1916, a new Department of State had been instituted, entitled the Department of Scientific and Industrial Research. A Fuel Research Board was appointed in 1917, and an experimental Station was established at Greenwich to investigate the fuel characteristics of coal and oil of all descriptions. Thus at last it became possible to develop on a becoming scale and with every promise of continuity the coal-quality researches which had been initiated by the Geological Survey under De la Beche and revived under Teall.

A further important stage was reached on the 1st April, 1918, when the National Physical Laboratory was transferred to the care of D.S.I.R. It was considered that the activities of this Laboratory were of a type unlikely to be undertaken by any combination of interests of lower denomination than the State.

Meanwhile arrangements were made to encourage the start and maintenance of other specialised bodies known as Co-operative Research Associations. These are self-governing bodies formed to serve the needs of various industries on a national basis. They are financed mainly by the industries themselves, but receive grants from the Department, related in amount to the money thus raised. In addition, D.S.I.R. support was to be given to individual workers engaged on approved objectives, and towards the training as research-workers of post-graduate students.

Fuel Research and the National Physical Laboratory were soon joined by other research institutes which, unlike the Research Associations just mentioned, were directly responsible to D.S.I.R. These in all cases but one were, like Fuel Research, special creations. The exception was the veteran Geological Survey, which on the 1st November, 1919, was handed over to D.S.I.R., thus severing a connection with the Board of Education that dated back to 1856 in Murchison's regime.

From all this it will be seen that the Department of Scientific and Industrial Research soon came very near to being a resurrection of De la Beche's comprehensive Geological Survey, except that its funds were vastly bigger and its educacational functions much more severely canalised. It had of course assumed another name; and thus it escaped from De la Beche's impossible conception that the best co-ordinator of such a body would always be found in the person of a geologist. D.S.I.R. may not yet have recaptured the scientific prestige which the Geological Survey enjoyed in the days, say, of Huxley and Hooker, Stokes and Murchison; but there is no reason to despair.

The transfer of the Geological Survey to D.S.I.R. was made in conformity with recommendations of two committees of the Ministry of Reconstruction. One of these committees dealt with Coal Conservation; and it advanced two additional suggestions affecting the Survey :—

(1) Completion of the primary six-inch survey of all coalfields.

(2) Compulsory notification and right of examination of all bores and sinkings expected to reach a depth of 100ft. or more.

To implement, as quickly as possible, the first of these two proposals and to facilitate continuous contact with mining operations for subjects other than coal, the Geological Survey Board (appointed by the Lord President) asked for and obtained a substantial increase of staff for the Survey—of which we shall speak more fully in the sequel. As regards rights in relation to bores and sinkings, these were, as we have already seen, established for oil in 1918. In 1926 they were extended to cover minerals; and in 1945-46, water.

It is pleasant to acknowledge that the Geological Survey has received kind treatment from its youthful step-mother. Between the Survey and the Advisory Council there stands the Geological Survey Board, mentioned above, which with its specialist understanding has proved consistently helpful and never dictatorial. The Chairmen of this important body have been Sir Francis Grant Ogilvie, 1920-30; Sir Franklin Sibly, 1930-40; and Sir Arthur E. Trueman, 1940- .

Naturally enough the skies have not always remained entirely unclouded. While the Geological Survey readily agrees that economic areas should enjoy preferential treatment, it also realises that, like the Ordnance Survey, it has a national and international duty to produce and keep up to date a map of the country as a whole. Moreover, its science is much more observational and less experimental than those of other research institutes under D.S.I.R. Perhaps on this account it alone as yet has realised the value of maintaining a specialist museum. Some day perhaps a visitor to Building Research or Water Pollution may find inspiration in exhibits illustrative of past and present achievements, not to mention future aspirations.

The most serious difficulty that has attended the assimilation of the Geological Survey into the ranks of D.S.I.R. concerns the fixing of a limit beyond which expenses must be charged in return for services rendered—though, so far as I am aware, it only came to a head in the early years of the Second World War. It is clear, for instance, that the National Physical Laboratory *must* charge a fee if it undertakes to test the watches or thermometers of some manufacturing firm. The Geological Survey, however, is rather differently situated. It has depended for its success in large measure upon the active co-operation of the public. The greater part of the economic information which it co-ordinates in its maps and memoirs has been gratuitously supplied by mining corporations, industrialists, landlords, county and town councils, mining and water engineers, not to mention countless private individuals. It has also received many of its most valuable museum specimens on the same generous terms. In keeping with this, for over a hundred years, it has endeavoured to place its non-confidential information freely at the disposal of inquirers who ask for more than appears in its published (and priced) maps and memoirs. A reply to a question may in some cases amount to little more than a reference to, or an explanation of, an available publication; but there is behind the Survey's maps and memoirs a wealth of accumulated data, which it would be absurd to attempt to print. Admittedly any inquiry takes time to answer, and many which reach the office concern trivialities—but even these latter often educate the staff as to what sort of information is wanted by the public. The more serious inquiries in peace time usually concern coal or water, and have come from professionals, frequently consultants. The Director holds himself responsible for encouraging this side of Survey activity, but always within limits. He cannot forget that his staff is, and ever will be, greatly in arrears in its routine attempt to cover the whole country with what can be accepted as satisfactory maps and memoirs.

Though anxious to be as little hampered as possible by 'repayment' practice, the Geological Survey recognises the value of such procedure in particular cases. For instance, it felt that it had gained when, in 1920, the printing of its maps by the Ordnance Survey came to be ranked as a 're-payment service.' The innovation, theoretically at any rate, simplified the planning of future publication, since there is still some truth in the old adage that he who pays the piper calls the tune.

In conclusion, it may be pointed out that, while the Geological Survey shares in the interests of all its comrades gathered under the D.S.I.R. banner, its closest contacts within the period covered by this booklet have been with those dedicated to the investigation of fuel, roads, building and water-pollution. Co-operation has been arranged. For instance, appropriate Geological Survey officers sit on the Coal Survey Committees of the Fuel Research Board set up in the various coalfields, while petrographical reports are furnished on road metal.

1920

FLETT SUCCEEDS TO DIRECTORSHIP

JOHN Smith Flett took over from Strahan in the second year of peace, 21st July, 1920. Howe at the same time followed Lamplugh as Assistant Director for England and Wales, since the latter, like Strahan, had passed the 60 year limit. The vacancy left by Flett in Scotland was filled by Gibson.

As a result of the representations of the Geological Survey Board the scientific establishment was now increased by sixteen fieldsmen to meet pressing coalfield and other economic needs. There should have been corresponding additions to the indoor staff, palæontological and petrological. Subsequent calls for help from the fieldsmen have in their multitude proved very difficult to answer, even with the assistance of outside experts. Still, the progress made as a result of the post-war influx has been very satisfactory.

By 1922 there were twelve officers of District Geologist rank: T. C. Cantrill, R. G. Carruthers, B. Smith, H. Dewey, W. B. Wright, C. E. N. Bromehead (in England and Wales); E. B. Bailey, M. Macgregor, C. H. Dinham (in Scotland); H. H. Thomas (Petrographer), F. L. Kitchin (Palæontologist) and W. F. P. McLintock (Curator and Librarian). Under these there served 38 Senior Geologists and Geologists (including an Assistant Curator). In addition, there were Technical and General Assistants, Draughtsmen, labourers, warders, messengers, cleaners, carpenters and charwomen.

McLintock, whose appointment is listed above, originally joined the Survey as Assistant Curator in 1907; but in 1921 he transferred to the Royal Scottish Museum where, since Goodchild's death in 1906, the care of the geological gallery had ceased to be a Survey appointment. His return was opportune, for he was destined to play a distinguished part in the transfer of Survey Headquarters from Jermyn Street to South Kensington, an operation which, as we shall see, presently became Flett's outstanding contribution to Survey life. McLintock in later years followed Smith and Bailey as Director.

We may further anticipate by cataloguing the changes that occurred on the Assistant Director and District Geologist levels before Flett retired in 1935 : —

Assistant Directors : 1925, Gibson retired ; Macgregor promoted (Scot.) ; 1931, Howe retired ; Smith promoted (Eng.).

District Geologists : 1925, J. E. Richey promoted (Scot.) ; 1927, Cantrill retired ; Dinham transferred to England ; 1928, G. V. Wilson promoted (Scot.) ; 1929, Bailey resigned (Scot.) ; 1930, T. Eastwood promoted (Eng.) ; 1934, Kitchin died (Palæontologist) ; J. Pringle promoted, 1935 ; Thomas died (Petrographer) ; J. Phemister promoted.

It will be noted that after Bernard Smith's promotion in 1931 there was an unfilled vacancy among District Geologists.

The rapid post-war recruitment did not introduce all the difficulties that would have attended such a move in normal times. There were in the post-war demobilisation pool several candidates who had already graduated in Geology, or could do so within a short period. The Geological Survey Board as one of its first moves had laid down that, in general, candidates for the Survey should have completed a ' University course for a Degree in Science with Honours in Geology.' It has been very exceptional for any but a first class honours graduate to be accepted since.

Quasi-simultaneous bulk enlistment did, however, lead to unevenness of promotion in after years. This applied even in regard to advancement to the grade of Senior Geologist, which was now firmly established, though, unfortunately, with an unsympathetic limit as to numbers. On the other hand, pay and allowances were improved, to bring conditions into line with those of other branches of the Civil Service.

The change was greater than was required to counterbalance increased cost of living, and helped to introduce early marriage and a desire for settled winter quarters.

DISTRICT OFFICES

The increase of staff could not be accommodated in the two existing Headquarters. It was decided to institute branch offices in certain coalfields, each in charge of a District Geologist. Soon the following dispositions were made :—

Newcastle under Carruthers to serve Northumberland and Durham.

Whitehaven under Smith to serve Cumberland.

York under Bromehead to serve Yorkshire.

Manchester under Wright to serve Lancashire.

Newcastle was placed under the Assistant Director for Scotland; the remainder, under the corresponding officer for England.

Opinions differ as to the balance of advantages that have accrued under this District Office arrangement. The gains are the more obvious, but the losses may be the more important. The former include all-the-year-round contact with the coalfield concerned. This does not help in field-work, but it is an important matter in watching bores, consulting mining plans and making underground examinations—and perhaps, above all, in maintaining personal relations with colliery staffs. The difficulties can be listed under two headings :—

(1) *Instability.*—A field unit, given a special task to overtake, generally moves on after a comparatively few years. Thus the Whitehaven office was closed in 1927, and the York office in 1938. Since then the staffs of these two units, with new objectives, have been based on the London office, enlarged in 1935.

(2) *Isolation.*—It is not good training for a small group of young Geologists to be isolated, with their attention concentrated upon one branch of geological research, and with deficient library, laboratory and personal aids. In his early years a Geologist should be given a variety of experience

with transfer from one District Geologist to another. This is easy if the District Geologists concerned share head-quarters, since the indoor work of the transferee can be re-gulated by arrangement; but any general attempt to carry out such a policy with a multitude of headquarters is bound to fail. Cognate with this trouble is the reluctance a Director must on occasion feel when faced with the proposition of moving an experienced Geologist of special aptitude from one district to another. The move may be desirable from the Survey point of view, and yet it may involve uprooting a household and upsetting the education of a young family. Accordingly, in practice, a newly enlisted Geologist is likely to be sent by accident to fill a vacancy in some outlying branch office, and there remain until, if he deserves it, he is promoted to be District Geologist and goes elsewhere. Not only is his experience very limited, but the staff he is eventu-ally called upon to lead probably regard him as an intruder with much less knowledge than they themselves possess.

The correct answer to the winter quarter problem lies, I am convinced, midway between over-centralisation and over-dispersal. Scotland is properly accommodated. England and Wales should have at least two, likely three, headquarters. Each of these should cater for a group of District units, with adequate library and other ancillary support, and with a varied menu of geological interests. In Scotland, since 1902, almost every Geologist has had two very different areas in hand, highland and coalfield, according to the season; and experience has shown that the result is good.

DISTRICT ORGANISATION DISREGARDED

From 1926 to 1929 and again during 1933 and 1934 Flett, on a small scale, threw District organisation overboard. His object was twofold. He wanted to accelerate mapping in the north of Scotland, including part of Sutherland, the Orkney Isles and the neighbourhood of Mallaig in Inverness-shire, and also to widen the experience of some of his coalfield Geologists of the North of England. Accordingly he sent picked men from York, Manchester and Newcastle to do part-time summer work with their Scottish colleagues. The

result was a nightmare for the District Geologists concerned
north of the Border. Team-work of a district unit, both in
the field and in publication, depends in large measure upon
day to day exchange of ideas *during the winter*. Such consultation was of course impossible for members of a team
dispersed between two, three and sometimes four winter
quarters.

As regards Orkney, where the geology is very simple, the
result was successful. The maps appeared in 1932, and the
inclusive memoir in 1935. This was largely due to Flett's
personal knowledge of the district. He supplied the petrographical chapter of the memoir, as well as a considerable
measure of coherence and driving power throughout. As for
the Sutherland rush, it attempted to clean up mapping which
had been started and dropped on many previous occasions.
We can at any rate say that it provided some of the material
with which H. H. Read had to cope in producing a memoir
that, as we shall presently see, appeared in 1931. The
Mallaig effort was a *de novo* operation, faced with splendid
opportunities coupled with normal Highland difficulties. Its
completion, entangled in the Second World War, has not
yet been accomplished.

SPEEDING PUBLICATION

Criticism has just been offered of Flett's readiness to disregard the requirements of team-work organised under District Geologists. It is pleasant to recall other experiments,
more or less on lines laid down by Teall, which, though un-
popular with his staff at the time, have since won gratitude.

The staff almost always resents publication of a colour-
printed edition of a one-inch map, unless preceded by special
revision to bring the mapping up to the most recent standard
of excellence. It is apt to forget that the public should not be
kept waiting longer than necessary for information already
in hand. A case in point is afforded by the one-inch maps
of the Scottish Southern Uplands. Between 1923 and 1933
Flett arranged for colour-printing of nine one-inch maps of
this region, carrying the results of the famous revision made
by Peach and Horne some 45 years earlier. Only three of

these sheets, dated 1889-93, were as yet available (hand-painted) in revised form; while the remainder, dated 1871-79, were in the old style. Admittedly the 1889-93 maps were much the most important of the lot, and were supplemented by a 10 mile to the inch map in the 1899 Silurian memoir; but it is a great thing that Flett released the remainder, while directing his staff to country which was either unmapped or much more in need of revision than the area concerned.

Similarly between 1921 and 1933 Flett somewhat eased the situation in the South of England by issuing a dozen colour-printed sheets based on partial revision. The favoured districts include Ramsgate, Brighton, Shaftesbury, Marlborough, Cirencester and Ipswich. Corresponding sheet memoirs were supplied by outside experts, Osborne White, L. Richardson and P. G. H. Boswell. In 1929 he also published a colour-printed map of Stonehaven on the east coast of Scotland. The land area covered by this sheet is very small, but geologically very interesting. It had been revised in detail by Robert Campbell, of Edinburgh University.

Perhaps we should have pointed out before now that the Ordnance Survey restarted colour-printing for the Geological Survey in 1919, and the following year produced a colour-printed geological map of Anglesey as a whole. A two-volume memoir had already appeared in 1919. This Anglesey map and memoir were the work of E. Greenly, who had been a member of the Geological Survey under Peach in the North-West Highlands from 1889 till his resignation in 1895. Thereafter he devoted himself to an unofficial six-inch geological survey of Anglesey. His work was gladly accepted by Teall and Strahan for Geological Survey publication. It is of a very high standard, though, as is usual in relation to an area of schistose rocks, it has raised as many problems as it has solved.

FIELD WORK AND PUBLICATION

At the start of Flett's directorate not much less than half the energy of the Survey was devoted to finishing Strahan's *Special Reports on Economic Resources,* and most of the remainder to coalfield revision. Work on the former soon dwindled, while that on the latter increased. Four English coalfields have already been specially mentioned as the sites of the new District offices. In addition broad areas were under revision in the Midlands of England under Cantrill and in Lowland Scotland under Bailey and Macgregor. The only English unit working with very minor coalfield attachment was that engaged on London and South-East England under Dewey. Even this made the first official survey of the concealed coalfield of Kent.

In Scotland, during 1919, Read alone was engaged in the Highlands. He had been invalided out of the Army in 1917 after combatant duty in Gallipoli; and had been sent next year by Flett to revise, on the six-inch scale, two one-inch sheets covering parts of the shires of Banff and Aberdeen— originally mapped in the bad early eighties on the one-inch scale. His welcome new maps with an inclusive memoir appeared in 1923. Meanwhile, in 1920, having finished part of the field work connected with this task, Read was placed in a unit stationed in Sutherland, at first under Macgregor, later, in 1926, under Richey. Its task of cleaning up, to which allusion has already been made, involved three one-inch sheets. One of these had been published hand-coloured in 1896 without a memoir; while the other two, started in the '80s, had never been completed. The resultant maps and memoirs appeared in 1925 and 1931, with Read as main author. They furnish a very valuable account of his views on the age and metamorphism of the Moine sediments, and on granitisation, a subject never more discussed than at the present time.

While the work was proceeding in Sutherland during the summers of 1920-23, another Scottish unit under Bailey finished the parts of Mull falling outside the main one-inch sheet already completed. It also surveyed neighbouring islands and the western part of Ardnamurchan. In the latter a Mull-like centre of Tertiary igneous rocks was mapped by Richey.

In 1924 and 1925 the Highlands were given a complete rest, so far as field work was concerned. This did not mean abandonment of Highland geology, for writing up of pre-war results, supplemented by what had since been accomplished, occupied much time indoors.

There was of course a glut of delayed publication to be dealt with, both in London and Edinburgh, the maps and memoirs of South Wales were completed, except for new editions, by 1921. The corresponding publications for North Wales started to appear in 1923, and continued until 1929. There were also non-economic memoirs to finish and produce. Among these the most important dealt with the volcanic history of Mull. Team work in this island had been carried on from 1907 to 1914 by nine fieldsmen, most of them only very minor participants, supported by Thomas as Petro-

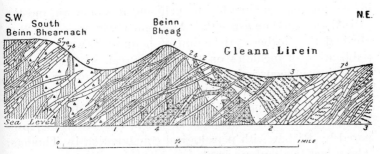

FIG. 33.—Flank of Loch Spelve anticline, Mull. 1, Moine Gneiss; 2, Mesozoic Sediments; 3, Tertiary Basalt Lavas; 4, Gabbro; 5′, Vent Agglomerate; 7a and b, Acid and Basic Cone-Sheets. (Quoted from Bailey, *Mull Mem.*, 1924, p. 237).

grapher; and it had revealed a truly fascinating story. Flett's opinion of it may be gathered from the following quotation taken from his *First Hundred Years of the Geological Survey of Great Britain:*—

> No part of Britain has proved more complicated than Central Mull, and the intricacy of the structure was often too great to be represented even on the six-inch maps. The history of the Mull volcanoes, and of the various stages through which their activity passed, makes one of the most wonderful chapters of the geology of Britain. Not only was the sequence of lava eruptions and of intrusions exceedingly difficult to decipher, but the tectonics also were of types not previously recognised. When the geological work on Mull was completed and the maps and memoirs issued, it was universally admitted that new lustre had been added to the records of the Geological Sur-

vey of Scotland. For originality and thoroughness the work controlled by Clough and Bailey in Mull is fit to stand comparison with the work done under Horne and Peach in unravelling the history and structure of the North-West Highlands. It was also an appropriate sequel to Harker's notable achievement in the survey of the southern part of Skye.

Before joining up in 1915 I had prepared a skeleton memoir on Mull. On my return in 1918 this skeleton had to be filled in with the help of my colleagues; and the map, which on account of its detail is regarded by the Ordnance Survey as their prize production in colour-print, had to be seen through its various stages. The map appeared in 1923, and the main Tertiary and Post-Tertiary memoir in 1924, followed by a Pre-Tertiary memoir in 1925. Flett played an important part in securing proper time for the field and indoor work, mostly carried out while he was either Assistant Director or Director. He had the further satisfaction of helping forward Survey publication of memoirs on two other great Scottish centres of Tertiary igneous activity, Arran, 1928, and Ardnamurchan, 1930. The former was entrusted to G. W. Tyrell, of Glasgow University, and may be regarded as a second edition of Gunn's North Arran memoir of 1903. The latter was prepared by Richey with petrological collaboration by Thomas. These last two authors in their private time also gave excellent accounts of the Mourne Mountains and Slieve Gullion, corresponding Irish centres. Richey thus became our foremost investigator in the field of British Tertiary igneous activity. As for Thomas, his services to Petrology have been great indeed among the Tertiary volcanoes of both Scotland and Ireland and their Early Palæozoic forerunners in Wales; but our first thought of him always conjures up the sacred circles of Stonehenge. In 1920, on the invitation of the Royal Society of Antiquaries, he undertook an examination of the so-called ' foreign ' stones, long a subject of inquiry; and he recognised them as transported from the far away Prescelly Mountains of Pembrokeshire, a truly enduring monument to human skill and devotion.

There is space for little more concerning the rich harvest of publication characteristic of Flett's regime. The survey of the completely concealed coalfield of Kent, which was started in 1930, is specially noteworthy since it broke new ground, so far as official investigation was concerned. Its results are clearly set out in Part ii of the Geological Survey's *Summary of Progress* for 1932. (The practice of publishing selected scientific papers gathered together in separately issued *Parts* of the *Summary*, and not merely as *Appendices*, began in 1927.) Here H. G. Dines deals with sequence and structure, while R. Crookall and C. J. Stubblefield respectively cover fossil plants and animals.

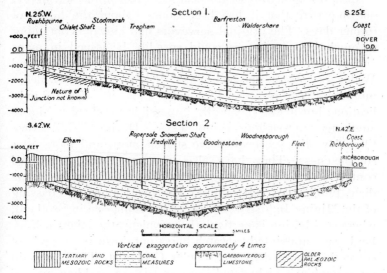

FIG. 34.—Horizontal Sections across Kent Coalfield. (Quoted from Dines, *Sum. Prog. for* 1932, pt. 2, p. 22.)

Coal had first been raised in Kent in economic quantities in 1913, but the establishment of the coalfield may be said to date from the early 1920's. Previous to the passing of the Mining Industry Act of 1926 there had been great difficulty in obtaining accurate information regarding the circumstances of the field. The Survey had, it is true, been able to publish two very important memoirs, in 1911 and 1923, dealing with the Mesozoic cover as revealed by boring; but it could produce nothing regarding the Coal Measures themselves beyond copies of such records as had already appeared in print. Most of its 1932 report is based upon information previously withheld, but now voluntarily placed at its disposal.

A memoir on another and more important concealed coalfield, the eastern continuation of the exposed coalfield of Yorkshire and Nottinghamshire, reached a second edition in 1926, written by G. V. Wilson. The first edition, 1913, had been by Gibson ; and a great deal of exploration had occurred in the interval.

Speaking generally of the coalfield revision of the Survey, one may say that it has been done without the hurry of former days. The original surveyors had aimed at obtaining as much information as could speedily be issued in maps and memoirs, and they had in many parts of England and Wales to work on one-inch maps. It is true that they filed a number of bore records additional to those intended for publication ; but it was physically impossible for them to aim at anything approaching completeness. During Teall's time till today, the surveyors have striven more and more after completeness. They have also in many cases maintained contact with colliery managements after satisfying the immediate publication programme. Moreover, since the passing of the Mining Industry Act, two Assistants, one in Scotland, where coal boring is particularly prevalent, the other in England, were appointed to watch bores put down in ground not currently allocated to a particular Geologist. They were, in my young days, nicknamed Boa-constrictors, and have proved invaluable. I have seen, as the years passed, coalfield after coalfield rescued from the Survey's half-forgotten past ; and I believe that the time is at hand when the decennial revision of active coalfields, asked for by the Coal Conservation Committee of 1906-7, will be more than achieved. Indeed, I think that, if individual Geologists were entrusted with the supervision of highly skilled Assistants, not merely decennial, but perennial, revision might be successfully attempted.

Hand in hand with more meticulous co-ordination of mining information has gone unhurried examination of field exposures and increasing attention to fossil evidence. This has proved particularly valuable to the mining community, which left to itself has seldom the specialist training for such studies, though increasingly conscious of their value, particularly in the interpretation of deep expensive bores. Outside experts, such as Kidston among plants, Bisat among goniatites and Trueman among non-marine lamellibranchs, have given every assistance to the Survey in their daily work, besides blazing the trail. Gibson, as we have already seen, did more in his English days than any other Survey contemporary to bring home to the mining fraternity the value of fossils and fossil experts. In later years all Field Units, perhaps especially those engaged in Lancashire and Yorkshire, have had conspicuous success in their employment of palæontological guides. In this connection Wright will long be remembered as a leader.

Kidston has been mentioned repeatedly in these pages. He was for many years unofficial Palæobotanist to the Survey. He undertook the naming of current collections, thus securing for himself much additional knowledge. He also started a great Survey memoir on *The Fossil Plants of the Carboniferous Rocks of Great Britain*, of which the first parts appeared in 1923. He died suddenly in 1924 while gathering further material in South Wales. He had been so impressed with the value of the Survey as a home of research that he bequeathed to it his own magnificent collection of plant impressions along with much supporting material. The whole constituted, according to Flett, 'the greatest single acquisition which the Survey's collections have ever received,' high praise indeed! It is still being worked over by Crookall, the Survey's official Palæobotanist, appointed largely to complete Kidston's great monograph.

It must not be supposed from anything which has been said above (when District offices came under criticism) that a Survey Unit engaged on a coalfield is likely to be confined to Coal Measures. As a rule it completes each one-inch sheet that it enters, and thus obtains an invigorating and healthy variety of experience. Then there are the ubiquitous problems bequeathed by the Quaternary. The Cumberland Unit found these particularly interesting. It had a relatively small coalfield to cover; and presently part of the staff moved on

14

to tackle the famous hæmatite field in adjacent Carboniferous Limestone—already described in considerable detail by their District Geologist, Bernard Smith, in a *Special Report,* 1920. Others of the unit made a long migration to the coalfield of the Forest of Dean, near the borders of South Wales.

The Southern Unit in the main dealt with the Cretaceous and Tertiaries of South-East England; but Dines from 1925 spent some of his time in the metalliferous field of Cornwall. He has already been mentioned for his work on the Kent coalfield.

In 1923, a novel publication was entrusted to this Southern Unit, to cover London with colour-printed six-inch maps. The London County Council proved extremely co-operative, and by 1935, the year of Flett's retirement, 15 out of a projected total of 42 quarter sheets had appeared.

A PROBLEM OF SCIENTIFIC LIBERTY

Here perhaps I may be permitted to return to a subject already introduced in connection with Horne's administration as Assistant Director for Scotland. Flett, when he succeeded to Horne's position and later when he held the Directorship in London, claimed that all scientific writings of the staff, which were intended for unofficial publication, should be submitted in advance for official permission. He sought, in fact, to abrogate the previous custom that scientific writings dealing with districts not on the official publication programme were free of this restriction; and I refused to give way.

I want it to be clear that no question was raised of my having at any time unfairly anticipated official publication, or stolen a march on a colleague, or indulged in unseemly criticism. My two faults came under two headings :—

(1) In certain interpretations of the Highland Schists my work was, in Flett's judgment, mistaken.

(2) I publicly reinterpreted districts already covered by the Survey and not as yet included in its official programme for revision.

In both these directions Flett considered that I brought discredit upon the Survey.

Flett thought that I was a useful officer in coalfields and among igneous rocks; and I have no complaint that from 1924 to 1929 I and my unit were not sent to the Highlands. Admittedly it may seem strange to outsiders that Flett during this time could think that he would get better understanding (if the Devil may so quote scripture) from babes and sucklings* brought from the North of England to work under conditions that precluded adequate training or supervision; but the reason is simple. Flett had noticed that several workers (myself the latest example), who had spent a considerable time in the Highlands, had produced theories upon which no agreement could be reached. He concluded that we had lost perspective through close contact with local difficulties, and that the stratigraphical and tectonic problems we conjured up were in essence imaginary. To him, looking on from a distance, the main issues seemed perfectly straightforward; and he considered that the best results might be expected from temporary employment of Geologists who had not become infected with the malaise of the district.

It is only fair to add that Flett partly inherited his distrust of my Highland interpretations from Horne; but Horne had frankly said he was too old to test them himself, and, after getting Clough and Maufe to check them in the field, he had acquiesced even to official publication. Furthermore, from time to time, I made important mistakes, for instance, the one already mentioned in regard to the stratigraphy of the Loch Leven area on the borders of Argyll and Invernessshire. I remember asking Carruthers, to whom I am especially grateful for correction in this matter, whether his reinterpretation of Loch Leven led him to doubt my interpretation of Ballachulish, the key area of the district as a whole. His reply was: 'Certainly not! Any damned fool could have worked out that country.' This was reassuring. Still, the fact remained that I had made mistakes; a fact that necessarily influenced onlookers.

*My reference to babes and sucklings must be read in its context. The men selected were among the best the Survey has ever been fortunate to possess.

Much more difficult to understand was Flett's announcement to me, soon after my return from the War, that Read's researches under his guidance in the East Highlands during the past two seasons had shown that my reading of Ballachulish and Fort William in the West was wrong! I marvelled at this feat of television, but obtained permission for Read to accompany me to Fort William—where, to Flett's regretful surprise, he reported that he saw the local geology exactly as I and others had seen it in the past.

During my official separation from the Highlands, whilst busily pushing forward the mapping and description of the

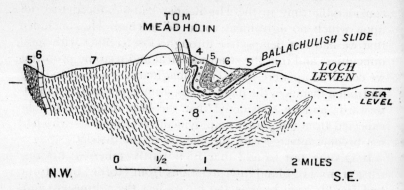

FIG. 35.—Section showing relation of Ballachulish Slide to Tom Meadhoin Fold. The Dalradian Schist formations are now known to be increasingly old from 4 to 8. (Quoted from Bailey, _Ben Nevis and Glen Coe Mem._, 1916, p. 42.)

Ayrshire coalfields, I was still able year by year to spend a fortnight of my holidays revising chosen localities. Careful preparatary study of field maps made by past members of staff allowed of wonderfully profitable concentration on critical exposures. To stop this an order was issued that, while Survey field maps were open to inspection by the general public, they were only to be shown to a member of staff after permission had been granted by the Director. It was obvious that I must look elsewhere for scientific opportunity. I applied for the Chair of Geology at Glasgow University, left vacant by Prof. J. W. Gregory's retirement, and was accepted, starting work 1st January, 1930. Though in the next seven years I often found it extremely hard work attempting to do justice alike to my duties as teacher and researcher, I felt continually grateful, for my scientific life had been saved.

I recognise the difficulty attaching to the subject which has just been outlined in relation to a particular case. I believe that most readers will hold that Flett correctly interpreted his duty and that a Civil Servant should surrender all right to independent publication. I hope not, for, as I have said already, if this comes to be the acknowledged rule, the chance of tempting a true scientist into the Civil Service will vanish, except in wartime.

UNDERGROUND WATER

Three special aspects of Flett's directorate, concerned with Water, Agriculture and Geophysics, remain to be considered before we turn to his creation of a new Museum and Offices.

Flett soon reinvigorated publication of Water Survey memoirs, which had slackened during the War. At first he was able to rely upon a continuation of outside help from Whitaker; but after the latter's death in 1925 he turned to an entirely non-Survey expert, L. Richardson. These two authors, Whitaker and Richardson, supplied five each of the twelve memoirs produced. A regrettable feature is that rainfall now received little or no attention. This falling away was probably connected with Mill's famous 'gift of British weather' to the nation, which dated from 1919. Previously, as a private individual, Mill had organised a vast unpaid British Rainfall Organisation, which from 1860 onwards published annual reports. In 1919, however, Mill stepped down, feeling the weight of years, and his organisation was gratefully taken over by the Meteorological Office of the Air Ministry.

Whitaker's last two memoirs, on Wiltshire, 1925, and Dorset, 1926, were posthumous, and appeared as joint-publications with Survey authors, F. H. Edmunds and W. Edwards, respectively. The two junior authors were sent for a considerable time to the field and told drastically to edit and condense Whitaker's compilations. This was in part determined by a desire to reduce the price of the finished article in view of high post-war printing charges. It was also in part due to an increasing realisation that unchecked records of wells that have been sunk through ill-defined strata are apt to be misleading, if presented verbatim to an innocent reader who may think that he should believe everything he sees in print. The restraint and selection exhibited in these two memoirs were maintained in their successors of the Flett period. Another valuable feature was the introduction in every case of a helpful geological map.

It will be remembered how from 1874 to 1895, that is during most of Ramsay and Geikie's director-generalships, a committee of the British Association, with Hull in the Chair and De Rance as Secretary, had investigated circulation of underground water. There is little doubt that its activities materially helped such members of the Survey staff as sought to foster official publication of data bearing on the subject. A milestone along this path is, of course, Geikie's 1899 inception of *County Water Supply* memoirs, which, as we have seen, prospered greatly under his successors. Concurrently there were several public inquiries into various aspects of water, mostly surface water, involving, for instance, salmon, sewage and power.

Following its York meeting in 1932, the British Association appointed a further committee, including Bernard Smith, recently promoted Assistant Director of the Geological Survey for England and Wales. Its function was to inquire into the position and prospects of an Inland Water Survey of Britain. It came to the conclusion that a central organisation was desirable, controlled perhaps by the Department of Scientific and Industrial Research. The appositeness of the inquiry, we may interpose, was emphasised by severe drought during 1933 and 1934.

In the latter year a joint deputation of the British Association and the Institute of Civil Engineers put the case before the Minister of Health. As a result, the Government decided on an Inland Water Survey Committee, which was appointed in 1935 by the Minister of Health for England and the Secretary of State for Scotland. Its object, as explained to Parliament, was to collect and correlate reliable records dealing with rivers and underground waters. The rivers were to be cared for by the two Ministers mentioned above, but as regards underground water the Committee thought : —

> The work of examining and securing the amplification of the information on this subject could best be done by the Geological Survey who have on their staff persons with the necessary knowledge and experience. We [the I.W.S. Committee] are therefore glad to report that the Committee of the Privy Council for Scientific and Industrial Research have agreed that the Geological Survey should assist in the work.

This statement appears in the First Annual Report of the Inland Water Survey Committee, of which Sir Henry Lyons was Chairman, and was published in 1936, the year after Flett retired. It shows the position reached at the end of his reign.

Public acknowledgment of the Geological Survey as keeper of the national records of underground water gave both additional responsibility and additional strength. Edmunds, who was already author or joint author of two Water Supply memoirs, was entrusted with the work that resulted from the Geological Survey's association with the Inland Water Survey Committee.

AGRICULTURE

An intimate relation between soil and underlying material, whether solid rock or drift, is often self-evident; so much so, that it seems incredible to a British geologist that a useful soil map of any considerable stretch of our country will ever be made by a worker unversed in the principles of Geology. In some cases the connection is crystal clear, as in the district covered by A. D. Hall and E. J. Russell in their delightful *Report on the Agriculture and Soils of Kent, Surrey and Sussex*. This, after completion at Rothamsted, was published in 1911 by the Board of Agriculture. Its authors found the Geological Survey map all that could be desired as a basis for their descriptions.

In other districts, however, the connection may be very elusive. For instance, the distribution of under-soil material may be complicated, in which case a geologist tends to generalise, and to include several lithological types in one of his mapped divisions; or, again, trouble may arise through a geologist entirely neglecting what is for him a mere surface film, whereas for a soil expert it may be the very stuff that matters. Moreover, much material may be introduced into a developing soil, by wind, water, or organisms (including farmers), which is not derived at all from the underlying formation—although the latter may be mistakenly credited with the rôle of a parent; and, equally, much may be selectively removed.

It is often thought by optimistic agriculturists that the Geological Survey could make soil maps in its spare time; but geological surveyors know that to prepare a creditable soil map of the country as a whole, even when geological maps of solid and drift are everywhere available on the six-inch scale, will be a most formidable task. It will require skill in field and laboratory techniques, and a knowledge of living creatures, of a quite non-geological character.

Some Survey geologists of pre-Flett times, for instance Kilroe and Woodward, and further back, but above all, Trimmer, felt particularly strongly the natural appeal of soil. Flett did much to foster this sentiment in his staff. He was himself stimulated by Sir Thomas Middleton, who from 1920-43 represented agriculture on the Geological Survey Board. The net result of several years of sympathetic effort may not seem very impressive; but probably it has been exactly what was needed and should prove very helpful in the future. Here we can do nothing more than list a few organisational steps, in all of which the Geological Survey participated, often represented by H. G. Dines and J. B. Simpson.

1925. Middleton presided over a conference of soil men. Small field parties of agriculturists and geologists tried co-operative mapping in seven counties. Foreign experts gave valuable assistance.

1926. A series of annual Soil Survey Field Meetings was

instituted—'the main purpose is to examine, map and compare the results reached by small groups of surveyors into which those members attending the meetings are divided up, with the object of gaining experience and ascertaining the degree of uniformity that can be reached by separate groups working on a common method.' One result of prolonged discussion this particular year was the provisional adoption of two models of field-auger.

1929. Great advantage was obtained from air photographs.

1930. Middleton attended the fifth Soil Survey Field Meeting. He records that previous sharp differences of opinion as to principles and methods have now given place to general agreement (see below under 1931). A Soils Survey Correlation Committee was established under the chairmanship of Prof. G. W. Robinson, of Bangor.

1931. Various agricultural centres at which soil mapping was in progress were visited by the Soils Survey Correlation Committee. As regards agreement, we learn that parent material offers the most suitable basis for primary classification of British soils; and as regards previous differences of opinion, we read that 'grouping by climatic regions, such as is being done on the Continent, has not been satisfactorily applied in this country.'

1934. The Soils Survey Correlation Committee was superseded by a Soil Surveyors' Conference. This was furnished with a standing Executive Committee with Robinson again in the Chair. At the request of the Ministry of Agriculture it was agreed that the Geological Survey should continue to be represented.

As a further contribution to agriculture the Geological Survey published two one-inch soil texture maps of Ayrshire, prepared by the West of Scotland College of Agriculture who worked in close touch with the Geologists responsible for the revision of the solid and drift of the area. Co-operation with the Forestry Commission was also arranged in their assessment of soil characters that influence the growth of timber.

Perhaps I may add that in after years I was consulted, as Director of the Geological Survey, on the institution of a Soil Survey. I was very sympathetic to the proposal, and advised that the two Surveys might be expected to give the best results if they operated as independent organisations, linked closely, I hoped, by friendly consultation.

GEOPHYSICS

Flett made a brave start in exploring the possibilities of geophysics from the Geological Survey's point of view. In this he had the enthusiastic support of Sir Francis Ogilvie, during the latter's chairmanship of the Geological Survey Board from 1920 to 1930. In the Board's Report for 1924 we read that consideration had been given at different times to 'the various methods that have been suggested for detection of underground deposits by accoustical, electrical, or gravitational means'; and that of these 'the gravitational method seems the most promising.'

The Anglo-Persian (Iranian) Oil Company, whose Chairman at the time sat on the Geological Survey Board, was anxious for unbiased discussion, and very willingly explained the Company's employment of the Eötvös torsion balance. This is a wonderful instrument devised by an Austrian scientist. It determines the rate of change of gravity from place to place, which, of course, after integration, allows of the mapping of gravity contours. The Company also offered a demonstration under working conditions. Accordingly McLintock and Phemister were sent in 1926 to Persia, where they critically examined and verified observations and deductions of the Company's geophysical staff. On their return they did good service in expounding the theory and practice of the Eötvös balance in the Survey's *Summary of Progress* and from several other convenient housetops.

The next step was to secure a balance for the Geological Survey and to experiment with it on home problems. The work was assigned to the same two skilful operators. The exercises chosen were as follows :—

1927. Basalt dyke cutting Trias marl, Swynnerton, Staffordshire. *Result:* A traverse across an expected, but concealed, position of the dyke got a clear indication of the dyke's presence, and a strong suggestion of its inclination.

1927-28. Drift-filled channel aligned with the Kelvin river, N.W. of Glasgow. *Result:* A rock barrier seems to block what had previously been taken as a buried channel of the Clyde. This result is probably trustworthy and, if so, is of great scientific interest.

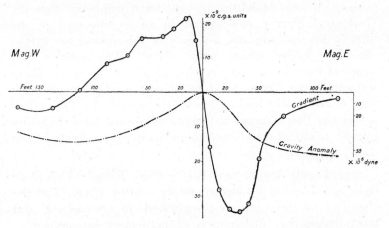

Fig. 36.—Components of corrected gravity gradients parallel to line of traverse across Swynnerton basalt dyke. (Quoted from McLintock and Phemister, *Sum. Prog. for* 1927, pt. 2, p. 7.)

1928-29. Pentland Fault, S.W. of Edinburgh. *Result:* An exact sub-drift position of the fault was suggested, and also certain structural accompaniments. Most of the gravity anomalies detected were ascribed to the presence of the Arthur's Seat volcanic rocks.

1930. Thrussington, Melton Mowbray district (following a magnetic survey, 1929, see below). *Result:* Gravity anomalies suggested an uneven sub-Trias floor of Precambrian rocks. Precambrian intrusions had been invoked in 1929 to account for magnetic readings, but, if present, could not, by gravity, be distinguished from associated Precambrian sediments. A known fault gave a clear signal.

Partly concurrently with the above gravity surveys, a series of magnetic surveys was undertaken with modern equipment. All except one (1930, an investigation of the Lornty dyke by McLintock and Phemister) were entrusted to A. F. Hallimond :—

1929. Swynnerton Dyke (see gravity series, 1927). *Result:* Sixteen traverses located the dyke again and again under cover, and showed its width and branching and, less certainly, its depth of cover.

1929. Melton Mowbray (it will be remembered that the Geological Survey co-operated in an examination of the already known magnetic anomaly of this district in 1917— see also gravity series, 1930). *Result:* The position and depth of intrusions, 'possibly granite,' were deduced. These intrusions were considered to belong to the Precambrian floor of the district and to be directly overlain by Trias. The associated Precambrian sediments suggested later (1930) by gravity readings could not, magnetically, be separated from overlying Trias.

1930. Lornty Dyke, near Blairgowrie. *Result:* This basic dyke could easily be located under shallow cover, and the character of the anomalies suggested an unexpected, and most interesting, distribution of permanent magnetism — since confirmed in the laboratory.

1930. Pentland Fault (see gravity series, 1928-29). *Result:* Rather vague support was obtained for some of the deductions of the gravity survey. Lack of detailed agreement is understandable since only parts of the Arthur's Seat volcanics are notably magnetic.

1930. Pipewell, Northamptonshire. *Result:* The Northampton Ironstone proved to be too weak a magnetic subject significantly to affect the local field.

In 1931 further geophysical exploration by the Geological Survey was suspended. This was partly due to pressure of work in relation to the impending transfer of the Offices and Museum of the Survey to South Kensington ; and partly, I imagine, to misgivings of the new Chairman of the Geological Survey Board. The instruments were accordingly lent for teaching purposes to the Imperial College of Science.

Flett's geophysical venture as a whole has proved of permanent value in that it brought the Geological Survey into contact with a great community of oil and water borers who seek aid from geophysical techniques. It is true that the gravitational work, carried out with the instruments available at the date, but since fortunately superseded, proved expensive both in time and money; and it is undeniable that similar effort directed to orthodox geological survey in other directions would have given a better harvest of results. Still it was important at the time to have a demonstration in our country by an independent body that geophysical survey is a genuine operation and not mere quackery (there are of course charlatans in the trade). The main criticism that can be offered is, I think, that money ought to have been set aside in advance to check by boring some of the geological deductions that were bound to follow. Comparatively little boring would have added enormously to the educational value of the experiment, for members of staff no less than for outsiders.

Some, perhaps, may think that problems of obvious economic value should have been selected for investigation. It would, however, have been difficult in such cases to have avoided all appearance of favouritism among conflicting interests of private enterprise.

TO SOUTH KENSINGTON

In April, 1923, it was found that the roof of De la Beche's Museum of Practical Geology in Jermyn Street required repair. The damage was due to settlement of the foundations. It is quite possible that the trouble started with a German bomb, dropped near at hand in Piccadilly on the 19th October, 1917. Had not some plaster fallen from the roof, it might have escaped notice for some years to come. As it was, to quote from Flett's *First Hundred Years of the Geological Survey* : ' The Museum was at once closed to the public as dangerous, but the staff continued to work in it as usual.'

The Geological Survey Board, in view of all the circumstances, revived a recommendation that had been made by a Departmental Committee in 1912, and pressed for transfer of Survey Headquarters to South Kensington, where a site was available on land purchased from the proceeds of the 1851 Exhibition. Next year, 1924, the Government decided, at least in principle, to adopt this procedure.

As a temporary measure elaborate timber supports were erected in the Museum, and thin sheets of wood were inserted to replace glass in its one-time transparent roof. At last, on the 4th of August, 1925, the building was reopened to the public. To quote again from Flett : ' The interior now presented a spectacle such as no other museum in the world could furnish.'

Meanwhile, plans were made for removal, in so far as this matter lay in the hands of the Survey. In 1925 Flett, accompanied by McLintock, visited museums at Copenhagen, Oslo, Stockholm, Berlin, Dresden, Prague, Vienna, Buda-Pesth, Munich, Frankfurt on the Maine, Strasbourg, Brussels and Paris. They found that those which had been built as museums showed a progressive and advantageous development of plan. They were particularly impressed with the design and furniture of the Riksmuseum at Stockholm and the Deutsches Museum at Munich ; and generally speaking they learnt much of value regarding display, labelling and illustration of exhibition material, and storage of reference specimens. All the recent museums had abundant ancillary accommodation for storage and research, including laboratories and libraries.

Financial stringency prevented the Office of Works from making any provision in their estimates for 1926-27, and again 1927-28, for the building of the proposed new Offices and Museum. It even came to be questioned whether the Survey required a museum of its own, since palæontology and mineralogy are principal features of the British Museum (Natural History) already at South Kensington. However, in July, 1927, a Royal Commission was appointed to consider and report on the condition and organisation of national museums in London and Edinburgh ; and in

November it took evidence from Flett, who put forward the Survey case in cogent terms.

After this there was little delay. On the 22nd December the Under Secretary of State for the Home Office announced in the House of Commons that the Royal Commission had advised the transfer of the Geological Museum to South Kensington at the earliest convenient moment, and that the Chancellor of the Exchequer hoped to give effect to this recommendation as soon as financial circumstances permitted. One last quotation from Flett : ' The period of suspense was over.'

Fortunately the financial difficulties of transferring the Survey from Jermyn Street to South Kensington, when properly faced, proved of much the same obliging character as those which have helped Columbia University in a succession of migrations from the centre of New York. The Government leased the Jermyn Street-Piccadilly site for £11,000 a year, which more than recoups it for the £245,000 expended on new buildings and furniture at South Kensington, on a site, it will be remembered, inherited from the 1851 Exhibition.

This site, situated on Exhibition Road, in what might fitly be called Princeconsortland, adjoins the British Museum (Natural History) on the west, and the Science Museum on the north; while to the east it faces the Victoria and Albert Museum, north of which stand the Huxley Buildings, the first to be occupied of a great series housing the Imperial College of Science.

Plans for the new buildings were prepared by Sir Richard Allison and Mr. J. H. Markam, of H.M. Office of Works, and the furniture was designed by other officers of the same department. There was, of course, constant consultation, in which Flett and McLintock played a very prominent part, assisted by Grant Ogilvie. The latter had been successively Director of the Royal Scottish (Edinburgh) and Science (S. Kensington) Museums, before becoming Principal Assistant Secretary of the Department of Scientific and Industrial Research, and, concurrently until 1930, Chairman of the Geological Survey Board.

A start was made at actual building in 1929. By 1931 progress was such that several members of the field staff were diverted to co-operate with their museum colleagues in developing the exhibitional detail of the master plan, since successfully put into operation. According to this, the basement of the new Museum is devoted to workshops and storage; the main floor and two galleries to the display of exhibits (main floor to illustrate principles, first gallery, regions, and second gallery, economic resources); while the top floor, with a superficial area of 16,000 square feet, houses ' reserve and study collections,' and is furnished with tables for the benefit of research workers. Alongside, and with easy communications, stand the library, laboratories, and staff working rooms.

Flett arranged that the regional displays of the second gallery should be made the subject of eighteen *Regional Guides* illustrating the geology of the whole United Kingdom. The preparation of these *Guides* proved very stimulating to their selected authors; and their appearance has been welcomed by a wide public, much wider than that which has easy access to the Museum. The *Guides* rank, in fact, among the Survey's best-sellers.

Building proceeded so satisfactorily that the *Summary of Progress* for 1932 foretold a transfer to be completed in stages during 1933. The prophecy seemed safe, since it was penned in the early months of 1933. Suddenly, however, the Government installed an International Monetary and Economic Congress, thus delaying the entry of the Survey until the beginning of 1934.

On the 3rd of July, 1935, the new Museum of Practical Geology was opened to the public by a great-grandson of the Prince Consort, no less a person than H.R.H. the Duke of York, since crowned George VI. The ceremony was attended by over 1,200 guests.

In the evening of the same day the Geological Society held a reception of delegates and guests in its rooms at Burlington House in Piccadilly. The occasion was particularly happy, for the opening of the new Museum coincided with the Centenary of the Geological Survey. Next day this latter

PLATE IV.
MUSEUM OF PRACTICAL GEOLOGY.
Top : Jermyn Street, main floor with two galleries above Lecture Hall.
Bottom : South Kensington, ready to receive exhibits.

[To face page 212.

event provided the subject of a special assembly in the lecture theatre of the Royal Geographical Society at Kensington Gore. Lord Rutherford presided, as Chairman of the Advisory Council of the Department of Scientific and Industrial Research. He pointed to the large and representative gathering of scientists drawn from all parts of the world (some 130 from overseas); and found in it a striking testimony to widespread respect and admiration surrounding the British Geological Survey. He might, perhaps, have added affection, for the Survey, with all its faults, still occupies a warm corner in the heart of international Geology.

Flett entered into the spirit of the harvest thanksgiving, and furnished an appropriate *résumé* of the long day's work. He was followed by speakers from abroad. Other festivities came later in the day.

After that, Museum and indoor functions were deserted in favour of the field. Three well attended excursions spent a week visiting South Wales, the Isle of Wight and Edinburgh, as the case might be.

Mention of Edinburgh recalls that Flett, in spite of his London preoccupations, succeeded in securing greatly improved Headquarters for Scotland in the form of a mansion in Grange Terrace, Edinburgh, which was occupied in 1927.

FLETT RETIRES

For my own part I never enter the extraordinarily successful new Museum of Practical Geology without a feeling of gratitude to Flett, to whom above all, with the whole-hearted support of his colleagues, the nation owes this great achievement. Very fittingly, having reached the goal of his latter years, he retired on the 30th September, 1935. He had already been knighted ten years previously.

Flett's next concern was to see through the Press an official volume, entitled *The First Hundred Years of the Geological Survey of Great Britain,* which is in no way superseded by the present booklet. He then settled down to produce a new edition of his old favourite, the Lizard memoir. The original edition, published in 1912, had been a joint work with Hill, who died in 1927. Meanwhile, in 1925, Miss

15

E. M. Lind Hendriks had begun an intensive search for fossils, to be richly rewarded by debris of Devonian plants from some of Hill's presumed pre-Devonian formations. The result was specially welcome, since it cleared up part of the uncertainty that attended, and still attends, the dating of wide tracts of De la Beche's killas. Flett checked Miss Hendrik's discoveries during a month spent on the ground in 1932, and produced a most helpful account in the corresponding *Summary of Progress*. A new edition of the map appeared in 1934; but a new edition of the memoir had to wait until his retirement gave Flett, during 1937 and 1938, the requisite time for its preparation. Then came a further postponement owing to the paper famine of the Second World War; so that the date of actual publication was 1946.

Flett also represented the Royal Society at the Jubilee celebrations in Canberra of the Australian and New Zealand Association for the Advancement of Science. He had scarcely returned from this antipodean venture when war was declared. He died in January, 1947, after having seen his country once more victorious, though again sadly mutilated.

1935

BERNARD SMITH, DIRECTOR

BERNARD SMITH was appointed Director in Flett's place, October, 1935. Dewey at the same time became Assistant Director for England and Wales, while Macgregor remained Assistant Director for Scotland. The officers of District Geologist rank were as follows :—

> *In England and Wales:* Carruthers (Northumberland and Durham); Wright (Lancashire); T. H. Whitehead, promoted to replace Bromehead (Yorkshire); Eastwood (Cumberland and Forest of Dean); Dinham (West Midlands and Cambridge); Bromehead, transferred to replace Dewey (Southern England).
>
> *In Scotland:* Richey (Renfrew and Mallaig); Wilson (East Fife and Skye).
>
> *Petrographer,* Phemister; *Palæontologist,* Pringle; *Curator,* McLintock.

As we have already seen, Edmunds, slightly before Flett retired, had been entrusted with preliminary work connected with the Inland Water-Survey Committee. Smith put Edmunds' duties on a permanent basis, thus establishing a very modest Water Unit. Edmunds ranked as Senior Geologist, and had an excellent Assistant assigned to his care in 1936.

A difficult time is likely to follow any great effort in war or peace. Flett's first task had been to bring back the Survey from fighting and advising to mapping and describing; and at the same time to complete Strahan's *Special Reports on Mineral Resources.* Similarly Smith had to begin by returning to their normal duties fieldsmen who had been in large measure absorbed in the preparation of the New Museum;

215

and concurrently he had to finish Flett's *Regional Handbooks,* most of which had not as yet appeared in print.

Smith was admirably suited for his task. Like Ramsay, Geikie and Strahan, he had been a fieldsman during the whole of his career, starting at the bottom and working his way by stages to the top. He further resembled Strahan in having made a decisive mark in the economic field—in his case among the coal and hæmatite of Cumberland and in problems of underground water. His heart was in his work, and he told me in answer to congratulations that he had attained the ambition of his life—a good augury for the future.

There was, of course, no question of neglecting the Museum, which in its fresh glory was attracting twelve times as many visitors as had its predecessor in the days of its decrepitude. Attendance in 1936 passed the 255,000 mark. Obviously an increase in its proper staff was required. There was already an Assistant Librarian of Geologist rank. Now two additional Geologists were recruited for curatorial duties; and these were soon supplemented by an extremely valuable Guide Lecturer. This busy officer had all too little time and space to meet public demands. For instance, he found it difficult to cater for the needs of children without sacrificing those of other seekers after truth. A solution of this particular trouble was found through discussion with a liaison officer of the London County Council. Henceforward the Lecturer conducted parties of school masters and left to them the responsibility of dealing with the children.

The main new result of the 1935 field season came from Mallaig on the west coast of Inverness-shire, where Richey and Simpson found that current-bedding allows of the establishment of a time sequence through an immense thickness of Moine Schists—a most encouraging discovery. The investigation of the largest landslip in Britain, in Trotternish, Skye, is also worth recalling. As regards coal, Smith was able to report that by the close of 1935 work on the six-inch scale had at least been started in all the coalfields of Britain, except in the minor, very complicated area of Bristol and Somerset. Not only so, but in the great majority of these fields six-inch mapping had been carried to temporary completion on more than one occasion. In keeping with this, next year, 1936, saw a second revision undertaken of the six-inch mapping of the Mid-Lothian coalfield in Scotland.

A new and very useful publication was begun in 1935 with an issue of *Economic Maps* on the scale of 1 : 1,000,000. The first two examples were entitled the *Coalfields* and the *Iron Ores of England and Wales*. The scale, 1 : 1,000,000, had already been adopted by the Ordnance Survey, on a basis of international agreement, for some of their own special maps; so that the Geological Survey contributions fitted happily into an existing series. It was intended to follow with others on the same scale (*Limestones* appeared in 1937), and to include among them a geological map of England and Wales. An independent scheme was at the same time developed for an official geological map of Scotland on the scale of one inch to ten miles, or 1 : 633,600. As we shall presently see, these plans underwent modification before they were carried very far.

UNDERGROUND WATER

In regard to Underground Water an important change was made in consequence of association with the Inland Water Survey Committee. Hitherto the Geological Survey records had been filed (and the corresponding *Water Supply* memoirs written) with reference to counties. The choice had certain advantages for County and Rural District Councils and for County Officers of Health. It was also in keeping with the practice of the Ordnance Survey, only recently abandoned, of publishing their six-inch maps on a county basis—with independent setting of meridians and with blank paper outside the particular county boundary ! As, however, the counties interlock in intricate fashion, there are many aspects of underground water resources which are sadly muddled by presentation within a county frame. Accordingly R. G. Hetherington, of the Ministry of Health, adopting a national outlook, urged the Geological Survey to discard their old system; and this was willingly agreed. Two possibilities were thus opened up. Classification might in future be based on catchment areas or else upon Geological Survey maps.

In the country as a whole, surface waters are much more important than underground waters, and strong pressure was brought to bear on the Geological Survey to tabulate and present all water data in terms of catchment areas defined by surface form. Such a procedure is, of course, convenient for surface waters, since it agrees fairly closely with what may be called Nature's own habits. On the other hand, it has only a comparatively vague correspondence with the realities of underground sources, and Smith and Edmunds did yeoman service in refusing to be trapped once more in areas with intricate boundaries. Thus it was eventually admitted that the Geological Survey should tabulate and publish their underground data with reference to their straight-margined Geological Survey one-inch maps (or quarter-inch maps for memoir purposes). At the same time, for the convenience of the statutory authorities known as Catchment Boards (one of which may be in charge of a group of natural catchment areas), the boundaries of officially defined catchment areas (simple or compound) have since been inserted on maps that accompany Geological Survey water publications.

MONTSERRAT

The value of the Geological Survey as an occasional source of trained personnel, even for extra-British studies, was once more demonstrated early in 1936. On this occasion the Royal Society, in collaboration with the Colonial Office, organised an expedition to Montserrat in the West Indies, to investigate a disquieting recrudescence of earthquakes and soufrières. A. G. MacGregor, with wide experience of Scotland's extinct volcanoes, was selected as geologist, and C. F. Powell, not a Survey man, as seismologist.

Montserrat is a volcanic island on the same great arc as St. Vincent and Martinique, though 150 miles to the north of the latter. It has staged no eruption, other than solfataric, since its discovery by Columbus; but it was clear to MacGregor that it had once been the site of a devastating *nuée ardente,* accompanied by dome or spine extrusion of typical Peléan character. MacGregor noted marked porosity as characteristic of fragments in the *nuée ardente* deposits, especially pronounced in the case of certain cognate xenoliths enclosed in those fragments. His studies of this porosity led him to accept Anderson and Flett's conclusion that *nuées ardentes* generate fresh supplies of gas during their riotous travel—a vital element in the avalanche theory. On the other hand, from a letter in *Nature,* 1946, it is clear that he follows Lacroix in accepting co-operation of laterally directed blast in the production of the 1902 disaster of Mt. Pelée.

THE END

Smith sat with Flett on the Royal Society Committee which originated the Montserrat expedition. He also, in the early summer of 1936, made himself familiar with the field work proceeding at home as far north as Mallaig. Then to the consternation of his friends he was quickly carried off by cancer of the stomach, dying on the 19th of August, 1936.

1 9 3 6

INTERREGNUM

IN October, 1936, I was asked to attend a meeting in London to discuss the situation arising out of Smith's sudden death. I do not feel at liberty to disclose with whom the discussion occurred, but the following letter, dated 22nd October, 1936, sufficiently indicates its scope :—

' Dear —

' In our conversation last Tuesday you asked me to put in writing the reply that I should make if I were offered the Directorship of the Geological Survey.

' I am prepared to accept such an offer supposing it is made on the clear understanding that I regard it as a duty for the Director to strive to continue in the ranks of active Research. I should accept as an obligation of honour what you spoke of as the " allotted task," but I am not prepared to subscribe to the defeatist proposition that this blocks the way to Research. In University life, Teaching and Research are accepted as twin ideals. For myself I see that the Teaching side of our Department [at Glasgow University] is secure, before I turn to the Research side. I think you understand that my wishes in regard to the Geological Survey are impersonal. If Director, I should wish to share to the full any opportunity for Research which seemed right and proper. If I found a man working loyally and whole-heartedly at the " allotted task," I should like to reward him with opportunities for additional work in directions where he had a voice in the choice of subject. There is, as you well know, no sharp line between the " allotted task " and Research, especially for the junior ranks, who do the bulk of the Survey's work.

' The last Director who insisted upon freedom of research for himself was Sir Archibald Geikie. My younger and more fruitful days in the Survey were lived under the influence of his tradition. I joined in 1902, shortly after Geikie's retirement, and found myself starting with £120 a year as a member of a wonderful band of enthusiasts. The staff numbered about 32 (not counting the Irish), and yet included seven Fellows of the Royal Society. I admit that Geikie. . . . At the same time we should be careful not to lose sight of the good that he did. . . .

'You asked me how the administrative side of the work would appeal to me. I have no aptitude for business or finance, but I think that this need not be too frightening. In regard to the running of the Survey I have very definite opinions. I should wish to encourage each in his own station to plan and work for the good of the whole. I should let the officers in charge of Scotland, and England and Wales, and the Museum, understand that it would give me much greater pleasure to support and adapt their schemes than to present them with my own. I should let the District Surveyors understand that each of them was virtually king in his own territory, trusted to carry out his " allotted task " with very considerable discretion. I should not for a moment resuscitate the system by which men were sent to the Highlands and Islands in the Summer, and returned to their English branch-offices for the Winter. As District Surveyor I never personally suffered from this mistake, but I sympathised to the full with my colleagues in nominal charge of these birds of passage.

'Lastly, I know that there are difficulties in any course : that, if I were successful in reawakening the individualistic pride and enthusiasm of the past, the men might forget that they were paid Servants of the State with very definite objects to fulfil. At the same time I think that they would respond to the call for team work. Also I have a great belief in outside publication as a help in administration. I should advocate it especially :

'(1) to call attention to matters of general interest that are dealt with fully in official reports ;

'(2) to present certain particulars in greater detail than is advisable in a carefully planned and balanced report.

' If after reading this lengthly statement, you tell me that it has been decided not to offer me the post I shall not be in the least offended. I enjoyed our conversation very much, and shall always feel a little proud that I have been consulted.

'Yours sincerely,

' E. B. BAILEY.'

My letter remained unanswered for a considerable time. Then an offer came and was accepted, on my own terms. It was decided that I should take over my new duties on the 1st of April.

1937

BAILEY RETURNS AS DIRECTOR

WHEN I returned to the Survey in April, 1937, I naturally inherited the officers of District Geologist and higher rank, who have already been listed under Bernard Smith. There was only one change: McLintock, while remaining Curator and Librarian, was given the additional post of Deputy Director, thus relieving me of much administrative work. The Scientific Staff of the time may be classified as follows according to rank and function (Senior Geologists and Geologists are grouped together as Geologists):—

1 Director; 1 Deputy Director (holding also the posts of Museum Curator and Librarian); 2 Assistant Directors; 8 District Geologists (*sensu stricto*, 6 in England and Wales, 2 in Scotland) with 29 Geologists; 1 Petrographer; 1 Palæontologist with 4 Geologists; 1 Museum Curator and Librarian with 5 Geologists; 1 Head of Water Unit; 1 Chemist (seconded from the Government Laboratories).

The following changes occurred in the upper ranks during my term of office, where E stands for England and Wales, and S for Scotland:—

Retired:—1937: Dewey, Ass. Dir., E; Pringle, Pal.; 1938: Wright, D.G., E; 1941: Wilson, D.G., S.

Promoted:—1937: Eastwood to Ass. Dir., E; T. I. Pocock to D.G., E; C. P. Chatwin to Pal.; 1938: T. Robertson to D.G., E (1941 transferred to S); 1941: F. M. Trotter to D.G., E; 1944: H. G. Dines to D.G., E.

It will be seen that Dines' promotion was supernumerary (unless we take into account the vacancy that had remained unfilled since 1931). He was not promoted earlier because of the impossibility, so long as the war lasted, of weakening his day to day connection with the metalliferous field of Cornwall and Devon. In 1944 this difficulty was overcome by placing him in charge of the peninsula, organised as a temporary sub-district.

It will also be noted that in accordance with precedent the Petrographer started without any whole-time staff of Geolo-list or Senior Geologist rank—though it is true that A. G. MacGregor was working as part-time fieldsman, part-time petrographer in Scotland, and other Geologists were helping as occasion arose. In 1943 Miss E. M. Guppy, previously an Assistant in the Petrographical Department, was promoted Geologist, while remaining under Phemister's charge. This afforded not only a welcome strengthening of the Petrographical Unit, but also the first example of a lady attaining Geologist rank in the Geological Survey.

Similarly, the Chemical Unit was with good cause increased from one to two in 1938, thanks to the helpful acquiescence of the Government Chemist.

A proposal to enlarge the newly constituted Water Unit was in like manner confirmed at Headquarters D.S.I.R., where it was recognised as a proper consequence of underground co-operation with the Inland Water Survey Committee. Accordingly, an additional Geologist was enrolled in 1937 and another in 1938 with this object in view. It was never intended that these recruits should spend their lives isolated in the Water Unit. Instead it was planned to establish a rotation of service among junior members of the Water and Field Units.

WHILE YET THERE WAS PEACE : WATER

It is a curious circumstance that the good progress made by the Water Unit of the Geological Survey soon proved to be the only thing that kept the Inland Water Survey Committee in operation. Sir Henry Lyons was incapacitated by failing health in 1938, and the Acting Chairman, Sir Clement D. M. Hindley, proposed the Committee's indefinite prorogation. He pointed out that it had been found impossible to obtain adequate financial support for proposals in regard to surface waters. On the other hand, the Geological Survey representatives demurred, since D.S.I.R., after accepting responsibility for underground waters, had loyally done its part. Accordingly, the Committee continued to function until war supervened.

At the risk of some repetition I shall at this stage outline what seem to me the main benefits that have resulted from the existence of the Inland Water Survey Committee, some accruing before, some during hostilities:—

Recognition of the Geological Survey's position in relation to underground water.

Establishment and reinforcement of the Geological Survey's Water Unit.

Acceptance of the Geological Survey's one-inch maps as defining unit areas for cataloguing underground water data.

Much closer liaison between the water specialists of the Geological Survey and their opposite numbers in the Ministry of Health.

Much more intelligent discussion of proposals for water legislation.

Discussion of policy, mentioned under the last heading, did not officially belong to the Inland Water Survey Committee, whose real task was one of fact-finding and publication—'of making available to Government Departments, water undertakers, industry, agriculture, canal owners and indeed to all who need it, information as to the yield, behaviour and quality of the country's water resources.' In addition, however, in 1937 a Central Advisory Water Committee had been set up to advise the Minister of Health for England and Wales on general water policy; and it is unnecessary here to distinguish too precisely between the activities of these two committees. Rather let us recall a sixpenny command paper entitled *A National Water Policy*, which was published in 1944 by the Ministries of Health and of Agriculture and Fisheries, together with the Department of Health for Scotland. This was prepared in close consultation with the Geological Survey, who among other things contributed a four-page appendix on *The Influence of Geological Factors on Water Supply in Great Britain.* Mention has already been made of a detail of the two Acts that followed for England and Wales in 1945, and for Scotland in 1946. It arranged for a compulsory notification to D.S.I.R. (in practice the Geological Survey) of intention to sink a well or borehole more than 50 feet deep in search of water, and for supply of a copy of the journal of any such sinking after completion.

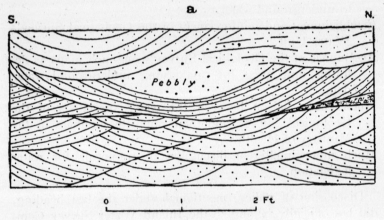

FIG. 37.—Current-bedding in Moine Schists, near Mallaig. (Quoted from Richey and Kennedy, *Bull.,* no. 2, 1939, p. 32.)

Only one important water publication dates from the pre-War period of my Directorate. It was written by S. Buchan and covers the County of London. Like its predecessors dealing with the London area, it was of outstanding merit, and was sponsored by the South of England Field Unit.

SURVEY BULLETIN AND NATIONAL ATLAS

The general field programme went steadily forward. Thus, mapping of the Forest of Dean coal and iron-ore field was completed, so that, in spite of the War, a covering memoir appeared in 1942 with Trotter as main author. A start was also made on the difficult Bristol-Somerset coalfield; while in Scotland the magnificent opportunity offered by the current-bedded Moines of Mallaig was developed to good purpose by Richey and Kennedy in a classical paper contributed to the second number of the Geological Survey *Bulletin*.

It must here be explained how this *Bulletin* came into being as a result of nothing more than a change of name. It will be remembered that Flett developed a Geological Survey magazine to hold scientific papers such as had previously appeared as appendices bound up with successive numbers of the *Summary of Progress*. Unfortunately, he gave his magazine no distinctive title. Each issue was merely called Part ii or Part iii of the *Summary of Progress* for such and such a year—the first for 1927 and the last for 1936. To make the existence of the magazine more apparent I changed its name to *Bulletin of the Geological Survey of Great Britain*. Nos. 1 and 2 appeared in 1939 before further publication was interrupted by the outbreak of war.

Another publication reform followed from action taken by a committee initiated at the Cambridge meeting of the British Association, 1938. The Chairman of the committee was Professor Eva G. R. Taylor, with Brigadier M. N. MacLeod, Director General of the Ordnance Survey, as an essential member. Its purpose was to prepare a scheme for a National Atlas of Great Britain. Its activities eventually led to the institution of a Maps Committee of the Ministry of Works and Planning (later Town and Country Planning) with the Brigadier in the chair; and to this I was appointed in 1942.

The scale chosen for the Atlas, which up to date consists of an assemblage of separately issued loose-leaf maps, is 1 : 625,000. This ratio is a sixteenth of 1 : 10,000,000, and is slightly larger than the traditional one inch to ten miles or 1 : 633,600. Like the latter, it enables Great Britain to be accommodated on two not over-large sheets, for which an east-west junction has been selected passing near Kendal and Whitby. Another feature of the plan is that these two sheets carry a unifying ten-kilometre grid. Moreover, the same grid, or its one-kilometre equivalent, is printed on all new issues of Ordnance Survey larger-scale maps. The general intention has been twofold : —

(1) to sweep away complications inherent in separate representation of England and Wales as distinct from Scotland, or of a particular county as distinct from its neighbours ;

(2) to supply Great Britain with a reference grid much more easy to employ than that given by longitudes and latitudes, though the latter of course continues essential for extra-British comparisons.

The maps of the National Atlas cover a wide range of subjects, such as topography, population, mining, industry, agriculture, communications, and land-utilisation in general —so dear to Dudley Stamp. It was recognised by all on the committee that geological maps, solid and drift, were of fundamental importance in such a series. Accordingly, I agreed that the Survey should modify the Flett-Smith programme of 1 : 1,000,000 and 1 : 633,600 publication of pure and economic geology to fit in with the new 1 : 625,000 scheme. The War made progress slow in these matters ; but it was a great pleasure eventually to welcome the appearance of the two-sheeted map covering the solid geology of Great Britain. It arrived some three years after my retirement, in the nick of time for the London session of the International Geological Congress held in 1948.

DISTRICT REORGANISATION

While these matters of detail were being arranged, I undertook a constructive review of the administration of Geological Survey field work, starting with England and Wales. I have always been a strong supporter of the District Geologist organisation, which had been consolidated under Teall ; but it seemed possible that it might be improved by extending its scope. Existing districts had in practice been built up of small areas, allotted in successive annual programmes, together with a vaguely recognised hinterland. An approach to more extensive and precise definition had resulted from the establishment of branch offices to serve

specific coalfields. Still, the vagueness of the scheme was
well illustrated in 1933, when the Forest of Dean was
coupled with the Cumbrian District, over the heads of units
working in Lancashire and the West Midlands.

The strength of the District Geologist organisation up to
date had resided in its concentration of field units under
adequate guidance upon particular maps. This, however,
led to comparative neglect of the greater part of the country.
Such neglect was fortunately never complete, as shown, for
instance, by the following list of national rather than district
publications instituted under various Director Generals and
Directors : —

> Palæontological Memoirs, Decades (De la Beche)
> Mineral Statistics (De la Beche)
> Memoir on the Iron Ores (Murchison)
> Quarter-inch Maps (Murchison, restarted under Geikie)
> Palæontological Memoirs, Monographs (Murchison)
> Stratigraphical Monographs (Geikie)
> Water Supply Memoirs (Geikie)
> Twenty-five-mile Map (Teall)
> Special Reports on Mineral Resources (Strahan)
> Regional Handbooks (Flett).

Provision for some of the needs of the neglected areas is
also evident in the *Report* for 1920, issued by the newly
constituted Geological Survey Board. Here it is stated that
collection of records of bores made in areas not currently
assigned to a District Geologist will be arranged for by the
Assistant Director concerned; and that ' survey work bearing on metalliferous mining . . . , in areas not at present under survey, will be assigned to officers selected in
each case in respect of their familiarity with occurrences of
the metal in question,' and acting under the general charge
of ' the District Geologist in the London District ' (at that
time Dewey).

In 1937 I decided to modify previous arrangements by extending and defining (in terms of one-inch maps) the existing holdings of the six District Geologists of England and
Wales, so that together they should include the whole of

16

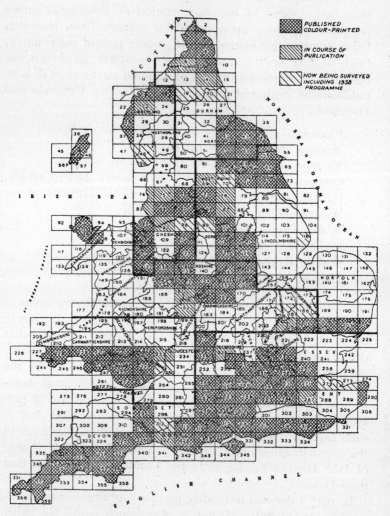

FIG. 38.—Heavy black lines outline Administrative Districts. (Quoted from Bailey, *Sum. Prog. for* 1937, p. 9.)

these two countries. The names chosen for the new super-districts were: Southern England; South Wales and Bristol; North Wales and Midlands; York to Suffolk; Cheshire to Cumberland; Northumberland and Durham.

The scope and intention of the reorganisation were, after frank discussion at a meeting of all the officers more particularly concerned, set out precisely in the Summary of Progress for 1937. Each District Geologist, it was explained, must take a personal interest in the welfare of the whole of his estate. For instance, he must arrange that contact be maintained with coalfields that have recently been revised, and in fact must strive for perennial revision wherever active development is proceeding. Also he must make a point of advising as to future annual programmes, and not merely treat them as something coming from above. To this end he must check in the field non-Survey published results, more particularly to expedite publication of official maps and memoirs in neglected areas.

On their side District Geologists agreed to aim at the production of well-balanced Sheet Memoirs, restricted in non-economic fields to about 100 pages—leaving much detail to be recorded in unofficial papers, the *Bulletin* or one-inch-sheet reference files, as might seem desirable.

In this plan two categories of research were in large measure lifted out of the district frame, so far as England and Wales were concerned. These were non-ferrous minerals and underground water. The first was placed under the Assistant Director, Eastwood, and the second under the Head of the Water Unit, Edmunds.

Two mineral districts were selected for 1938, with H. G. Dines continuing in Devon and J. V. Stephens starting in Derbyshire. It was arranged that these officers should keep in touch with the local District Geologist, though directly responsible in their metalliferous work to the Assistant Director. Such metalliferous work was not to occupy more than a part of any particular Geologist's field season, and its results were to be presented in special memoirs. Only brief *résumés* would appear in the Sheet Memoirs produced by District Geologists.

In the short trial period vouchsafed before the outbreak of war, the possibilities and difficulties of the new approach were not finally resolved. During 1938, only one District Geologist, Carruthers, realised his opportunity of helping in a neglected area. The corresponding *Summary of Progress* tells how he personally started and finished a revision of the old, but good, six-inch mapping of the Hexham one-inch map, Northumberland. ' The work was done on the 6-inch scale, but attention was confined to critical sections and those of outstanding clarity : mineral veins were reserved for a future and more specialised enquiry.' It is probable that some such action would have been taken before long by other District Geologists; and dual seasonal programmes might easily have been evolved, comparable with those normal in Scotland since 1902. As regards non-ferrous minerals, the progress made was fully up to expectations. The results achieved by the infant Water Unit were also most encouraging.

Though, as just stated, the Water Unit made an encouraging start in its uphill task, war came before one could be certain of the ultimate measure of its success. From the first it enjoyed the confidence of the water engineers and borers of South-East England. It also bravely tackled the confused mêlée of well records which had been accumulating for many years in the Survey archives, together with recent accessions unloaded by the Ministry of Health. Moreover, it began to prepare a memoir on the eastern half of the quarter-inch map-sheet, No. 15. This particular area, including Oxford and Northampton, covers a large part of the catchment area of the river Nene, selected by the Inland Water Survey Committee for special study. The results eventually appeared in a *Wartime Pamphlet,* dated 1942. Meanwhile, it was a feature of the pre-War activities of the Water Unit that considerably more attention than heretofore was given to seasonal fluctuation of water tables.

BURDEN OF INQUIRIES

We now come to a vital question, namely, the effect upon the Geological Survey of outside inquiries concerning underground water. These inquiries, mostly from South-East England, are more numerous than those relating to any other branch of geology, even coal-mining. They often bring with them valuable additional information; and their consideration is on the average highly educative. On the other hand, answering inquiries takes time; and, before I rejoined the Survey, water inquiries had come to be one of the main impediments to normal map and memoir publication. It was my earnest hope that the Water Unit, once it had been firmly established, would take over this Survey responsibility. It could be trusted, I felt sure, to seek any necessary advice from the Field Units and in return to keep the latter cognisant of discoveries of mutual interest; while at the same time it could free them for their essential map and memoir production.

The field staff of the time did not altogether welcome this idea. They had been reconciled for the most part to special *Water Supply* memoirs—although the Liverpool sheet memoir as late as 1923 includes an excellent unsegregated water component; but they clung tenaciously to the privilege of answering water inquiries. Most Survey men want to feel that they are useful; and most of them get this feeling much more easily by answering an inquiry than by writing a contribution to a memoir that, experience tells them, is unlikely to appear in print for years to come.

Especially devoted to question-answering were some of my most trusted District Geologists, who, naturally, with long experience had become past masters in the art. Unfortunately direct answers by District Geologists are often given at the cost of co-ordination of their subordinates' publication efforts. What was I to do? The time did not seem ripe for drastic action. The Water Unit was still in its infancy, and before it could take over more work it must grow both in experience and numbers. It had already shown great promise; but the time did not seem ripe—and then came the War, which removed for the next few years all thought of normal map and memoir production.

The trouble I have just elaborated in relation to Field Units answering water inquiries was paralleled to some ex-

tent in the Petrographical Unit. Here much time was spent
in answering problems raised, for the most part, by sister
branches of D.S.I.R., such as Building Research and Road
Research. As the Petrographer had, previous to the War,
no staff of his own of Geologist rank, Geological Survey
memoirs had in some cases to wait impatiently for their
petrographical chapters. In this case the obvious remedy
seemed a strengthening of the Petrographer's staff; and as
recorded above, a first step was taken in this direction in
1943.

INTERNATIONAL GEOLOGICAL CONGRESS

A quite unrelated feature of the early years of my
Directorate must now be recorded. In 1937 the International
Geological Congress met in Moscow. It was its second visit
to Russia, and it was fully time that England should act as
host again after an interval of approximately 50 years. The
Lord President of Council, Ramsay MacDonald, responsible
to Parliament for D.S.I.R., agreed that the Geological Survey might furnish substantial assistance and that the Survey
buildings might be used as Headquarters. The Geological
Society then took the matter in hand and invited the Congress to London for 1940. This invitation was accepted.
McLintock was selected as one of the General Secretaries,
while I became Chairman of the Excursions Committee. Sir
Thomas Holland, a former Director of the Geological Survey of India and Principal of Edinburgh University, was
elected President-designate. His interests, especially on the
economic side of Geology, and his competence in handling
committee work, gave him special qualifications for the post.
We worked in those dark days of appeasement for a meeting which we knew would have to be postponed. It was a
struggle for all concerned. For us on the Survey there were
two other tasks on hand : to run the Survey as if peace would
continue, an impossible conception; and to collaborate with
scientific colleagues in preparing for inevitable war.

After the War, Holland died and Read, late of the Survey, but now Professor of the Royal School of Mines, was
elected in his place. Beyond the time limits of this booklet

he successfully presided in 1948 over one of the most inspiring meetings of the famous Congress, where, in spite of difficulties of money, food and transport, courage and hope found continuous expression in lively scientific intercourse.

PRIVATE RESEARCH

Three important items of private research, carried out by Davidson, Kennedy and Simpson, reached partial fruition while yet there was peace.

Davidson undertook an elaborate investigation of the Lewisian Complex as developed in Harris of the Outer Hebrides. It was published by the Royal Society of Edinburgh in 1943.

Kennedy, in preparing museum specimens for the move to South Kensington, had been impressed by the distribution of injection-metamorphism in the Scottish Highlands either side of the Great Glen Fault. This led him to suspect that the fault displacement was of wrench or tear type and some 65 miles in extent. He looked for independent evidence and found extremely suggestive support in similarities of two truncated outcrops of granite complexes occurring with the required separation, the one at Strontian on the north-west side of the fault, the other at Foyers on the southeast. He read a paper on the subject to the Geological Society in the spring of 1939, though he deferred full publication until 1946.

Simpson nightly studied under the microscope the pollen in Scottish coals of Tertiary and Mesozoic age. His contribution to our knowledge of the floras concerned has been exceedingly welcome. It received good mention in Sir Albert Seward's Presidential Address to the British Association meeting in 1939 at Dundee, a meeting that was dispersed by the outbreak of war. I could not be present, as by that time it was clear that appeasement had run its course.

COAL COMMISSION

The passing of the Coal Act of 1938 constituted a momentous happening in British life. The immediate effect upon the Geological Survey was next to nothing; but from the first it was clear that its subsequent influence must be far reaching. Accordingly it seems appropriate to give some account of the conditions introduced.

The Act laid down that on the 1st July, 1942, previous multiplicity of privately held royalties should be ' unified ' under the ownership and control of a specially appointed public body called the Coal Commission. This meant nationalisation of all coal worked or unworked, and of all coal mines. It did not, however, mean nationalisation of coal undertakings. In future coal was to be owned by the nation, but until further notice it would continue to be worked by private enterprise. The Coal Commission would be owner,* not operator. It would not disturb existing leases beyond, so far as possible, simplifying those that had grown up piece-meal, and amalgamating others where this seemed in the public interest—compulsory amalgamation powers were con-veyed by the Act, but were so circumscribed as to be of doubtful validity. In granting new leases the Commission would ask for as high a rent as it thought reasonable ; would aim at securing efficiency and diligence ; and would consider each proposition as part of a co-operative whole. Financed by advantageous loans guaranteed by the Treasury, the Commission would have to adjust its income to cover, not only its working expenses, but also the interest and sinking fund connected with compensation transactions. Moreover, it had very wide responsibilities for surface damage, and these were not easy to assess. No doubt at some period in its career it would invest money in exploratory boring ; but the Geological Survey was informed that such action was not likely to be taken in the initial years.

The Coal Commission on appointment consisted of five permanent members, who had to cut themselves adrift from all other connections with the industry. Their Chairman, Sir Ernest Gowers, had a long experience of administration of mining legislation, having been Permanent Under-Secre-

---

*This statement may easily be misunderstood because the term coalowner continued in common use after July, 1942, in the sense of coal-lease-holder. Also, as we shall presently see, operation came under the control of the National Coal Board in 1942, though at first as a temporary war measure.

tary for the Mines Department of the Board of Trade as far back as 1920.

There was never talk of confiscation. Compensation was to be based upon the hypothetical value of the fee simple of all unworked coal and of all coal mines, on the supposition that these properties were sold in the open market by a willing seller. Coal, known or unknown, which at the vesting date possessed (in the opinion of the valuators) no market value, would be taken over free of charge. Registration of existing ownership had already started under an Act of 1937. Claims for compensation had to be submitted by 1st January, 1939.

An inclusive sum of £66,450,000 was allotted by Parliament to cover compensation. Its amount had been fixed by a special tribunal on the basis of 15 years' purchase of the anticipated royalty values of 1942. The sharing of this total was entrusted to an independent, temporary Central Valuation Board under the chairmanship of Lord Reading. The first task of this Board was to divide Great Britain into ten Valuation Regions, to each of which it assigned a definite part of the whole, ranging from £13,515,000 for Northern England to £1,196,100 for Southern. These regional totals in turn were to be apportioned by Regional Valuation Boards, upon which the principal local royalty owners were to be represented. The underlying idea was that each owner could be trusted to see that any excessive claim by a neighbour would be appropriately scaled down.

Fortunately no attempt was made to divert the Geological Survey to help in gathering valuation data, except where specifically geological advice seemed desirable—as often as not where a claim was advanced in relation to unproductive formations. The Regional Valuation Boards employed mineral surveyors, who looked forward rather gloomily to a lean time bound to follow this temporary glut of employment. The work was carried on with surprisingly little postponement during the War, for it was important to get it over and done with. Vesting day actually materialised on the appointed 1st July, 1942; but the first regional valuation was not completed till September, 1943, and the last till

March, 1945. The total valuation amounted to £64,559,559;
and so on the average had to be scaled up to fit the allotted
£66,450,000. The variation from region to region was considerable. For instance, in Yorkshire 24/10¼d. was paid per
£1 of valuation, while in Kent only 14/5½d. Payment was
made as soon as possible in every case. In fact partial payment to account was general, since compensation carried
interest from the day of vesting.

SECOND WAR DIRECTORATE

Early in 1939, D.S.I.R., the Home Office and the Office
of Works came to an arrangement whereby certain accommodation in the museum-basement and office-block of the
Geological Survey buildings was earmarked for Headquarters of the London Civil Defence Region. This latter
was one of several administrative regions into which the
whole country was divided, mainly for air raid precautions,
but *in extremis* for local self-government till communications should be restarted. The preliminary reconditioning
was carried out in good time, and, as the fateful 4th September approached, certain officers of the new organisation took
up residence.   ,

From the first I accepted the newcomers as the Survey's
guests, welcome partners in what was sure to prove a life and
death struggle. As time proceeded I did all I could to meet
their claims for increased *lebensraum,* retaining for myself
and staff no more than was required on an austerity basis for
war efficiency.

There were at the beginning two Commissioners in charge
of London Region. One of them was Sir Ernest Gowers. He
was generally at Headquarters, and in quieter moments
sometimes remembered that he was Britain's coalowner-in-
chief. The other, Admiral Evans of the Broke, was for the
most part out and about, settling disputes with kindly understanding and bringing reassurance to the harassed and home-
less. On one occasion, after I had been temporarily buried
by a VI or Doodlebug, the Admiral visited the scene of the
accident and stirred local enthusiasm by declaring the devastation to be the worst in his wide experience. I suspect it

was a *cliché;* but a colleague had already confided that he did not know whether to condole or congratulate.

I have wandered from the starting post. The first day of war brought a sense of immediate usefulness to the Survey staff. There was urgent need for rapid reinforcement of many important buildings in the Metropolis. Sandbags must meet the emergency until, within about a year, they could be gradually replaced by bricks and mortar. A committee of all interests had considered the proposition in advance. The Admiralty had declared that sand transport must not clutter up the river, and the Army and Home Office had been equally positive that it must not block railways and external roads scheduled for military traffic and evacuation of women and children. Bromehead, representing the Geological Survey, undertook to list the London parks and open spaces that could be trusted to supply what was wanted— the requisite information was already available on the 6-inch geological maps. Excavators, mobilised in readiness, got to work as soon as war was declared.

The consequent saving of money was estimated by the Civil Defence authorities at £125,000. This merely means that the original cost would have been some £125,000 higher if the sand had been bought from normal extra-London sources. It takes no account on the credit side of the value the sandpits presently assumed as repositories of London's bomb-debris; or on the debit side of expenses later incurred in restoring surface. It does, however, help to indicate that the Survey played a useful part in a major operation in the initial stages of the war.

Another cause for self-congratulation was the recent appearance of the Survey's memoir on the underground water of the County of London. Here, by good fortune, was an up-to-date census of all the internal water resources of the capital, including the location and capacity of every important pump.

The experience of the previous war had been taken to heart in planning action for what was seen to be coming; and the Survey was fortunate in having as its Assistant Directors Macgregor in Scotland and Eastwood in England and

Wales, the leading geological experts of the day on the coalfields and other mineral depositories of their respective
countries.

It was obvious that routine map and memoir production
should cease immediately hostilities were declared and that
the Survey should aim at acting in a consultant fashion to
the forces and supply agencies at home and abroad, especially in regard to : —

(1) home mineral resources, with a wartime importance
    enormously enhanced by need to economise in ship-
    ing and foreign exchange;
(2) underground water for new airfields, camps and fac-
    tories; and
(3) subterranean facilities for storage and personnel.

Before proceeding further it is well to point out that in
some respects the wartime prospect was very different for the
Survey in 1939 from what it had been in 1914 : in the first
place, advances in aeronautics gave the enemy comparative
freedom of access; in the second, there was to be no admission of members of the Geological Survey's scientific staff,
Geologists or Assistants, into the fighting ranks (except for
F. W. Anderson, who had made certain by joining the Terri-
torials, but was soon diverted to bomb-penetration experiments); and lastly, the 1939 War brought an immediate
paper famine.

Air Risks. Amplification of air risks was responsible for
the widespread call for subterranean accommodation alluded
to above under heading (3). In anticipation of the War the
Admiralty, especially, had established underground storage
for oil, etc., and in every case had sought advice from the
Geological Survey. Similar help was frequently in demand
at later stages, and in one instance, where extensive tunnels
and chambers were prepared to house a factory on the Welsh
Borders, a geologist was deputed for some months to act as
resident consultant.

The probability of air attack brought domestic problems
as well. Air raid precautions (A.R.P.), including fire watching and first aid, were installed at once, to begin with on a

voluntary basis. C. F. Davidson was appointed A.R.P.
Officer, and gave tireless service. In 1940, when a call came
for Home Guards to defend London Regional Headquarters,
the response was instantaneous. In these matters the personnel of the Survey and Civil Defence naturally co-
operated.

The safeguarding of the Survey material had also to be
carefully considered. The Museum was closed to the public
on August 25th, although, as in the previous war, responsible inquirers, mostly from Service, Supply and other
Government Departments, had access to the Offices and
Library. At the outbreak of hostilities McLintock took up
permanent residence. To him belonged the main responsibility for care of our property. At first it was decided to retain and protect the collections and books as far as possible
within our own building, taking advantage of the strongest
part of the basement. Mounting air risks, however, combined
with expansion of London Regional staff led in 1941 to
evacuation of everything not urgently needed for war-work.
Exhibition material, unless considered irreplaceable, was
stored in emptied rooms in the Victoria and Albert Museum
across the way (these rooms were comparatively small and
separated by thick walls); while what was classed as irreplaceable, whether exhibited or no, was dispatched to University College, Bangor, North Wales. Transport in the
latter case was by rail and involved moving 164 great cabinets full of specimens, 10,000 books, enormous numbers of
micro-photo duplicates of field-maps, bore records, etc.,
8,000 other negatives, and the ' standard copy ' collection of
Geological Survey maps. The operation was completed
within six weeks, and the evacuated material was placed in
charge of a Survey officer, who was able to transmit particular specimens or books to Headquarters on demand.
Similar evacuations on a less extensive scale were undertaken from the Scottish, Newcastle and Manchester offices.

In the event Survey material in Survey care suffered no
war loss, if we disregard comparatively trifling damage to
buildings : the Office Block at South Kensington received a
direct, though glancing, hit on September 10th, 1940, which

broke half the windows of the combined building; and the Museum endured a very near miss on April 19th, 1941, which broke the remainder. The glass roof had long since been replaced, so that the second bomb completed out deglazing; and the two of them were so timed that the process cost us not a single casualty ! It was indeed a happy day when we realised that the last of the plate glass was gone, though it was some weeks before cloth windows and black curtains allowed of lights other than flashlamps in the greater part of our home. Fortunately, before this, London Region operational work had been safely transferred to a bomb-proof citadel sunk to groundwater level alongside the Museum.

In other directions we came to sad grief. Our stocks of un-issued maps and un-issued memoirs, in the care respectively of the Ordnance Survey and the Stationery Office, were almost completely destroyed by bombing. The loss was indeed heavy, but the plates and stones from which the maps had been printed escaped undamaged.

Retention of Staff. In expectation of war, the Government entrusted registration of scientists to the Royal Society. I felt bound to agree to the treatment of professional geology as a reserved occupation, from which active combatants could not be drawn. It was probably wise from the all-country impersonal standpoint; but it caused cruel heart-burnings for many within and without the official circle. Presently, however, the escape of the Army from Dunkirk, and the sense of partnership engendered by the bombardment of London brought a considerable degree of comfort.

The Army took very few, I think too few, geological consultants on to its staff, preferring in large measure to come to the Survey with specific problems. We have already seen how Professor W. B. R. King, no longer on the Survey, was invited back to the Army as soon as war was declared. He was Head Geologist to the Army, especially concerned with the Western Front. He occupied a room in the Survey Offices when in England, and needless to say could rely on any assistance he desired. F. W. Shotton, a University lecturer, unconnected with the Survey, accompanied the Desert Rats. He was associated with the geological high-light of the war, which helped in planning of Alamein by revealing the existence of a considerable and readily available pocket of underground water lying right on the route of the pro-jected advance. J. V. Stephens, with engineering as well as geological qualifications, secured the only post offered to the Survey, and did good work throughout the Italian cam-paign. I myself had the great privilege of six short weeks in Malta during the early part of 1943. The trip was planned before Alamein, to see whether increased water could be obtained for irrigation to lessen the food-load carried by heroic convoys; but before my arrival Alamein had been fought, and the Desert Rats on one side and Stalingrad on the other kept the enemy fully occupied. My visit was one of a series made by scientists flown in to help, if possible, in the island's struggle for existence. Before I left a Nuffield Professor had arrived to do what he could to stop a trouble-some epidemic of infantile paralysis.

Let us return to Britain. To maintain the Geological Sur-vey's strength, the age limit was suspended for the duration, and a few experienced external geologists were enlisted on a temporary basis.

Paper Famine. Immediately war was declared, publica-tion of normal Geological Survey memoirs was postponed; so that during hostilities only three examples, all of special economic significance, made an appearance. These were Macgregor's *Synopsis of the Mineral Resources of Scotland*, Edwards, Wray and Mitchell's *Geology of the Country around Wakefield* and Trotter's *Geology of the Forest of Dean Coal and Iron-Ore Field*. In addition, electrotype copies were taken of certain memoirs which were ready for printing off in 1939; and then the ordinary type was broken down and used in other connections. This fate overtook Flett's second edition of *Lizard and Meneage*, W. J. Arkell's *Weymouth*—a successor to Strahan's *Purbeck* of 1898—and Richardson's *Witney*. The two latter were instances of Sur-vey memoirs written more or less completely by outside ex-perts, and they owed their inception to Bernard Smith.

It was still open to the Survey to meet the war situation by planning a succession of printed memoirs comparable with

Strahan's *Special Reports on Mineral Resources;* but such memoirs would have taken long to write and longer still to print. Accordingly it seemed preferable to accept an alternative based on an offer of the Stationery Office to produce a quick succession of multigraphed reports, short but adequately illustrated.

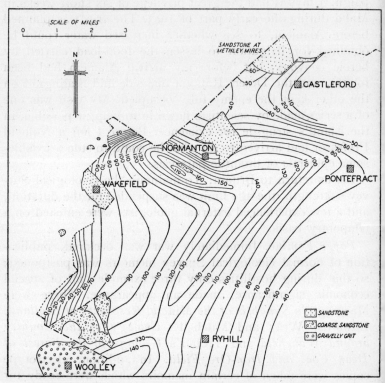

FIG. 39.—Woolley Edge Rock. Outcrop ornamented. Isopachytes in feet. (Compare *Fig.* 12, p. 88.) Quoted from Edwards and Wray, *Wakefield Mem.,* 1940, p. 80.)

The resultant *Wartime Pamphlets,* as they came to be called, dealt with restricted subjects and received consecutive Arabic numbers for the sake of ready reference—all except the first few carried lists of previous issues. The Arabic numbering was determined by the expected date of appearance of the first part of any particular pamphlet.

Often, however, pamphlets consisted of several separate parts. Thus *Wartime Pamphlet* No. 4 appeared in Parts i to vi published in 1st edition from June to September, 1940. In such a case, Roman numbering was allotted to the individual parts as determined by natural sequence in the planned treatment of the subject concerned.

There are in all 47 numbers with 107 parts. Each part on the average carries 42 pages, mounted in semi-stiff covers, and measures 13 inches by 8 inches. Their only drawback is a propensity to lie hid, whether on bookshelf or table. Apart from this bad failing they are of very serviceable size for tabular matter, maps and other illustration. Also their limitation of subject made it easy to supply information to inquiring specialists without waste of paper on collaterals which, for the time being, might be wanted only by somebody else. Moreover, it allowed of intensive preparation by one or more members of staff, working with the exhilaration that comes from a prospect of immediate publication. This welcome tonic was supplied by a splendidly co-operative spirit that animated all ranks in a newly established branch of the Stationery Office, whose sole purpose was rapid, accurate copying of war-worthy material.

Wartime Pamphlets continued to appear till 1949, but as 93 of the total of 107 parts dated from the actual period of hostilities in Europe, ending in April, 1945, they fully justified their pugnacious title. These 93 parts may be roughly classified as follows : : —

> Water, 48; Scottish Limestones, 8; Coal and Oil Shale, 7; Refractories, 7; Iron Ores and Magnetic Survey, 5; Phosphates, 3; Felspar, 3; Mica, 2; Sand and Gravel, 2; and Barytes, Diatomite, General (for the Lothians), Glauconite, Ochre, Peat, Slate, Tin, one apiece.

Not only did these pamphlets supply many immediate needs, but also they insured that a great mass of carefully co-ordinated facts would be handed on from war to peace, when normal memoir production could be resumed.

17

Enough has been said of conditions governing war work. Let us turn to a few definite aspects of the Survey's achievement. It was, I believe, just of a kind the Country had a right to expect, useful though non-spectacular. The story is easy to put together, for McLintock, my successor as Director, has already given an excellent summary, appended to the annual *Report of the Geological Survey Board* for 1945.

WATER

As already indicated, the position of the Geological Survey in relation to underground water had been materially strengthened in consequence of the initiation of the Inland Water Survey Committee in 1935. On the outbreak of hostilities a bold plan, proposed by Eastwood, was put into immediate operation. A hitherto impossible concentration of man-power was diverted from other subjects to set in order all available information in anticipation of demands which were bound to follow. Actually, between 1940 and the end of the war in Europe, the Geological Survey reported on 305 sites for the Air Ministry, 252 sites for the War Department, 163 for the Ministry of Works, and 15 for the Admiralty, besides many others for various public and private undertakings. Characteristic activities were : preparation of emergency schemes for the populations of London and East Anglia in the event of widespread disruption of water mains ; provision of maps showing prospects of underground water throughout the whole region of the Army's Southern Command ; and siting of bores to supply six American camps in the Midlands.

The preliminary work, which started in September, 1939, amounted to much more than methodical filing of information already in the Survey's possession. Well-drillers and consultants readily opened their books, and all their records were collected. Moreover, field parties were organised and systematic correspondence undertaken to mark sites precisely on 6-inch maps and to obtain surface levels, water levels, casing details, pumping facilities, yield, etc.

These results, combined with critical summaries of the

strata pierced, furnished the bulk of the 48 parts of *Wartime Pamphlets* dealing with water. Here are found introductory remarks on the hydrogeology of the district concerned, followed by orderly catalogues of annotated well records, with adequate site-maps, each catalogue and map covering a Geological Survey one-inch sheet. In England 12,800 well records in 110 one-inch sheets are thus recorded; and in Scotland the corresponding figures are 830 in 27 (though the English one-inch sheets are smaller than the Scottish, the country they represent is much more dependent on underground water). For many sites, separate records of associated wells are quoted; but where this is the case each group-record has been counted merely as one in the above enumeration. Also no records of wells under 20 feet in depth have been reproduced.

The 48 parts cover much of the South of England, East Anglia, the Midlands, Lincolnshire, Lancashire, Yorkshire and Co. Durham, together with the east coast of Scotland from Berwick, through Edinburgh and Dundee to Banchory. Norfolk is not included with the rest of East Anglia as it was made the subject of a less fully checked report supplied at the urgent request of the War Office in 1940.

Twenty Geologists (2 temporary) and 7 Assistants (4 temporary) are named as authors on the title pages of these pamphlets. The value of work done by Assistants was a very welcome feature of the campaign. The Water Unit was responsible for about half the output, with A. W. Woodland, assisted by J. Lee, as mainstays of the operation. Among the many outside the Water Unit, who co-operated in the good work, Buchan deserves special mention. Collection of detailed evidence extended far beyond the limits reached at any time by publication, and supplied reliable advance information for the answering of inquiries.

Edmunds was for the most part busy with consultant work, and the advice he was able to give with the Survey organisation behind him was, I think, the most important war-contribution made by anyone on our staff. He showed a thorough understanding of the outlook of the practical man, and was ever ready to discuss matters on the site itself. Five District

17A

Geologists were at the same time largely concerned with water inquiries, and especially valuable service was given by Dinham and Bromehead. Business was thus transacted quickly and surely, without any accumulation of arrears.

As was inevitable, the growth of aerodromes and camps raised problems of sewage disposal, to ensure that underground sources of water should escape contamination. Here naturally the Geological Survey often co-operated with their opposite numbers in the Ministry of Health.

Before leaving the subject of water, I may perhaps refer to a difficulty which confronts the Army, and might at any time develop in the sister services. Several Army officers and other ranks believe in the practical value of water divining or dowsing. On the other hand, the majority, among those who matter most, think that water divining is as unsubstantiated as the soothsaying upon which our military forefathers, in a remote past, set considerable store. Disagreement between the supporters and opponents of the dowsing technique did to an appreciable extent hamper military operations during the recent War, for provision of water is as vital for fighting as is that of food, clothing or weapons.

On various occasions our patriotic Press comforted home readers with accounts of the wise use our army was making of dowsers. This not unnaturally brought a strong protest from the Head of the Water Unit of the United States Geological Survey which I transmitted through the usual channels. At the same time I persuaded an Honourable Member to ask a question on the subject in the House of Commons. Below is given the result, dated 19th January, 1942 :—

> *Question:* To ask the Secretary of State for War to what extent the War Office is relying upon dowsers for advice on water supply, and in what theatres of war; whether this action has been taken with the approval of the Government's Scientific Advisers; and whether he has any information regarding the reliability of advice given by dowsers during the course of the present War.

> *Answer:* The War Office does not rely on dowsers for advice on water supply in the United Kingdom, and so far as I know the only place where they have been tried is the Middle East. The report of their performance showed a very small percentage of successes, and orders were issued that scientific methods only were to be used.

The non-dowsing faction of the Army derived considerable pleasure from this interchange, which may have had something to do with my subsequent elevation to Honorary Membership of the Royal Engineers.

MINERALS

Current Coal Mining. Since coal had been for long the main peace-time occupation of the Survey, it was felt that its interests could temporarily be entrusted to a reduced proportion of the staff. This view antedated the superfluity of coal output, which followed the collapse of the French market. Without doubt new armament factories would prove very hungry customers; but a vast amount of co-ordinated knowledge was already in existence, upon which it would be easy to draw. Obviously, important bores must be visited and interpreted, and problems raised by particular colliery managers must be examined; but field work might for a time be reduced to a minimum so as to free staff for other subjects.

Only four *Wartime Pamphlets* appeared on coal before hostilities in Europe closed, two dealing with Scotland, and two with England. They all made a feature of the practical advantages that result from study of fossils. In this respect Macgregor and Richey, the Survey authors for Scotland, co-operated with palæontologists of Glasgow University; while Mitchell in England was supported by Stubblefield and Crookall.

Coal Board. We must now turn aside for a moment to an event of great national importance that occurred in the year 1942. A Ministry of Fuel and Power developed out of the Mines Department that had been established in the Board of Trade in 1920. This new Ministry, acting through a National and several Regional Coal Boards, undertook responsibility for policy and general conduct of mining operations, but not for day to day details of management. It also assumed control over allocation of coal supplies.

Thus in 1942 British coal found itself permanently nationalised under the Coal Commission, while British coal mining and selling were temporarily, according to first intentions, nationalised under the Coal Board. It lies beyond the time-scope of this booklet to tell how in post-War days the Coal Board has become permanent and has absorbed its predecessor, an early associate now practically incognito.

Opencast Coal. Broadly speaking mineral exploitation proceeds in stages from the outcrop to further and further subterranean depths. War needs, however, led to a curious temporary reversal of practice in relation to coal. In 1941 someone raised the question of possible worth-while near-surface reserves of coal still extant in our country. There are only very incomplete records of outcrop working in past centuries, and mining has for long tended to avoid shallow depths, so as to escape special problems of surface damage, risks of flooding and general uncertainty as to extent. When consulted as to prospects I confess I held out little hope that the ' old men ' had spared enough to repay the cost of gleaning. Fortunately, however, the Mines Department decided to investigate; and several districts, especially in the Notts-Derby-Yorkshire field, have since proved amazingly fruitful.

In this great eastern coalfield, not only have the ' old men ' left untouched an unexpected proportion of near-outcrop coal, but the seams themselves are characterised by a low and steady dip which renders them ideal subjects for opencast working with modern mechanical excavators. Even so, working costs are high in terms of money, though not of man power; and in most localities extraction would not be justified except in days of combined coal and man-power shortage.

Wartime opencast working was started in 1941 by the Mines Department of the Home Office. Sites were chosen in Warwickshire in positions suggested by Geological Survey maps. The operation was entrusted to Professor J. A. S. Ritson, of the Royal School of Mines. At an early stage it was reported that ' a very large number of sites have to be abandoned owing to old workings.'

Control was transferred in 1942 to the new Ministry of Fuel and Power and, thanks largely to the initiative of F. S. Sinnett, Director of Fuel Research, it has continued, since July, 1942, to be for the most part carried out in close contact with both Fuel Research and the Geological Survey.

There was naturally some confusion to begin with. The new Ministry soon decided that the mechanical fieldwork belonged to civil, rather than mining, engineering, and deputed the production side of the venture to the Ministry of Works, while retaining disposal of output in its own hands. The man in command at the Ministry of Works was Major-General K. C. Appleyard, and he was furnished with a considerable staff of his own coupled with outside boring and excavating contractors. At first Appleyard was a little out of touch with scientific departments, and left it to the boring firms to prospect. If they presented an acceptable proposal they secured a contract to bore. Soon, however, the Geological Survey was regularly called in at the initial stage to indicate likely areas, after which the opencast staff made local inquiries—the fact that the Geological Survey was known and trusted by colliery officials helped considerably to moderate not unnatural antipathies.

The amount of assistance given by the Geological Survey steadily increased. In most areas officers started by adding surface advice to their more normal coalfield duties; but from the latter half of 1942 Edwards and Buchan had to devote themselves extensively to crop investigation, working from Wakefield and Chesterfield respectively. Mitchell, at the same time, was heavily engaged in the Midlands. They all thoroughly enjoyed the mining camp atmosphere of the adventure. Naturally they not only gave advice, but also recorded information afforded by the consequent temporary exposures. In Yorkshire the Survey was able at once to suggest suitable prospecting areas, two of which yielded over 1,000,000 tons apiece. In the Notts-Derby area, not recently revised, a special set of wartime prospecting maps was prepared for the Directorate of opencast mining.

Fuel Research's most vital contribution consisted in reporting on the quality of coal found in exploration bores, and in indicating the depth at which this quality became good enough to warrant extraction. Other important matters dealt with in relation to any particular occurrence included the washing requirements of the coal as quarried, and its keeping possibilities.

In spite of urgent wartime need for coal production and at the same time for economy of man power, opencast working was strictly regulated to prevent, so far as possible, the production of permanent unsightly deserts. It was laid down that consent must be obtained from the Ministries of Agriculture and of Town and Country Planning before any specified site might be opened up; and to avoid vexatious disturbance no coal under 3 feet in thickness was to be considered.

In practice the soil was stripped and kept separate from the rest of the overburden, and replaced after re-levelling of the worked area—this cost about $7\frac{1}{2}$d. per ton of coal. From November, 1941, to December, 1944, the total tonnage of coal excavated amounted to 14,375,000 (by August, 1945, this figure had risen to 29,000,000), and involved the handling of about eight times as much overburden. The total cost (including transport) averaged about 40/- per coal-ton.

Major Lloyd George, speaking as Minister of Fuel and Power in the House of Commons in 1945, said that he could not agree that land was being destroyed. He had inspected many sites and had consulted many farmers, and had found satisfaction with the measures of rehabilitation. He had even found one farmer who assured him that his land had been returned to him in better heart than ever before. On the other hand, the common man does hear farmers continually grumbling, and is assured by them that their grievance extends beyond the time limit of present devastation.

It was fortunate for the country that on the 1st July, 1942, when coal in general became national property, coal available for opencast working changed ownership free of charge. Scarcely any of it could have been claimed on the 1st January, 1939, to affect the market value of the land where it lay. Presently, in 1944, the Government as a temporary war measure took possession and control of land where coal was likely to occur.

Coal in the Future. Partly for immediate war purposes, but largely for a planned post-War future, Fuel Research about 1943 started a nation-wide survey of the quantitative distribution of the various qualities of British coal. They received great assistance from the information recently collected by the Valuation Boards, now handed over to the Coal Commission, and also, of course, from the Geological Survey.

At about the same time, Eastwood, on the latter's behalf, set in motion the preparation of a series of separate one inch to the mile seam-maps for each major coal seam in England and Wales. These maps show outcrop, principal faults, variations of thickness, depth contours, limits of working and shaft and bore records. Their production often involves correlation of a multiplicity of coal names, which may in the past have been attached to a single seam worked from a number of collieries. Such correlation has always been a Survey aim, and has become increasingly important with unification of ownership. Good progress was made with these seam-maps, copies of which were supplied on completion to Fuel Research, the Coal Commission and the Ministry of Fuel and Power.

Another example of taking thought for the morrow was furnished in 1942 by the appointment by the Secretary of State for Scotland of a Scottish Coalfield Committee :—

> to consider the present position and future prospects of coalfields in Scotland and to report—
>> (a) what measures should be taken to enable the fullest use to be made of existing and potential resources in these coalfields; and
>> (b) in this connection, what provision of houses and other services will be required for the welfare of the mining community.

The Committee started circumspectly, for its Chairman and Secretary travelled to London to call upon Edward Appleton, Secretary (that is Chief) of the Department of Scientific and Industrial Research. On my recommendation they were promised unlimited aid from Macgregor and his Edinburgh staff. The resultant *Report,* issued as a command paper in 1944, is an extremely valuable and broadbased publication with four main headings : *Geology; Present Position and Future Prospects; Housing; Subsidence.* It is pleasant to find in its Introduction that D.S.I.R. is singled out for special thanks :—

> We are particularly indebted, the acknowledgement continues, for the assistance given by Dr. Murray Macgregor, Assistant Director of the Geological Survey of Great Britain, whose services have been

continuously at our disposal; his expert and detailed knowledge of the coal resources of Scotland has been invaluable, and the ungrudging manner in which he has co-operated with us throughout our investigation must be recorded. Our thanks are also due to him and to the staff of the Scottish office of the Geological Survey of Great Britain for the maps, diagrams and descriptions which are included in this Report.

The example set by the Secretary of State for Scotland stirred the Minister of Fuel and Power to emulation. In 1945 and 1946 ten *Regional Survey Reports* appeared dealing with the coalfields of England and Wales. Their general scope is much the same as that of their Scottish forerunner, but they sometimes include an additional section on *Drainage*. In all cases, though in varying degrees, important help was supplied by officers of both the Geological Survey and Fuel Research.

Oil-Shale. Owing to the special wartime importance of oil a detailed revision of the West Lothian oil-shales was undertaken on Macgregor's advice as soon as war commenced. Richey, as District Geologist, took a large share in this work. With two Geologists and two Assistants he produced three parts of a *Wartime Pamphlet* that will, I hope, provide a model for future interim reports on mining regions that are undergoing active development. The illustrations include geological maps, which with their representation of bore sites and underground features are almost equivalent in utility to new editions of the existing published 6-inch maps. A particularly refreshing feature of this oil shale revision was its careful planning. For instance, more than usual advantage was taken of the capacity of available Assistants.

Low-Phosphorus Iron Ore. The division between low- and high-phosphorus is set at 0.02 per cent. P, on a basis of 50 per cent. Fe. In our country the low-phosphorus ores that are worked occur as veins or replacements, and the high-phosphorus ores as bedded sediments. Immediately before the war the Survey had completed map revisions of the hæmatite replacements found in Cumberland and the Forest of Dean. *The Geology of the Iron Ore Field of South Cumberland and Furness* was issued in 1941 as a *Wartime*

Pamphlet; while the Forest of Dean was covered, as we have already noticed, in a normal memoir in 1942.

In 1934 a University lecturer, J. T. Whetton, had found detectable magnetic effects in relation to certain small, proved, unworked lodes of hæmatite near Millom in Cumberland, though as is well known *pure* hæmatite is practically non-magnetic. Four years later Hallimond, investigating for the Survey, obtained similar results. Accordingly, Whetton and Hallimond co-operated in presenting a detailed report on this trial area to *Bulletin* No. 2 of the Geological Survey. In this it was demonstrated that, with due precautions taken, a hæmatite vein 15 feet wide could be detected under 60 feet of cover.

This preliminary investigation had the unanimous support of the Geological Survey Board. It established the possibility of profitable geophysical exploration, while leaving it to the operating companies to follow up the matter through private agencies. When war broke out I thought that a new position had arisen, and that the Survey ought to use its knowledge and personnel to prospect. Output of hæmatite had been falling off, and a find of new veins would have greatly helped the country. Here alone among my various wartime proposals, I met with a certain amount of opposition from the Geological Survey Board; though eventually magnetic prospecting was permitted. It was carried out by Geological Survey teams acting under Hallimond and H. Shaw, the latter freely lent by the Science Museum. To my great disappointment no addition accrued to the mineral resources of our country. In fact, the only benefit that could be claimed was that certain areas were shown to be barren of shallow ore without incurring the expense of a boring campaign.

In the Pennines Dunham by more normal geological research reinvigorated the working of a group of sideritic replacements, fed laterally into hospitable beds of limestone from fissure veins (see *Wartime Pamphlet* No. 14, 1941). Jointly with the Home Ores Department of Iron and Steel Control of the Ministry of Supply, he supervised a drilling campaign involving 15,000 feet of cored boring which resulted in the location of a new ore-body containing 100,000 tons.

In Scotland the Home Ores Department investigated three Geological Survey pre-War discoveries of magnetite, in the Shetlands, Tiree (phosphatic) and Skye. The two former are parts of ancient schistose complexes; the Skye occurrence is a reaction product of Tertiary igneous activity. The Shetland magnetite seems to amount to 18,000 tons, of which 1,000 were brought to the surface during development. Further progress was arrested, since it was not considered wise to incur the cost of installing shipping facilities.

High-Phosphorus Iron Ore. The bedded iron ores of Britain occur mainly in the Carboniferous and Jurassic, and also to a small extent in the Cretaceous. Among the Mesozoic ores only those of Cleveland receive notice in the Geological Survey Memoir on *The Iron Ores of Great Britain,* published 1856-1862. Their fellows farther south are, however, included in vols. xii, 1920 (general occurrence), and xxix, 1925 (petrography and chemistry), of the *Special Reports on the Mineral Resources of Great Britain.* The petrographical account by Hallimond in vol. xxix is of great theoretical and practical value; but here I must focus attention on vol. xii. In it Cleveland ores, for the most part worked from mines, were described by Lamplugh, whose task was made relatively easy by the pre-existence of good Geological Survey six-inch maps. The ores south of the Humber, mostly worked opencast, were described by Wedd and Pringle, who had to base their investigations mainly on one-inch maps. It is these southern occurrences which today supply most of Britain's iron ore.

On the outbreak of war Eastwood asked for and obtained a revision of the Jurassic ores of England. In Cleveland the six-inch mapping of the past sufficed for immediate purposes, and revision amounted to little more than bringing Lamplugh's figures and estimates up to date. This was done in *Wartime Pamphlet* No. 23. Total reserves were estimated at 370,000,000 tons

The areas south of the Humber received much fuller attention. By 1944 some 800 square miles had been mapped on

the six-inch scale by a team of eight Geologists under White-
head as District Geologist. Close contact was maintained
with the Controller of Home Ores; and operating companies
were supplied with manuscript maps and typed reports, as
well as verbal discussion on such matters as the planning of
working faces and of exploratory boring. Naturally fossil
bands in the cover proved of considerable value. Their outcrops, when mapped, furnish natural contour lines defining
the depth at which iron ore is to be expected at any particular
locality. Reserves were estimated at 2,300,600,000 tons, with
a further 838,500,000 tons according to the nature of future
demand.

The rocks of the Midland ironstone field include a considerable proportion of mobile clays. They have accordingly
often adjusted their disposition, with production of minor
folds and faults, to meet changes in distribution of load introduced, very gradually, by erosion of the present day valley
system. Much additional insight into these adjustments was
obtained, with results which were definitely helpful to the
quarry managers concerned. The scientific implications were
dealt with in a paper published by the Geological Society in
1944 with S. E. Hollingworth as its main author.

Apart from its wartime value the six-inch mapping of the
iron ore fields south of the Humber will serve as a welcome
nucleus for post-war publication of maps and memoirs in a
relatively neglected tract of England. The memoirs will, of
course, include special volumes giving a full treatment of
the ores themselves.

Non-Ferrous Ores and Minerals. In 1940 a Non-Ferrous
Ores Committee was set up by the Ministry of Supply and
met regularly at short intervals for more than two years in
the Geological Survey conference room, under the Chairmanship of Sir William Larke. W. C. C. Rose, of the Survey Staff, was whole-time Secretary, and Eastwood and
Macgregor Assessors. Following the loss of Malaya this
Committee gave birth early in 1942 to a corresponding Non-
Ferrous Minerals Development Control, which moved to
quarters of its own in the City. Rose now became an

Assistant Controller, and R. O. Jones, also seconded from the Survey, took his place as Secretary. The Geological Survey continued in closest liaison, and reported on almost every project which came up for consideration.

In Ireland Eyles, of the Scottish branch of the Survey, undertook an investigation of bauxite deposits known to be interbedded among the Tertiary basalts of Antrim; and was the first Survey man to be entrusted with the organisation of a boring campaign carried out by contractors. He found considerable supplies, which, though somewhat ferriferous, were accepted under protest at aluminium factories, thus contributing to the easing of shipping difficulties. Two hundred and fifty thousand tons were mined before the war ended, and a further reserve of 500,000 tons was proved.

In Cornwall and Devon, Dines and his associates did all they possibly could to maintain production of tin and tungsten. A higher output of the latter was reached in 1944 than in any year except 1916. This tungsten success was essentially due to installation of a new mill at Hemerdon, near Plymouth, to deal with a large low-grade deposit, already worked during the 1914-1918 War. It was a subject that could be tackled opencast, and so did not require highly trained miners.

Within the present century, war experience has emphasised twice over the difficulty of bolstering up at short notice a decadent mineral industry. A glorious past means only too often that the more readily proved and accessible material has already been taken to limits set by rock or water. Once a mining company finds its property on the downgrade, it naturally feels less and less disposed to spend money on exploration and equipment. It prefers to take what is certain rather than risk the dropping of a bone for the sake of a shadow. Meanwhile, skilled labour seeks other employment, and recruits hang back. In fact, to swell wartime output it is often requisite to have pre-war proof of reserves coupled with a pool of skilled personnel. Fortunately, however, the value of information gathered under war conditions, and eventually published, may in the future prove to be very considerable. A decision may some day be taken to nationalise non-ferrous metals, and to treat their further exploration on such a scale that inevitable failures are likely to be cancelled out by an occasional discovery.

Away from Cornwall and Devon, mineral veins attracted most attention in the North Pennines, where Dunham did outstanding work. Mining brought no increase to the annual output of lead and zinc; but sampling of zinc ore on dumps in the Alston Moor area justified the erection of a treatment plant capable of handling 1,000 tons per day, and this helped matters considerably in 1944.

Barytes was in a better position. During the twenty years preceding 1939 average production in Britain had been about 50,000 tons, and consumption 90,000. From 1939 to 1945 average production mounted to about 90,000 tons, and met essential needs. The North Pennines supplied half the British total. The largest single producer, however, was at Gass Water in Ayrshire. Scottish sources were dealt with during hostilities in *Wartime Pamphlet* No. 38 by MacGregor.

Perhaps Dunham's most immediately valuable service was to give warning of an impending shortage of fluorspar, resulting from the increasing output of steel. Fluor, like tungsten, has only become of value in comparatively recent times. Before 1890 it was either left in lead and zinc mines or thrown on to refuse dumps. Since then it has become an essential flux in certain steel processes (unfortunately reducing the agricultural value of basic slag), and also a commercial source of hydrofluoric acid. From 1919 to 1939 annual output (partly for export) had averaged 36,000 tons. From 1940 to 1944 this was stepped up to 46,000.

It has recently been estimated that proved reserves of readily worked fluor are equally distributed in mines and dumps. During the accelerated attack of the war years both sources were drawn upon. One important bit of help given by the Survey was a reinterpretation of the shape of a particular fluor body in Derbyshire. In this connection miners drawn from the Royal Canadian Engineers rendered good service, for they were able to teach home miners a useful Canadian technique.

Here for a moment I must turn aside to express gratitude to Colonel Colin Campbell and the Royal Canadian Engineers under his command. The assistance they rendered, free of charge, to the British Ministries of Supply and Air in their efforts to win minerals and water was one of the many wonders of the War. Colonel Campbell at home was Canada's Minister of Public Works, and his Commander-in-Chief, General Macnaughton, was head of the same great country's Department of Scientific and Industrial Research —which undoubtedly explains a good deal.

It will be recalled how for long the Canadian troops were held in impatient reserve in Great Britain. Their engineers, however, were busy from the first. They brought with them a fund, raised, I believe, among mining companies, to enable them to help with any experiment which aimed at strengthening the fighting efficiency of the Empire. Several times I attended inspections at Aldershot and elsewhere, and witnessed their brilliant execution of directly combatant exercises. Again and again I heard of their boring and mining explorations ranging from Shetland to Cornwall—my Survey colleagues were often partners in these enterprises.

One tough proposition was presented by the portage of a compressor of about a ton in weight from the sea shore of Loch Nevis in Knoydart, near Mallaig, up to a mica-pegmatite located by Kennedy on an abrupt slope at a height of 1,800 feet. This heavy load had to be manhandled by some fourteen men with block and tackle, hauling it on log rollers over an unprepared surface.

I did not see this Canadian victory, but later on in September, 1943, I stumbled on British troops in action on the same site. I had been celebrating Mussolini's fall by taking four days with a colleague in Rhum, where a visit was required to look at some olivine rocks of possible value as refractories. On two of the four days the weather had been equinoctial with rain horizontal. The weekly steamer returned us to Mallaig in time to charter a motor launch to look at the Knoydart mica quarry, only nine miles distant. Imagine our amazement to find the place in the hands of a commando. To train for the Normandy beaches our troops had made a zig-zag pack-horse trail up to the quarry. It had taken them a fortnight, where Scotland's weather is at its worst; and their only shelter for night was provided by sleeping bags and waterproof sheets !

The Knoydart pegmatite was the richest source of mica found by the Scottish surveyors in an intensive search, the results of which were made the subject of a *Wartime Pamphlet* by Kennedy and Lawrie. The books of mica run up to eighteen inches, and very exceptionally two feet, in diameter. The quality is excellent.

Mica is an essential wartime mineral for electric apparatus used in aeroplanes. The Non-Ferrous Mineral Development Control, for whom the Geological Survey prospected, was able to produce a small but useful contribution from the Scottish Highlands; but the cost was acknowledged to be prohibitive as soon as extreme urgency abated. It was much cheaper at any time to fly in supplies from India, if planes could be spared.

A more bulky return, for no labour at all on the part of the Geological Survey, was secured in connection with potash felspar required for the manufacture of pottery. Pre-war supplies had come from Scandinavia. An early inquiry answered by the Survey led to a successful quarry being opened on a pegmatite in Harris in the Outer Hebrides. The material took more hand-picking than was desirable, and most of it did not give a pure white product; but for the war period it made our country self-sufficient. The tonnage shipped amounted to 17,530.

Limestone belongs to a different category, since in regard to it Britain, as a whole, has never been dependent on outside supplies. On the other hand, Scotland is relatively poorly endowed. Accordingly, on Macgregor's suggestion, the Scottish staff made a careful survey of local resources. Several members, including Robertson, Simpson and J. G. C. Anderson, contributed to eight parts of a *Wartime Pamphlet* covering the country as a whole. Full field information was supplemented by no less than 218 chemical analyses specially made for the purpose at the Macaulay Soil Institute—a fine example of co-operation.

It was not found possible to maintain the immediately pre-War output, which had risen since agricultural liming had received a subsidy ; but in several cases useful sources were opened up or further developed where transport from England or Wales was particularly costly. Instances are afforded by shell sands near John o' Groats and crystalline limestones near Fort William, Blair Atholl and Dufftown.

Enough has been said to give a general idea of the Survey's wartime activity in the Mineral field. We may perhaps add one other example because it is of a kind dear to the heart of the scientific apologist. In 1872 and 1878 Judd announced his discovery of Upper Cretaceous deposits in the Hebridean area. Among other occurrences he noted a white sandstone at Loch Aline on the mainland side of the Sound of Mull. When the area came to be mapped by the Geological Survey this outcrop was carefully traced, but at the time it was not realised that it might have economic value. Presently, however, in 1922, I visited the Lochaline exposure to follow up a clue I had found in Mull. I suspected that the sand making the white sandstone had originally been blown into the Chalk sea from an adjacent desert shore —thus throwing a new light on the remarkable absence of river-borne mud which is characteristic of the Chalk of England and France. I found the evidence strongly corroborative, and was also much impressed by the extreme purity of the friable sandstone. A percentage analysis showed 99.69 SiO_2 with only 0.02 Fe_2O_3. Thus Britain had at last a first class optical-glass sand, and one that was ideally located for transport by sea (the sandstone has so little cohesion that 60 per cent. disintegrates on blasting for extraction).

The information was published in Survey memoirs and communicated to successive landlords, and also on several occasions to the Admiralty. The latter need optical glass for their instruments and had long been anxious to learn of a native source of sand suitable for its production. For years, however, practically nothing happened. Under normal conditions optical-glass sand can be shipped in quantity from Holland, Belgium and France.

It came, therefore, as a great relief to hear from the Admiralty, when Hitler overran the Channel ports in 1940, that a Glasgow firm had interested itself in the Lochaline deposit, and that all promised well. The promise was fulfilled, for on the 12th March, 1946, My Lords Commissioners of the Admiralty formally communicated their thanks to the Secretary, D.S.I.R., and informed him that the Lochaline sand had been used in large quantity and had been found ' after treatment superior in quality to that [previously] obtained from continental sources.'

As a sand mine the Lochaline working is unique. The deposit lies at a low angle, and is 20-25 feet thick with a 4-foot roof of Tertiary mudstone overlain by a great thickness of basalt lavas, constituting part of the Mull volcano, the whole cut by occasional basalt dykes. The main mine has been driven 1,000 feet into the hillside from the outcrop, and from its galleries the sandstone is worked in rooms 15-20 feet high, 30-40 feet wide and 120-130 feet long. No timber is required for support. After washing the sand shows an average Fe_2O_3 content of only 0.011 per cent. In 1941 some 21,000 tons were shipped, and by the Autumn of 1948 the total exceeded 250,000 tons.

Anyone passing up the Sound today sees the processing, storage and loading equipment at Lochaline pier, overlooking a conspicuous strand of white spilt sand. On the grassy slope above are clustered a couple of dozen prefabs built by the County Council to house the immigrant employees.

HYDRO-ELECTRIC POWER

In 1926 the Electricity Act established Electricity Commissioners and a Central Electricity Board for Great Britain as a whole. The Commissioners were to divide the country into districts, and to plan intercommunicating grid schemes. The Board in turn was to control generation and high-tension transmission within the several districts. Before long the system was in working order for all districts except Northern Scotland, defined to include a small proportion of Scottish Lowlands together with all the Highlands and Islands to the north and west.

In 1931 the Commissioners did indeed prepare a scheme for Northern Scotland, but it was never put into action. Instead, what has been called 'an unofficial adaptation of certain features,' was negotiated. Most of the District south-east of the Caledonian canal and some small part to the north-west of the same were to continue to be developed by undertakers already vested with parliamentary powers; while the remainder was left for later consideration. Only two undertakers were of real importance in this matter, so far as public supply was concerned. They were the Grampian Company, relying mainly on water power, and, a long way behind, the Aberdeen Corporation, with a coal installation. To help the Grampian Company to finance its local distribution, and at the same time to benefit the country at large, the Central Electricity Board contracted to take a very substantial part of the company's output for use farther south. The company already had an independent contract for export in the same direction.

As will be readily understood, the difficulty of fitting Northern Scotland into the framework of the 1926 Act depended on the fact that its characters are extreme. It has a superfluity of water power considered from the local standpoint, and an attenuated population. Although these features recur to some extent in Southern Scotland, Lakeland, Wales and the tideway of the Severn, they do not in these places characterise a region comparable in extent with Northern Scotland. Broadly speaking, therefore, Britain electrically consists of two contrasted divisions :—

(1) the bulk of Great Britain, where electricity production depends essentially on coal, and where it is reasonable to aim at a rough balance between district production and consumption; and
(2) Northern Scotland, where electricity production depends essentially on water and topography, and where domestic supply, of even a considerable part of the whole, can only be undertaken economically *if it is possible to attract electro-metallurgical or electro-chemical industries into the District, or, alternatively, to export a profitable stream of power southward out of the District.*

The earliest developments of Northern Scotland's hydro-electric possibilities were undertaken by manufacturers of aluminium, with little or no thought of public supply. Here we find the Foyers scheme, which went into production in 1896; the Kinlochleven scheme, 1909; and the Lochaber scheme, 1929. Of these, the Lochaber scheme was geologically much the most important, since it involved the driving of three tunnels, the longest of which leads from Loch Treig to Fort William, a distance of fifteen miles.

In relation to the Lochaber scheme, at any rate, the Geological Survey received far more than it gave. Many visits were made to the great tunnel while under construction, during which mutually useful discussions occurred and specimens were taken; but the detailed record was compiled by the resident engineers, as section by section the funnel face was washed free of dust preparatory to lining with concrete. One of these engineers was Ben N. Peach, jun., son of the great Survey geologist of former days. Looking back upon this investigation, I wonder if the Survey had any right of access. These tunnels were not mineral mines, and were not, I have since been informed, inspected for safety by the Mines Inspectorate. At any rate the question of trespass was never raised.

The next developments in Northern Scotland were undertaken for public supply, and were due to the Grampian Company, responsible for schemes at Rannoch and Tummel, which came into operation in 1930 and 1933. Meanwhile, the first Scottish scheme for public supply had come into being at the Falls of Clyde in 1926; but this belonged to Central Scotland. The subsequent Galloway scheme, operating more or less in partnership with the Central Electricity Board, was situated in Southern Scotland.

In 1941 the Secretary of State for Scotland appointed a Committee on Hydro-Electric Development in Scotland. It gave most attention to Northern Scotland, where alone conditions were notably anomalous. It reviewed carefully the performance of the Grampian Company, and decided that this great undertaker would not have done better for the country if it had been working as a non-profit-earning public corporation. Much greater progress might, indeed, have been made, with immense advantage to the country's

18

peace and war potential; but, as the Committee puts it, successive Governments and Parliaments seem to have been determined neither 'to develop the resources themselves nor allow anyone else to do it.'

Under all the circumstances the Committee found existing conditions unduly muddled. 'At present,' they said, 'there is no policy for the development of the water power resources nor any authority to frame one and to ensure that it is carried out.' It therefore advised the separation, at Board level, of Northern Scotland from the rest of Great Britain.

This and concomitant recommendations of the Committee were adopted in the Hydro-Electric Development (Scotland) Act of 1943. The North of Scotland Hydro-Electric Board was set up to work with, but not under, the Central Electricity Board. To maintain close liaison, the latter provides one of the five members constituting its new companion.

The North of Scotland Board's first duty was to provide a Development Scheme. This, after approval by the Electricity Commissioners, was confirmed by the Secretary for State for Scotland in 1944. It has been added to as time proceeds.

The Board's development schemes cover all proposals up to date for new production within the district, and for resultant distribution :—

(1) to ordinary consumers within the District—using Authorised Undertakers, such as the Grampian Company, as middlemen in previously allotted portions of the District;

(2) to any large power users subsequently entering the District; and

(3) to the Central Electricity Board for use farther south.

The Northern Board has to give priority to furnishing supplies to ordinary consumers of its District; but it also has to make its schemes pay their way as a whole. This latter condition will be essentially determined by sales to large users attracted to the District and to the Central Electricity Board. To avoid price-cutting, the charges to the latter are fixed by those paid to the most efficient steam-power plant in Britain (hypothetically transferred to Central Scotland and supplied with Scottish coal). A Treasury guarantee of dividends on money raised for expenses enables the Board to finance itself at a low rate of interest, and to face initial losses with confidence, although it is a condition that all Treasury advances must eventually be repaid.

The Board is furnished with two independent Committees to ensure that Amenity and Fishery interests will be kept prominently in view at all stages of its work. Altogether, consideration of schemes has been made much simpler, quicker and cheaper than heretofore.

Broadly speaking, the Board's distribution area is equal in area to that of the Grampian Company, and lies, with minor exceptions, to the north-west of the same. The development schemes confirmed up to the end of 1945 include the provision of eight new hydro-electric power stations, half of them in the Board's own distribution area, and half in that of its Grampian neighbour. They also include eight distribution schemes, all, of course, in its own area.

In framing its programme the North of Scotland Board receives assistance from the Meteorological Office and the Geological Survey. The former supplies rainfall maps, discusses drought possibilities and assists in enlisting voluntary rainfall observers in the higher, less inhabited parts of the District. The Geological Survey furnishes reports on suggested sites for dams, power stations, tunnels and aqueducts. In return it has been promised all possible facilities for making observations and records.

The activities of the North of Scotland Hydro-Electric Board cannot on any basis be reckoned as war work. They were started as a contribution to the hard struggle which was bound to follow eventual victory. The organisation of the Geological Survey's small but useful share was left in the hands of the Assistant Director, Murray Macgregor.

ACCOUNTANCY

Reference has already been made to occasional difficulties that have arisen between the Geological Survey and Headquarters of the Department of Scientific and Industrial Research on the subject of repayment and accountancy. In the early years of the Second War these difficulties became acute. Other branches of D.S.I.R. were doing splendid war work

that was paid for by Service or Supply Departments;
whereas, measured by the yardstick of financial receipts, the
Geological Survey's direct war work was small.

This last circumstance was easy to understand. When the
Survey was asked to give advice on any matter that I considered of military importance I saw to it that the advice was
given in the shortest time possible, only asking for travelling
expenses from the party concerned. If my men had passed
out of my control for a noteworthy period, it would have
seemed reasonable to require repayment for their services,
including salary, costs and overheads. My interpretation,
however, of what should be charged for and what should not
was inclined to be more generous than that of D.S.I.R.
Headquarters; and this sometimes led to strong differences
of opinion between me and Headquarters officers in the interpretation of the financial instruction to the Department
that it should charge the Defence Ministries for services
rendered.

My position never became quite untenable. I had always
the support of the Geological Survey Board, and eventually
my Chief, Appleton, for whom I had unbounded respect,
came to my rescue with a judgment reminiscent of the wisdom of Solomon. Inquiries addressed to the Geological Survey must henceforth be divided into two halves, called major
and minor. The major must be paid for by the Department
that benefits. The minor may be undertaken at the Director's
discretion. From that time on the Survey continued its good
work without more blame than attached, perhaps, to the following aphorism : ' My Geological Director,' Appleton used
to say, ' is different from the rest. The others break some of
the rules some of the time, but he breaks them all without
ceasing.'

Looking back, I think that most of the difficulties that
have arisen between the Survey and the Headquarters of
D.S.I.R. were due to differences in the ages of the two
organisations. We, with a history of over a hundred years,
could not help, sometimes, regarding D.S.I.R. as being relatively immature and apt, in the early stages, to impose too
little confidence in the Director of the survey. I remember

my surprise when I returned to the Service to find two apparently innocent examples of Flett's audacity spoken of in hushed whispers at Headquarters. Towards the end of the First World War he had, without waiting for orders, gathered relevant geological data in regard to schemes for a Channel tunnel and a Forth to Clyde ship canal. For three-quarters of a century the Geological Survey had been expected to be able to answer geological questions put to it by the Government; and to Flett it had seemed mere common sense to equip himself with evidence on these two questions, in regard to which so important a public Department as the Admiralty had already expressed an interest.

Be this as it may, in 1944 I had a refreshing experience, when Headquarters itself became increasingly involved in uranium. Very naturally they turned to the Geological Survey for counsel in regard to sources of supply. Forgetting my orders, I did not ask what arrangements would be made about accountancy of pay, pension and overhead expenses, I merely placed Davidson at their disposal. He had already shown high competency in supplying information in regard to military aspects of the geology of many overseas areas. Now he was flown across the Atlantic, to return covered with appreciation. Today he is in charge of a new Atomic Energy Division of the Geological Survey.

GOODBYE

Towards the close of 1944, victory was well in sight. Optimists expected to be in Berlin by Christmas, but progress was a little delayed by Rundstedt's offensive in the Ardennes. I felt it was time for me to go, for two good reasons. Firstly, drastic reorganisation was in sight, and those who were young enough to look forward to functioning under the new conditions should be given maximum opportunity to help in their framing. Secondly, I knew there was a strong desire on the part of the juniors to say goodbye to the older generation.

Already before the Second World War had burst upon us there had been a block in promotion, owing to the quasi-simultaneous enrolment of sixteen Geologists following the close of hostilities in 1918; and this had since been accentuated by the wartime retention of a number of seniors beyond the normal age limit. The impatience of the younger members was partly determined by a laudable desire to try their prowess at higher levels while in the prime of manhood; and partly by a very natural hope in home circles for an increase in pay.

A chance offered, when a leading firm of Consulting Engineers told me that they had an important irrigation and power scheme in hand in Iran, to which the Foreign Office attached high priority as affording an opportunity of exchanging service for sterling. The firm had been asked by the Iranian Government to supply a geological report, and it wanted me to suggest some suitable geologist who would be willing to go. With the ready consent of Headquarters I offered myself; and so had the exhilarating experience on retirement in April, 1945, of stepping into an aeroplane instead of an arm chair.

' Why did he go?', said Appleton in reply to a question from a young friend, ' Why did he go? Adventure, boy, Adventure.'

So our story ends, though not its subject.

LONG LIVE THE GEOLOGICAL SURVEY

INDEX

ERUPTIVE ROCKS
by S. J. SHAND

Their Genesis, Composition, Classification and their Relation to Ore-Deposits, with a Chapter on Meteorites

5th Impression (4th Edition)   *30s. net*

" By far the most complete and satisfying text now available to put into the hands of the advanced student of the subject."—*Nature.*

" At last we have a book on rocks which the chemist can read with satisfaction."—*Journal of the American Chemical Society.*

" This work is now one of the best and most up-to-date English texts concerning eruptive rocks."—*Bulletin of the Imperial Institute.*

" The volume can be highly recommended for use by advanced students." —*American Journal of Science.*

" Those who are equipped to read Professor Shand's book will find here a wealth of material and interpretation which will prove of extreme value and stimulation."—*Natural History.*

" Presents a conspectus of the controlling features of a wide field of knowledge more clearly and in simpler language than has ever been done before."—*Geographical Journal.*

" Students who use this book will be grateful for the clear, straightforward presentation of facts and theories."—*American Scientist.*

" The discussions are brief and critical, and they preserve an excellent balance between the field, the laboratory, and the geochemical data."— *Science.*

SILICATE ANALYSIS
by A. W. GROVES

A Manual for Geologists and Chemists. With Chapters on Check Calculations and Geochemical Data

Second Edition revised and enlarged

Foreword by Professor Arthur Holmes   *Demy 8vo. 25s. net*

The aim of the author of this book is to provide a practical and up-to-date laboratory handbook for the analysis of rocks and silicate minerals, and of the silicates—both natural and artificial—used in industry.

The needs of various types of workers are borne in mind—the analyst with no special training in petrology; the analyst who is both a chemist and a petrologist; and the geologist wihout special training as an analyst, who requires to understand the methods of silicate analysis so that he may be able to guide the analyst in his work. " Silicate Analysis " thus differs from previous books dealing with the chemical analysis of silicates in that, in addition to the chemistry, it also gives the requisite amount of mineralogy and petrology.

In this revised, enlarged edition the best alternative methods or methods for special conditions have been added and reference has been made to all the more promising work, methods and suggestions published subsequent to the first edition. The range of most useful qualitative tests has been expanded.

The new matter is not confined to analytical methods; much of it is of a more general character, though all closely bearing on the problems of the silicate analyst. The section on geochemical data has been considerably expanded, while that on the recalculation of mineral analyses has been entirely re-written, giving a greater insight into the methods employed by the mineralogist in interpreting and checking chemical analyses.